E. B. Uvarov was born in ... at Haberdashers' Aske's Hampstead School and the Imperial College of Science. He graduated in chemistry in 1929 and spent two years in biochemical research. In 1932 he taught science at Bertrand Russell's School: this was followed by two years as biochemist and technical manager to a firm of food manufacturers. From 1935 to 1944 he was senior chemistry master at Dartington Hall and subsequently at Taunton School. For the following eleven years he was head of the Technical Information Bureau of a large industrial organization, before going into independent practice as a scientific literature consultant and translator.

D. R. Chapman was born in 1926. He was educated at Collyer's School, Horsham, and later held a Natural Science Postmastership at Merton College, Oxford. Since graduating in 1948 with first-class honours in physics, he has been engaged in textile research.

Alan Isaacs was born in London in 1925 and educated at St Paul's School and the Imperial College of Science and Technology, where he graduated in 1946. He was then engaged in fundamental research into combustion problems associated with rocket propulsion and was awarded a Ph.D. in 1950. At the same time he was a part-time teacher of English and Mathematics at the Polish University College in London. Dr Isaacs is the author of *Introducing Science*, and *The Survival of God in the Scientific Age*, both available in Penguins.

A Dictionary of Science

E. B. UVAROV

AND

D. R. CHAPMAN

REVISED FOR THE THIRD EDITION BY
ALAN ISAACS

PENGUIN BOOKS

Penguin Books Ltd, Harmondsworth, Middlesex, England
Penguin Books Inc., 7110 Ambassador Road, Baltimore, Maryland 21207, U.S.A.
Penguin Books Australia Ltd, Ringwood, Victoria, Australia

—

First published 1943
Reprinted 1944
Second edition 1951
Reprinted 1952, 1954, 1956, 1958, 1959, 1960, 1961, 1962
Third edition 1964
Reprinted 1966, 1968, 1969

—

Copyright © E. B. Uvarov and D. R. Chapman, 1943
New material for third edition copyright
© Alan Isaacs, 1964

—

Made and printed in Great Britain
by Cox & Wyman Ltd, London, Reading and Fakenham
Set in Monotype Baskerville

Foreword to the 1964 Edition

IN revising a dictionary of this size and scope, inevitably the problem must be not what to put in but what to leave out. This revision has been made with two criteria in mind: first, to keep the original flavour of Uvarov's work, particularly in the case of entries that needed to be re-written, and second, to include only those new words that have come into use in the last decade which are of predominantly scientific rather than technological usage. From the rapidly expanding field of electronics, for example, only the more fundamental words have been included – the Penguin *Dictionary of Electronics* provides a more comprehensive coverage of the technological aspects of the subject. Nevertheless, most of the basic terms used in solid state and microwave physics will be found in this edition.

Probably the largest number of new entries relate to nuclear physics and what may be loosely called space science (including artificial satellites, radio astronomy and cosmology), for it is in these fields that progress has been most rapid in the last ten years. On the chemical side less radical revision has been necessary, though the dictionary has been brought up to date where necessary (e.g. synthetic rubbers and plastics, transuranic elements, chelation compounds, etc).

The earlier editions of this dictionary have dealt primarily with the pure sciences of physics, chemistry, mathematics, and astronomy. However, it was felt that, in view of the widespread interest in the advances that are currently being made in biochemistry, molecular biology, and biophysics, this edition should include a smattering of the key words used in these disciplines. Further and fuller treatment of these words will usually be found in the Penguin *Dictionary of Biology*.

The network of cross-references has been maintained throughout this edition, and cross-references are indicated in the text by the use of italics. Italics have not been used, however, for the elements, as the dictionary lists all the elements (including transuranic elements). Trade names are marked with an asterisk.

Finally, it is necessary to add that during the course of this revision too many reference books and indulgent colleagues have been consulted to permit individual acknowledgements to be made.

A.I.

Abbreviations used in the Text

A°.	Absolute (temperature)
At. No.	Atomic number
A.W.	Atomic weight
(astr.)	Astronomy; as used in astronomy
(bio.)	Biochemistry; as used in biochemistry (or biology)
b. p.	Boiling point
C.	Centigrade
c.c.	Cubic centimetre
(chem.)	Chemistry; as used in chemistry
cm.	Centimetre
conc.	Concentrated
F.	Fahrenheit
f.p.	Freezing point
gm.	Gram
°K.	Degrees on the Kelvin (absolute) scale
Km.	Kilometre
lb.	Pound
(math.)	Mathematics; as used in mathematics
mm.	Millimetre
m.p.	Melting point
(phot.)	Used in photography
(phys.)	Physics; as used in physics
S.G.	Specific gravity
sq.	Square
temp.	Temperature
wt.	Weight

A Dictionary of Science

AB–. A prefix attached to the names of practical electric units (e.g. *ampere, volt*) to indicate the corresponding unit in the *electromagnetic system* (e.g. abampere, abvolt).

ABERRATION (astr.). Variation in the apparent position of a *star* or other heavenly body, due to the motion of the observer with the *Earth*.

ABERRATION, CHROMATIC. Formation, by a *lens*, of an image with coloured fringes, due to the *refractive index* of *glass* being different for *light* of different *colours*. The light is thus dispersed (see *dispersion of light*) into a coloured band. The effect is corrected by the use of *achromatic lenses*.

ABERRATION, SPHERICAL. Distortion of the image produced by a *lens* or *mirror* due to different rays from any one point of the object making different angles with the line joining that point to the *optical centre* of the lens or mirror (see *mirrors, spherical*) and coming to a focus in slightly different positions.

ABRASIVE. A substance used for rubbing or grinding down surfaces; e.g. *emery*.

ABSCISSA of a point *P*, in *analytical geometry*, is the portion of the *x* axis lying between the *origin* and a point where the line through *P* parallel to the *y* axis cuts the *x* axis. See Fig. 5, page 70.

ABSOLUTE. Not relative; independent. E.g. *absolute zero* of temperature, as distinct from zero on an arbitrary scale such as the *Centigrade scale*.

ABSOLUTE ALCOHOL. *Ethyl alcohol* containing not less than 99% pure ethyl alcohol by weight.

ABSOLUTE EXPANSION of a liquid. The true *expansion*, not relative to the containing vessel. The coefficient of absolute expansion is equal to the sum of the coefficient of relative or apparent expansion of the liquid and the coefficient of volume expansion of the containing vessel.

ABSOLUTE THERMODYNAMIC TEMPERATURE. Temperature measured on the *Kelvin scale of temperature*. The magnitude of the degree absolute is the same as on the *Centigrade scale*, but to convert temperatures on the Centigrade scale to degrees absolute (A° or °K) add 273. See *absolute zero*.

ABSOLUTE UNITS. System of *units* in which the least possible number of independent *fundamental units* is used.

ABSOLUTE ZERO. Zero on the absolute temperature scale (see *absolute thermodynamic temperature*). The lowest temperature theoretically possible; $0°K = -273 \cdot 16°C$ or $-459 \cdot 69°F$.

ABSORPTION EDGE. The *X-ray wave-length* at which a discontinuity appears in the intensity of an X-ray *absorption spectrum*.

ABSORPTION OF GASES. The *solution* of *gases* in *liquids*. Sometimes also applied to the absorption of gases by *solids*.

ABSORPTION OF RADIATION. *Radiant energy* is partly reflected, partly transmitted, and partly absorbed by the surface upon which it falls, the absorption being accompanied by a rise in *temperature* of the absorbing body. Dull black surfaces absorb the greatest proportion of the incident energy, and brightly polished (reflecting) surfaces the least. Surfaces which are the best absorbers are also the best radiators. See *radiation*.

ABSORPTION SPECTRUM. A *spectrum* consisting of dark lines or bands which is obtained when the *light* from a source, itself giving a continuous spectrum, is passed through a *gas* into a *spectroscope*. The dark lines or bands will occur in the same position as the coloured lines in that substance's *emission spectrum* and will be characteristic of the substance. When the absorbing medium is in the *solid* or *liquid state* the spectrum of the transmitted light shows broad dark regions which are not resolvable into sharp lines. Characteristic *X-ray* and *ultra-violet* absorption spectra are also formed.

ABSORPTIVITY of a surface. The fraction of the *radiant energy* incident on the surface which is absorbed. The absorptivity is a pure numeric, but is often referred to as 'absorptive power'. From *Kirchhoff's laws* it follows that the absorptivity is equal to the *emissivity*.

ABUNDANCE. The ratio of the number of *atoms* of a particular *isotope* in a mixture of isotopes of an *element*, to the total number of atoms present. Sometimes expressed as a percentage, e.g. the abundance of $^{235}_{92}$ U in natural uranium is $0 \cdot 71\%$

ACCELERATION. Rate of change of *velocity*; measured as a change of velocity per unit time.

ACCELERATION DUE TO GRAVITY, *g*. *Acceleration* of a body falling freely in a *vacuum*; varies slightly in different localities as a result of variations in the distance from the centre of mass of the Earth. Standard accepted values = $980 \cdot 6$ cm./sec./sec. at latitude $45°$; $981 \cdot 19$ cm./sec./sec. at Greenwich ($32 \cdot 17$ and $32 \cdot 19$ ft/sec./sec. respectively).

ACCELERATOR (chem.). A substance which increases the rate of a *chemical reaction* (i.e. a *catalyst*), particularly in the manufacture of *vulcanized rubber*.

ACCELERATOR (phys.). A machine for increasing the *kinetic energy* of charged particles (e.g. *protons, electrons, nuclei*) by accelerating them in *electric fields*. In *electrostatic generators* (see also *Van der Graaff generator* and *tandem generator*) the acceleration is achieved directly by using a very high *potential difference*. In multiple accelerators a lower potential difference is used repeatedly to give the particle successive increments of energy. Multiple accelerators are classified as *linear accelerators* or cyclic accelerators. See *cyclotron, synchroton, synchro-cyclotron, betatron*, and *bevatron*.

ACCEPTOR. An imperfection in a *semiconductor* which causes *hole* conduction.

8

ACCUMULATOR, storage battery, secondary cell. Device for 'storing' *electricity*. An *electric current* is passed between two plates in a *liquid*; this causes chemical changes (due to *electrolysis*) in the plates and the liquid. When the changes are complete, the accumulator is charged. When the charged plates are joined externally by a *conductor* of electricity, the chemical changes are reversed, a current flows through the conductor till the reversal is complete, and the accumulator is discharged. In the common lead accumulator, the liquid is *sulphuric acid* of *specific gravity* 1·20 to 1·28, the positive plate when charged is lead peroxide, PbO_2, and the negative plate is spongy lead. During discharge both plates tend to become lead sulphate, $PbSO_4$, and the specific gravity of the acid solution falls. Discharge should not be continued beyond the point at which the S.G. reaches 1·15, otherwise an insoluble sulphate of lead, not decomposed on re-charging, may be formed. When this occurs, the cell is said to be sulphated. Nickel-iron (Ni-fe*) accumulators are also widely used, in which the negative plate is iron and the positive plate is a nickel oxide. In these cells the liquid is a 20% solution of *potassium hydroxide*.

ACETAL. An *organic compound* of the general formula $RCH(OR')_2$, where R is hydrogen or an organic *radical*, and R′ is an organic radical. Term is generally applied to $CH_3CH(OC_2H_5)_2$, a liquid, b.p. 104° C.

ACETALDEHYDE. CH_3CHO. Colourless liquid with a pungent fruity smell, b.p. 21° C. Formed by the *oxidation* of *ethyl alcohol*; further oxidation gives *acetic acid*. Used as an intermediate in the manufacture of many *organic compounds*.

ACETAMIDE. CH_3CONH_2. Colourless crystals, m.p. 81° C., odourless when pure. Used industrially as a *solvent*, etc.

ACETANILIDE, antifebrin. $C_6H_5NHCOCH_3$. White crystalline solid, m.p. 112° C. Used as an *antipyretic*.

ACETATE. A *salt* or an *ester* of acetic acid.

ACETATE PLASTICS. *Plastics* made from *cellulose acetate* (see also *rayon*).

ACETIC ACID. CH_3COOH. The *acid* contained in *vinegar* (3 to 6%). Colourless corrosive liquid with a pungent smell; m.p. 16·6° C., b.p. 118·1° C. Solidifies at low temperatures to 'glacial acetic acid'. Commercially obtained from *pyroligneous acid*, from vinegar made when *alcohol* is oxidized by the action of *bacteria*, and by the *oxidation* of *acetaldehyde*. Used in the manufacture of *cellulose acetate* and in other industries.

ACETIC ETHER. See *ethyl acetate*.

ACETONE, dimethyl ketone. CH_3COCH_3. Colourless inflammable liquid with a pleasant smell. B.p. 56·5° C. Used as a *solvent*, especially in the production of *rayon*.

ACETYLENE, ethyne. C_2H_2. Colourless, poisonous, inflammable *gas*. Made by the action of water on *calcium carbide*, CaC_2, or by the action of an electric *arc* on other *hydrocarbons*. Used as a starting material for many *organic compounds*, and for *welding* on account of the high flame *temperature* (about 3300° C.) it produces when burnt in oxygen. (See *oxy-acetylene burner*.)

ACHROMATIC LENS. *Lens* free from chromatic *aberration*, giving an image free from coloured fringes. Consists of a pair of lenses, one of *crown glass*, the other of *flint glass*, the latter correcting the *dispersion* caused by the former.

ACID. Substance which liberates *hydrogen ions* in *solution*; substance which contains hydrogen which may be replaced by a *metal* to form a *salt*; substance having a tendency to lose *protons*. Many acids are corrosive, have a sour taste, and turn *litmus* red.

ACID AMIDES. See *amides*.

ACID DYES. Group of *dyes*, nearly all *salts* of *organic acids*; used chiefly for dyeing wool and natural silk from an acid dyebath.

ACID RADICAL. A *molecule* of an *acid* without the *acidic hydrogen*. E.g., the *bivalent* sulphate *radical*—SO_4, from *sulphuric acid*, H_2SO_4, is present in all sulphates.

ACID SALT. An *acid* in which only a part of the *acid hydrogen* has been replaced by a *metal*. E.g. *sodium bicarbonate*, $NaHCO_3$.

ACID VALUE of a fat or oil. Measure of the free *fatty acid* present; the number of *milligrams* of *potassium hydroxide* required to neutralize the free fatty acids in one gram of the substance.

ACIDIC. Having the properties of an *acid*; the opposite of *alkaline*.

ACIDIC HYDROGEN. That portion of the hydrogen in an *acid* which is replaceable by *metals* to form *salts*.

ACIDIMETRY. Determination of the amount of *acid* present in a *solution* by *titration*. See *volumetric analysis*.

ACIDOLYSIS. *Hydrolysis* by means of an *acid*.

ACOUSTICS. The study of *sound*.

ACRE. British unit of area. 4840 square yards.

ACRIFLAVINE, 3:6-diaminomethylacridine chloride hydrochloride. Yellow substance used as an *antiseptic*.

ACROLEIN. CH_2:CH. CHO. Colourless liquid with an irritating smell. B.p. 52·5° C.

ACRYLIC ACID, CH_2:CH.COOH. Corrosive liquid, m.p. 13° C., b.p. 141° C. Derivatives form the basis of the important *acrylic resins*.

ACRYLIC RESINS. Class of *plastics* obtained by the *polymerization* of derivatives of *acrylic acid*. They are transparent, colourless, and *thermoplastic*; widely used, especially if a clear, transparent material is required.

ACRYLONITRILE, vinyl cyanide. CH_2:CH.CN. Colourless liquid, b.p. 78° C. Used in the manufacture of *plastics*, synthetic *rubbers*, and artificial textile fibres.

ACTINIC RAYS. Portion of the *Sun's* radiation rich in *ultra-violet radiation*, having a strong effect on a photographic plate.

ACTINIDES, actinons. The name of the group of *elements* with *atomic numbers* from 89 (actinium) to 103; analogous to the *lanthanides*. See Table 5, page 335.

ACTINIUM. Ac. Element. A.W. 227. At. No. 89. Radioactive. See *radioactivity*.

ACTION. The product of *work* and time. *Planck's constant* of action is measured in the *C.G.S.* units of *erg*-seconds.

ACTIVATED ALUMINA. Aluminium oxide which has been dehydrated in such a way that a porous structure of high surface area is obtained. Activated alumina has the power of adsorbing *water vapour* and certain gaseous *molecules*. Used for drying air and other gases.

ACTIVATED CARBON, active charcoal. Carbon, especially charcoal, which has been treated to remove *hydrocarbons* and to increase its powers of *adsorption*. Used in many industrial processes for recovering valuable materials out of gaseous mixtures; as a deodorant; and in *gas masks*.

ACTIVATION (phys.). The process of inducing *radioactivity*.

ACTIVE MASS (chem.), in the Law of *Mass Action* is taken to mean the *molecular concentration* of the substance under consideration.

ACTIVITY. The number of *disintegrations* of a *radioactive* material per unit time. See *curie*.

ACTOMYOSIN. A complex of two *proteins*, actin and myosin, which is the major constituent of muscle. The contraction of muscles is due to the shortening of actomyosin fibrils.

ACUTE ANGLE. Angle of less than 90°.

ADDITION COMPOUND. Chemical *compound* formed by the addition of an *atom* or group of atoms to a *molecule*. E.g. *phosgene*, $COCl_2$, is an addition compound of *carbon monoxide*, CO, and chlorine, Cl_2.

ADENINE. 6-aminopurine. $C_5H_3N_4NH_2$. A *purine* base occurring in *nucleic acids*, which plays a part in the formulation of the *genetic code*. Also occurs in *adenosine triphosphate*.

ADENOSINE TRIPHOSPHATE, ATP. A *nucleotide* of importance in the transfer of *energy* within living *cells*. One of the phosphate groups can be readily transferred to other substances, in the presence of the appropriate *enzymes*, and with it goes a considerable amount of stored energy. It is as a result of the transfer of these phosphate groups that energy is made available in cells for chemical synthesis, muscle contraction, etc. ATP which has lost one phosphate group becomes the diphosphate (ADP). Adenosine is a *nucleoside* consisting of *adenine* and D-ribofuranose.

ADHESION. Sticking to a surface. The effect is produced by *forces* between *molecules*.

ADHESIVES. Substances used for sticking surfaces together; e.g. *glues*, cements, etc.

ADIABATIC. Taking place without *heat* entering or leaving the system.

ADMITTANCE. The reciprocal of *impedance*.

ADRENALINE. Epinephrine. 3, 4-dihydroxy-α-(methylaminoethyl) benzyl alcohol, $C_9H_{13}NO_3$. *Hormone* produced by the adrenal glands. Used in medicine.

ADSORBATE. The substance which is adsorbed on a surface. See *adsorption*.

ADSORPTION. Concentration of a substance on a surface; e.g. *molecules* of a *gas* or of a dissolved or suspended substance on the surface of a *solid*.

AELOTROPIC. See *anisotropic*.

AERIAL (U.S.A., antenna). That part of a *radio* system from which *energy* is transmitted into, or received from, *space* (or the *atmosphere*).

AEROBIC. In the presence of free oxygen.

AEROLITES. *Meteorites*; especially those consisting of stony material rather than iron.

AERO METAL. Casting *alloy* consisting chiefly of aluminium, zinc, and copper.

AEROSOL. A dispersion of *solid* or *liquid* particles in a *gas*; e.g. *smoke*.

AETIOLOGY (U.S.A., etiology). The science or philosophy of causation. Used in medicine to mean the science of the causes of disease.

AFFINITY (chem.). Chemical attraction; *force* binding *atoms* together.

AFTER-DAMP. Poisonous mixture of *gases*, containing *carbon monoxide*, formed by the explosion of *fire-damp* (*methane*, CH_4) in coal-mines.

AFTER-GLOW. A glow sometimes observed high in the western sky after sunset. Caused by fine dust particles in the *upper atmosphere* scattering the *light* from the *Sun*.

AFTER-HEAT. *Heat* generated in a *nuclear reactor* after it has been shut down, by the *radioactive* substances formed in the *fuel elements*.

AGAR-AGAR. A *gelatin*-like material obtained from certain seaweeds. Chemically related to the *carbohydrates*. A *solution* in hot water sets to a firm jelly, which is used as a base for *culture media* for growing *bacteria*.

AGATE. Natural form of *silica*, SiO_2. Very hard, used for knife-edges of *balances*, for mortars for grinding hard materials, and in ornaments.

AGONIC LINE. Line of zero *magnetic declination*.

AIR, THE. See *atmosphere*.

AIR THERMOMETER. See *gas thermometer*.

ALABASTER. Natural opaque form of *hydrated* calcium sulphate, $CaSO_4.2H_2O$.

ALBUMENS, ALBUMINS. Group of water-soluble *proteins* occurring in many animal tissues and fluids; e.g. egg-white (egg albumen), milk (lactalbumen), and blood (serum albumen).

ALBUMINOIDS. See *scleroproteins*.

ALCHEMY. Predecessor of scientific *chemistry*. An art by which its devotees sought, with the aid of a mixture of mysticism, *astrology*, practical chemistry, and quackery, to transmute *base metals* into gold, prolong human life, etc. Flourished from about A.D. 500 till the Middle Ages, when it gradually fell into disrepute.

ALCOHOL, ETHYL. See *ethyl alcohol*.

ALCOHOLOMETRY. The determination of the proportion of *ethyl alcohol* in spirits and other *solutions*; usually performed by measuring the *specific gravity* of the liquid at a standard *temperature* by a specially graduated *hydrometer*.

ALCOHOLS. Class of *organic compounds* derived from the *hydrocarbons*, one or more hydrogen *atoms* in *molecules* of the latter being replaced by *hydroxyl groups*, – OH. E.g. *ethyl alcohol* (ordinary 'alcohol') is C_2H_5OH, theoretically derived from *ethane*, C_2H_6. Alcohols which contain more than one hydroxyl group are called *polyhydric alcohols*.

ALDEHYDE. See *acetaldehyde*.

ALDEHYDES, THE. Class of *organic compounds* of the type $R—C{\displaystyle <}{O \atop H}$ where R is an *alkyl* or *aryl radical*.

ALDOL, beta-hydroxybutyraldehyde, $CH_3CH(OH)CH_2CHO$. Thick oily liquid formed by the *condensation* of *acetaldehyde*.

ALGEBRA. Branch of mathematics dealing with the properties of and relationships between quantities by means of general symbols.

ALGEBRAIC SUM. The total of a number of quantities of the same kind, with due regard to sign. Thus the algebraic sum of 3, − 5, and − 2 is − 4.

ALGIN. A loose term for *alginic acid* or its sodium *salt*.

ALGINIC ACID. A complex *organic compound* related to the *carbohydrates*, found in certain seaweeds. Used for preparing *emulsions* and as a thickening agent in the food industry; its *salts*, the alginates, can be made into textile fibres which are *soluble* in *alkalis* and are used for special purposes.

ALGORITHM, algorism (math.). A systematic mathematical procedure which enables a problem to be solved in a finite number of steps. Problems for which no algorithms exist require *heuristic* solutions.

ALIDADE. Instrument for measuring vertical heights and distances.

ALIPHATIC COMPOUNDS. *Organic compounds* containing open chains of carbon *atoms*, in contradistinction to the closed rings of carbon atoms of the *aromatic compounds*. Comprise the *paraffins*, the *olefins* and the *acetylenes* as well as all their *derivatives* and *substitution products*.

ALIQUOT PART. A divisor of a number or quantity which will give an *integer*. Thus 3 is an aliquot part of 6, but 5 is not.

ALIZARIN, 1:2 dihydroxyanthraquinone, $C_{14}H_6O_2(OH)_2$. Orange-red crystalline *solid*, m.p. 289° C. Colouring matter formerly extracted from the root of the madder plant, now made synthetically. Used in dyeing with the aid of *mordants*.

ALKALI. Soluble *hydroxide* of a *metal*, particularly of one of the *alkali metals*; term is often applied to any substance which has an alkaline reaction (i.e. turns *litmus* blue and neutralizes *acids*) in solution. See also *base*.

ALKALI METALS. The *metals* lithium, sodium, potassium, rubidium, and caesium; belonging to Group 1 of the *periodic table*.

ALKALIMETRY. Determination of the amount of *alkali* present in a *solution*, by *titration*. See *volumetric analysis*.

ALKALINE. Adjective applied to an *alkali*; opposite of *acidic*.

ALKALINE EARTH METALS. The *bivalent* group of *metals* comprising beryllium, magnesium, calcium, strontium, barium, and radium belonging to Group 2 of the *periodic table*.

ALKALOIDS. Group of *basic* organic substances of plant origin, containing at least one nitrogen *atom* in a ring structure in the *molecule*. Many have important physiological actions and are used in medicine. E.g. *cocaine, nicotine, quinine, morphine*.

ALKYD RESINS. See *glyptal resins*.

ALKYL RADICALS. *Univalent hydrocarbon radicals*, particularly those derived from hydrocarbons of the *paraffin series*, and having the general formula C_nH_{2n+1}. E.g. methyl, CH_3—; ethyl, C_2H_5—.

ALLOMERISM. A similarity in the crystalline structure of substances of different chemical composition.

ALLOTROPES, allotropic forms. See *allotropy*.

ALLOTROPY. The existence of a chemical *element* in two or more forms differing in physical properties but giving rise to identical chemical *compounds*. E.g. sulphur exists in a number of different allotropic forms.

ALLOY. A composition of two or more *metals*; an alloy may be a *compound* of the metals, a *solid solution* of them, a heterogeneous *mixture*, or any combination of these.

ALLUVIAL. Deposited by rivers.

ALLYL RESINS. Synthetic *resins* formed by the *polymerization* of chemical *compounds* containing the allyl group, $CH_2 = CH - CH_2$—.

ALPHA PARTICLE, α-particle. Helium *nucleus*; i.e. a close combination of two *neutrons* and two *protons* (see *atom, structure of*), and therefore positively charged. Alpha particles are emitted from the *nuclei* of certain *radioactive elements*. See *radioactivity*.

ALPHA RAYS, α-rays. Streams of fast-moving *alpha particles*. Alpha rays produce intense *ionization* in *gases* through which they pass, are easily absorbed by *matter*, and produce fluorescence on a fluorescent screen.

ALTAZIMUTH. Instrument for the measurement of the *altitude* and *azimuth* of heavenly bodies.

ALTERNATING CURRENT. A flow of *electricity* which, after reaching a maximum in one direction, decreases, finally reversing and reaching a maximum in the opposite direction, the *cycle* being repeated continuously. The number of such cycles per second is the *frequency*.

ALTERNATOR. A machine for producing electrical *alternating currents*.

ALTITUDE. 1. Height. 2. Altitude of the Sun, or other heavenly body, is its angle of *elevation*.

ALUDEL. See *udell*.

ALUM, potash alum. $K_2SO_4.Al_2(SO_4)_3.24H_2O$. Crystalline potassium, aluminium sulphate. The *compound* occurs naturally and is used as a *mordant* in dyeing, for fireproofing, and other technical purposes.

ALUMINA. Aluminium oxide, Al_2O_3. Occurs naturally as *corundum* and *emery*, and in a *hydrated* form as *bauxite*. (See also *activated alumina*.)

ALUMINIUM. Al. Element. A.W. 26·9815. At. No. 13. Light white *metal*, S.G. 2·7, m.p. 659·70° C., ductile and malleable, good *conductor* of electricity. Occurs widely in nature in *clays*, etc.; extracted mainly from *bauxite* by *electrolysis* of a molten mixture of purified bauxite and *cryolite.* The metal and its *alloys* are used for aircraft, cooking utensils, electrical apparatus, and for many other purposes where its light weight is an advantage.

ALUMINIUM BRASS. *Brass* containing small amounts of aluminium.

ALUMINIUM BRONZE. *Alloy* of copper containing 4%–13% aluminium.

ALUMS, the. Double *salts* of the general formula

$$M_2SO_4.R_2(SO_4)_3.24H_2O,$$

where M is a *univalent metal* such as sodium, potassium, or ammonium, and R is a *tervalent* metal such as aluminium or chromium.

ALUM-STONE. See *alunite.*

ALUNITE, alum-stone. Natural *compound* of potassium and aluminium sulphate and aluminium hydroxide, $K_2SO_4.Al_2(SO_4)_3.4Al(OH)_3$. Used as a source of potash *alum.*

AMALGAM. *Alloy* of mercury.

AMALGAMATION PROCESS for gold. Gold-bearing rock or sand, after crushing, is treated with mercury, which forms an *amalgam* on the surface of the gold. The amalgamated particles are allowed to stick to amalgamated copper plates, the rest of the ore being washed away; they are then removed, the mercury is distilled off in iron *retorts*, and the remaining gold purified by *cupellation.*

AMATOL. Explosive mixture of 80% *ammonium nitrate* and 20% *T.N.T.*

AMBER, succinite. A fossil *resin*, derived from an extinct species of pine. Obtained from mines in East Prussia, and found on seashores. Contains *succinic acid.* Yellow to brown solid, used for ornamental purposes.

AMBERGRIS. Grey or black waxy material which occurs (probably as the result of disease) in the intestines of the sperm whale. Used in perfumery.

AMERICIUM. Am. *Transuranic element*, At. No. 95. *Radioactive.* Member of the *actinide* series. Most stable *isotope*, $^{243}_{95}$Am, has *half-life* of 8.8×10^3 years.

AMETHYST. Violet variety of *quartz*; impure crystalline *silica*, SiO_2.

AMIDES. Group of *organic compounds* formed by replacing hydrogen *atoms* of *ammonia*, NH_3, by *organic acid radicals.* E.g. *acetamide*, CH_3CONH_2.

AMIDOL*. Hydrochloride of 2:4-diaminophenol,

$$C_6H_3(OH)(NH_2)_2.2HCl,$$

used in *photography* as a developer.

AMINES. Compounds formed by replacing hydrogen *atoms* of *ammonia*, NH_3, by organic *radicals.* Classified into primary amines of the type NH_2R; secondary, NHR_2; and tertiary, NR_3. See also *quaternary ammonium compounds.*

AMINO ACID. A *carboxylic acid* which contains the *amino group* —NH_2. These acids are the units which link together into *polypeptide* chains to form *proteins*; they are therefore of fundamental importance to life. Some twenty different amino acids occur in nature, all of which have the general formula: R—CH—NH_2—COOH. See Table 3, page 333. 'Essential' amino acids are those which an *organism* is unable to synthesize and therefore has to obtain from its environment. There are eight 'essential' amino acids for man.

AMINO GROUP. The *univalent* group —NH_2.

AMINOPLASTIC RESINS. Synthetic *resins* derived from the reaction of *urea*, *melamine*, or allied amino compounds with *aldehydes*. Form the basis of *thermosetting* moulding materials.

AMMETER. Instrument for the measurement of *electric current*. In moving iron ammeters, a strip of soft iron is caused to move in the *magnetic field* set up by the current flowing through a coil; for the measurement of *direct current*, the more accurate moving coil instruments contain a permanent *magnet* between the poles of which is pivoted a coil carrying the current to be measured. In each type of instrument a pointer attached to the moving portion moves over a scale graduated in *amperes*.

AMMONAL. Mixture of *ammonium nitrate*, NH_4NO_3, and aluminium. Used as an *explosive*.

AMMONIA. NH_3. Pungent-smelling *gas*, very *soluble* in water to give an *alkaline solution* containing *ammonium hydroxide*, NH_4OH. Obtained synthetically from atmospheric nitrogen (see *Haber process*) and as a by-product of *coal-gas* manufacture. Used in refrigeration, and for the manufacture of *explosives* and *fertilizers*.

AMMONIUM CHLORIDE, sal ammoniac. NH_4Cl. White *soluble* crystalline *salt*, used in *dry cells* and *Leclanché cells*.

AMMONIUM HYDROXIDE. NH_4OH. *Compound* presumed to exist in *aqueous solutions* of *ammonia*; name is often applied to the *solution*.

AMMONIUM NITRATE. NH_4NO_3. White *soluble* crystalline *salt*, m.p. 169·6° C., decomposes on heating to form *nitrous oxide*, N_2O, and water. Used in *explosives*, e.g. *ammonal*, *amatol*.

AMMONIUM RADICAL. NH_4—. *Univalent radical* which has not been obtained free, but in *compounds* behaves similarly to an *alkali metal*, giving rise to ammonium *salts*.

AMMONIUM SULPHATE, sulphate of ammonia. $(NH_4)_2SO_4$. White *soluble* crystalline *salt*, obtained as a by-product of *coal-gas* manufacture, used as a *fertilizer*.

AMORPHOUS. Non-crystalline; having no definite form or shape.

AMPERE. Unit of *electric current* approximately equivalent to the flow of 6×10^{18} *electrons* per second. The absolute ampere, which is one-tenth of an ab-ampere (see *ab-*), is equal to 1·000165 International amperes. The International ampere was originally defined as the unvarying current which when passed through a *solution* of *silver nitrate*, deposits silver at the rate of 0·00111800 grams per second. Redefined in 1948 as the intensity of a constant current which, if maintained in two parallel, rectilinear *conductors* of infinite length, of negligible circular section and placed at a distance of one *metre* from one another in vacuo, will produce between the conductors a *force* equal to 2×10^{-7} *M.K.S.* *units* of force per metre of length.

AMPERE-HOUR. Practical unit of quantity of *electricity*; the amount of electricity flowing per hour through a *conductor* when the current in it is one *ampere*. 3600 *coulombs*.

AMPERE-TURNS. A measure of *magnetomotive force*. The product of the number of turns in a coil and the current in *amperes* which flows through it.

AMPHOTERIC. Chemically reacting as *acidic* to strong *bases* and as *basic* towards strong *acids*. E.g. the amphoteric oxide ZnO gives rise to zinc *salts* of strong *acids* and zincates of the *alkali metals*.

AMPLIFIER. An *electronic* device which increases the strength of a signal fed into it, by obtaining *power* from a source other than the input signal.

AMPLITUDE (phys.). If any quantity is varying in an oscillatory manner about an equilibrium value, the maximum departure from that equilibrium value is called the amplitude; e.g. in the case of a *pendulum* the amplitude is half the length of the swing. For a *wave motion*, e.g. *electromagnetic waves* or *sound* waves, the amplitude of the wave determines the amount of *energy* carried by the wave.

AMPLITUDE MODULATION. Principal method of transmitting information by *radio* waves. The *amplitude* of a *carrier wave* is modulated (see *modulation*) in accordance with the *frequency* of the signal to be transmitted.

AMU. See *atomic mass units*.

AMYL. The *univalent radical* C_5H_{11}—.

AMYL ACETATE. $CH_3COOC_5H_{11}$. *Ester* of *amyl alcohol* and *acetic acid*. Colourless *liquid*, b.p. 148° C., with a smell of pear-drops. Used as a *solvent* for lacquers, in perfumes, and as a flavouring.

AMYL ALCOHOL. $C_5H_{11}OH$. Colourless *liquid* with a characteristic smell. Exists in several isomeric forms (see *isomerism*). Commercial amyl alcohol consists mainly of *iso*-amyl alcohol,

$$(CH_3)_2 : CH.CH_2.CH_2OH,$$

b.p. 131·4° C., and is obtained from *fusel oil*. Used as a *solvent*.

AMYLASES. Group of *enzymes* capable of splitting *starch* and *glycogen* into *sugars*. Found in many plants and animals (e.g. the pancreatic juices of mammals).

AMYLOPECTIN. A form of *starch* which consists of *molecules* containing between 10 and 25 chains, each chain comprising about 20 *glucose* units. In amylopectin molecules, unlike *amylose* molecules, these chains are joined by cross-linkages so that a highly branched structure is formed.

AMYLOSE. A *starch* component structurally related to *cellulose*. Consists of *molecules* containing between 10 and 25 chains, each chain comprising about 20 *glucose* units. In amylose molecules, unlike *amylopectin* molecules, these chains are joined end to end, giving an unbranched chain of between 200 and 500 glucose units.

AMYLUM. See *starch*.

ANABOLISM. Part of *metabolism*, comprising the building-up of complex substances from simpler material, with absorption and storage of *energy*.

ANAEROBIC. In the absence of free oxygen.

ANAESTHETIC. Substance used in medicine to produce insensibility or loss of feeling.

ANALGESIC. Substance used in medicine to relieve pain.

ANALOGUE COMPUTER. A *computer* in which numerical magnitudes are represented by physical quantities such as *electric current*, *voltage*, or *resistance*. See also *digital computers*.

ANALYSIS (chem.). Decomposition of substances into their *elements* or constituent parts; term usually applied to chemical or physical methods of determining the composition of substances. See *colorimetric*, *gravimetric*, *qualitative*, *quantitative*, *spectrographic*, and *volumetric analysis*.

ANALYTICAL GEOMETRY, co-ordinate geometry. Form of *geometry* based upon the use of *co-ordinates* to define positions in *space*.

ANASTIGMATIC LENS. *Lens* designed to correct *astigmatism*.

ANATASE. Crystalline form of natural titanium dioxide, TiO_2.

ANEMOMETER. Instrument for measuring the speed of wind.

ANEROID. Without liquid. The aneroid barometer is an instrument for measuring atmospheric pressure; it consists of an exhausted metal box with a thin corrugated metal lid. Variations in atmospheric pressure cause changes in the displacement of the lid; this displacement is magnified and made to actuate a pointer moving over a scale by means of a system of delicate levers.

ANGLE. Formed by two lines (generally straight) meeting at a point. Measured in degrees, $360°$ being the angle traced by the complete revolution of a line OA about a point O until it returns to its original position, or in *radians* (see *circular measure*).

ÅNGSTRÖM UNIT, Å.U., 10^{-10} metre, $\frac{1}{10000}$ *micron*. Unit of length, especially for measurement of *wave-lengths* of *light* and intra-molecular distances.

ANGULAR ACCELERTAION. Rate of change of *angular velocity*.

ANGULAR DISTANCE. Distance between two bodies, measured in terms of the *angle* subtended by them at the point of observation; used in *astronomy*.

ANGULAR MOMENTUM. The product of *moment of inertia* and *angular velocity*. For the angular momentum of *elementary particles* see *spin*.

ANGULAR VELOCITY. Rate of motion through an *angle* about an *axis*. Measured in *degrees*, *radians*, or revolutions per unit time.

ANHYDRIDE. Anhydride of a substance is that which, when chemically combined with *water*, gives the substance. E.g. *sulphur trioxide*, SO_3, is the anhydride of *sulphuric acid*, H_2SO_4.

ANHYDRITE. Naturally occurring form of calcium sulphate, $CaSO_4$.

ANHYDROUS. Without *water*; often applied to *salts* without *water of crystallization*.

ANILINE, phenylamine, aminobenzene. $C_6H_5NH_2$. Colourless oily *liquid* with a peculiar smell, b.p. 184·4° C. Made by the reduction of *nitrobenzene*, $C_6H_5NO_2$, which is obtained from *benzene*, C_6H_6, extracted from *coal-tar*. Used in the manufacture of many important products, including *dyes*, *drugs*, and *plastics*.

ANILINE DYES. *Dyes* prepared or chemically derived from *aniline*.

ANIMAL CHARCOAL. Material containing 10% carbon and 90% inorganic matter, chiefly calcium phosphate, $Ca_3(PO_4)_2$, obtained by charring bones and other animal substances. Used as a decolorizing agent.

ANIMAL STARCH. See *glycogen*.

ANION. Negatively charged *ion*; ion which, during *electrolysis* is attracted towards the *anode*.

ANISOTROPIC, aelotropic. Possessing different physical properties in different directions; e.g. certain *crystals* have a different *refractive index* in different directions.

ANNEALING. Very slow regulated cooling, especially of *metals*, to relieve *strains* set up during heating or other treatment.

ANNIHILATION RADIATION. The *electromagnetic radiation* which results from the collision, and subsequent annihilation, of a particle and its corresponding *anti-particle*. In the collision between an *electron* and a *positron* the annihilation radiation usually consists of two *photons* of γ-radiation emitted in opposite directions. The *energy* of the annihilation radiation is derived from the *mass* of the annihilated particles according to the *mass-energy equation*.

ANNUAL VARIATION of *magnetic declination*. Very small regular variation which the magnetic declination undergoes in the course of a year.

ANNULAR. Ringed. E.g. annular eclipse; annular space, i.e. the space between an inner and outer ring.

ANODE. Positive *electrode*. See *electrolysis* and *thermionic valve*.

ANODIZING. Producing an *oxide* coating on a metallic surface by making it the *anode* in an electrolytic bath (see *electrolysis*).

ANOMALY (astr.). Term used to describe the position of a *planet* in its *orbit*.

ANTENNA. See *aerial*.

ANTHRACENE. $C_{14}H_{10}$. White crystalline *hydrocarbon* with a blue *fluorescence*; often yellowish due to impurities. M.p. 217° C. Obtained from *coal-tar*; used in the manufacture of *dyes*.

ANTHRACITE. Hard form of *coal*, containing more carbon and far less *hydrocarbons* than other forms. Probably the oldest form of coal.

ANTI-. Prefix denoting opposite, against. E.g. *antichlor*.

ANTIBIOTICS. Chemical substances produced by *micro-organisms* such as moulds and *bacteria*, which are capable of destroying bacteria or preventing their growth. Numerous antibiotics have been discovered in recent years, the first of which was *penicillin*.

ANTIBODY. A *protein* produced by animal plasma *cells* (of the reticulo-endothelial system) as a result of the presence of an *antigen*. Specific antigens stimulate the formation of specific antibodies. The function of the antibodies is to combine chemically with antigens and thereby to render them harmless to the *organism* which they are invading. As parasitic *organisms* and *viruses* produce, or are associated with, specific antigens, the consequent antibody formation provides a defence mechanism against these invading parasites. Once produced, antibodies persist in the bloodstream and therefore confer enduring immunity against the infecting organisms of antigens. Immunity to disease by inoculation is brought about by injecting antigens into the bloodstream with the object of stimulating the formation of antibodies. See also *vaccine*.

ANTICHLOR. Substance used to remove chlorine from materials after *bleaching*. E.g. *sodium thiosulphate*, $Na_2S_2O_3$.

ANTIDOTE. Remedy for a particular poison, which generally acts chemically upon the poison, thus neutralizing it, making it *insoluble* or otherwise rendering it harmless.

ANTIFEBRIN. See *acetanilide*.

ANTI-FREEZE. Substance added to water in radiators of motor-car engines in order to lower the *freezing point* of the water. *Ethylene glycol*, $CH_2OH.CH_2OH$, is frequently used.

ANTIGEN. A *protein* or *carbohydrate* which is foreign to an *organism* and which is capable of stimulating the formation of *antibodies*.

ANTI-MATTER. Hypothetical *matter* composed of *anti-particles*. Anti-hydrogen, for example, would consist of an anti-proton and an orbital *positron*. While theoretically possible, the existence of anti-matter in the Universe has never been detected. Contact between anti-matter and matter would result in the annihilation of both with the production of *annihilation radiation*.

ANTIMONY. Sb. (Stibium.) Element. A.W. 121·75. At. No. 51. Brittle crystalline silvery-white *metal*, S.G. 6·69, m.p. 630° C., expands on solidifying. Occurs as the *element*, *oxide*, and *sulphide* (stibnite, Sb_2S_3). Extracted from its ores by roasting the ore and reducing with carbon. Used in *type metal* and other *alloys*.

ANTINODES. Points of maximum displacement in a series of stationary waves. Two similar and equal *wave motions* travelling with equal *velocities* in opposite directions along a straight line give rise to antinodes and *nodes* alternately along the line. The antinodes are separated from their adjacent nodes by a distance corresponding to a quarter of the *wave-length* of the wave motions.

ANTI-PARTICLE. Every *elementary particle* has a corresponding real or hypothetical anti-particle, of equal *mass* but opposite *electric charge*, with which annihilation can take place. The anti-particle of the *electron* is the *positron*. Anti-*neutrons*, anti-*neutrinos*, and anti-*protons*, amongst others, have been detected.

ANTIPYRETIC, febrifuge. Substance used medically to lower the body *temperature*.

ANTISEPTIC. Preventing the growth of *bacteria*.

APATITE. Natural phosphate and fluoride of calcium, $CaF_2.3Ca_3(PO_4)_2$. Used in the manufacture of *fertilizers*.

APERTURE. Opening; in optical instruments, the size of the opening admitting light to the instrument. In spherical *mirrors* or *lenses*, the diameter of the reflecting or refracting surface.

APERTURE SYNTHESIS. The use of two small *aerials* in a *radio telescope* to synthesize a large *aperture*. This principle can be used both with *parabolic reflectors* and *radio interferometers*, but is usually best employed in conjunction with an *unfilled aperture*.

APLANATIC. If any reflecting or refracting surface produces a point image at B of a point object at A irrespective of the angle at which the rays fall on the surface from A, then that surface is said to be aplanatic with respect to A and B.

APOGEE. The moon or any other Earth *satellite* is said to be in apogee when it is at its greatest distance from the Earth.

APOTHECARIES' FLUID MEASURE.

    1 minim = 0·0591 c.c. (about 1 drop).
    60 minims = 1 fluid drachm = 3·55 c.c.
    8 fl. dr. = 1 fluid ounce = 28·41 c.c.
    20 fl. oz. = 1 pint   = 568 c.c.

APOTHECARIES' WEIGHTS. See *Troy weight*.

APPARENT DEPTH of a *liquid* viewed from above is less than the true depth, owing to the *refraction* of *light*. The ratio of the true depth to the apparent depth is equal to the *refractive index* of the liquid.

APPARENT EXPANSION. Relative expansion of a *liquid*. See *expansion of liquids*.

AQ. (chem.). Symbol denoting *water*; e.g. H_2SO_4.aq. is *aqueous sulphuric acid*.

AQUA FORTIS. Concentrated *nitric acid*, HNO_3.

AQUA REGIA. Mixture of concentrated *nitric* and *hydrochloric acids* (1 to 4 by volume). Highly corrosive liquid which dissolves gold and attacks many substances unaffected by other reagents. Turns orange-yellow owing to the formation of nitrosyl chloride, $NOCl$, and free chlorine.

AQUAMARINE. Bluish form of *beryl*.

AQUEOUS. Watery. Usually applied to *solutions*, indicating that *water* is the *solvent*.

ARC, ELECTRIC. Highly luminous discharge, accompanied by a *temperature* of over 3000° C.; produced when an *electric current* flows through a gap between two *electrodes*, the current being carried by the *vapour* of the electrode; e.g. the common carbon arc is formed between two carbon rods, and constitutes a very bright source of *light*. In the same way metallic arcs are formed between two similar metallic surfaces.

ARC LAMP. Technical application of the electric *arc* to produce a very bright *light*. The *carbon arc* lamp consists of an electric arc between two carbon *electrodes*, with suitable automatic mechanism for striking the arc and drawing the carbons closer together as they are vaporized away. The mercury arc lamp is important for laboratory use.

ARC OF CIRCLE. See *circle*.

ARCHIMEDES' PRINCIPLE. The apparent loss in *weight* of a body totally or partially immersed in a *liquid* is equal to the weight of the liquid displaced. See *buoyancy*.

ARE. Metric unit of area, 1 square dekametre, 100 square metres, 119·60 square yards.

AREA. Measure of surface; measured in 'square' units of length, e.g. square inches.

AREA, BRITISH UNITS.

$$1 \text{ square inch} = 6\cdot4516 \text{ square cm.}$$
$$144 \text{ sq. ins.} = 1 \text{ sq. foot} = 929 \text{ sq. cm.}$$
$$9 \text{ sq. ft} = 1 \text{ sq. yard.}$$
$$30\tfrac{1}{4} \text{ sq. yds} = 1 \text{ sq. pole.}$$
$$40 \text{ sq. pls.} = 1 \text{ rood.}$$
$$484 \text{ sq. yds} = 1 \text{ sq. chain.}$$
$$4 \text{ roods} = 4840 \text{ sq. yds} = 1 \text{ acre.}$$
$$640 \text{ acres} = 1 \text{ sq. mile} = 2\cdot590 \text{ sq. km.}$$

AREA, METRIC UNITS.

$$1 \text{ sq. centimetre} = \cdot155 \text{ sq. inch.}$$
$$10,000 \text{ sq. cm.} = 1 \text{ centare, } 1 \text{ sq. metre.}$$
$$100 \text{ sq. m.} = 1 \text{ are.}$$
$$100 \text{ ares} = 1 \text{ hectare, } 2\cdot4711 \text{ acres.}$$
$$100 \text{ hectares} = 1 \text{ sq. kilometre, } \cdot3861 \text{ sq. mile.}$$

ARGENTIFEROUS. Silver-bearing.

ARGENTITE, silver glance. Natural silver sulphide, Ag_2S. Important ore of silver.

ARGOL, tartar. Reddish-brown crystalline deposit consisting mainly of potassium hydrogen tartrate, which separates in wine-vats.

ARGON. A. Element. A.W. 39·948. At. No. 18. *Inert gas.* Occurs in the air (0·9%). Used for filling electric lamps and in fluorescent tubes at a pressure of about 3 mm. of mercury.

ARITHMETICAL PROGRESSION. *Series* of quantities in which each term differs from the preceding by a constant common difference. For an A.P. in which the first term is a, the common difference d, the number of terms n, the last term L, and the sum of n terms S,

$$S = \frac{n}{2}\{2a + (n-1)d\}$$
$$\frac{n}{2}(a+L)$$
$$L = a + (n-1)d.$$

ARMATURE. The coil or coils, usually rotating, of a *dynamo* or *electric motor*. Also more widely used as any part of an electric apparatus or machine in which a *voltage* is induced by a *magnetic field*, e.g. in gramophone pick-ups, electromagnetic loudspeakers, *relays*, etc.

AROMATIC COMPOUNDS (chem.). *Organic compounds* derived from *benzene*.

ARSENIC. As. Element. A.W. 74·9216. At. No. 33. Steel-grey brittle crystalline substance. Occurs combined with sulphur as *realgar*, As_2S_2, *orpiment*, As_2S_3; with oxygen as *white arsenic*, As_2O_3; with some *metals* and as the *element*. *Compounds* are very poisonous, and are used in medicine and for destroying pests.

ARSENICAL PYRITES. See *mispickel*.

ARSENIOUS OXIDE, *white arsenic*, 'arsenic'. As_2O_3.

ARSINE. Hydrogen arsenide, AsH_3; intensely poisonous colourless *gas*.

ARTIFICIAL RADIOACTIVITY. See *induced radioactivity*.

ARYL RADICALS. Organic *radicals* or groups of *atoms* derived from *aromatic compounds*; e.g. *phenyl*, C_6H_5—.

ASBESTOS. Name given to a variety of fibrous *silicate* minerals, mainly calcium magnesium silicate. Used as a heat-insulating material and for fire-proof fabrics.

ASCORBIC ACID, *vitamin* C. $C_6H_8O_6$. White crystalline *solid*, m.p. 192° C., occurs in fruits and vegetables.

ASEPTIC. Free from *bacteria*.

ASH. Incombustible residue left after the complete *combustion* of any substance. Consists of the non-*volatile*, *inorganic* constituents of the substance.

ASPHALT. Black, semi-solid sticky substance composed of *bitumen* with mineral matter. Consists mainly of complex *hydrocarbons*. Occurs naturally in asphalt lakes or in deposits mixed with sandstone and *limestone*; made artificially by adding mineral matter to bitumen. Used in road-making and building.

ASPIRATOR. Apparatus for drawing a current of air or other *gas* through a *liquid*.

ASPIRIN, acetylsalicylic acid. $CH_3COOC_6H_4COOH$. White solid, m.p. 133° C. Used in medicine as an *antipyretic* and *analgesic*.

ASSAYING. Analysing for one constituent of a *mixture*, particularly the estimation of *metals* in ores.

ASSOCIATION (chem.). Under certain conditions, e.g. in *solution*, the *molecules* of some substances associate into groups of several molecules, thus causing the substance to have an abnormally high *molecular weight*.

ASTATIC COILS. Arrangement used in sensitive electrical instruments; coils so arranged that the *resultant* external *magnetic field* which they produce when an *electric current* passes through them, and the *electro-motive force* induced in them by an external magnetic field, are zero.

ASTATIC GALVANOMETER. A type of moving *magnet galvanometer*, in which two equal small magnets are arranged parallel but in opposition at the centres of two oppositely wound coils, the system being suspended by a fine torsion fibre. Since the resulting *magnetic moment* is zero, the Earth's *magnetic field* exerts no controlling *torque* on the moving system. Instead, the restoring torque is supplied by the suspending fibre and is made very small by using a fine *quartz* fibre; the sensitivity of the galvanometer is thus very large.

ASTATIC PAIR of magnets. Arrangement of *magnets* used in *astatic galvanometers*.

ASTATINE. At. The element At. No. 85, the last member of the *halogen* group and the only one without a stable *isotope*.

ASTEROIDS, planetoids, minor *planets*. A belt of some 1500 small bodies, none exceeding 300 miles in diameter, rotating round the *Sun* in orbits between those of *Mars* and *Jupiter*.

ASTIGMATISM. Defect of *lenses* (including the eye) caused by the curvature being different in two mutually perpendicular *planes*; thus *rays* in one plane may be in focus while those in the other are out of focus, producing distortion. Astigmatism of the eye is corrected by the use of cylindrical lenses.

ASTRO-COMPASS. Instrument for determining direction relative to the *stars*. Unaffected by the errors to which *magnetic* or *gyro compasses* are subject; used to determine the errors of such instruments.

ASTROLOGY. The ancient art, or pseudo-science, of predicting the course of human destinies by indications derived from the positions and movements of the heavenly bodies.

ASTRONOMICAL UNIT. The mean distance from the centre of the *Earth* to the centre of the *Sun*. Approximately $92 \cdot 9 \times 10^6$ miles.

ASTRONOMY. Scientific study of the heavenly bodies, their motion, relative positions, and nature.

ASYMMETRIC. Not possessing *symmetry*.

ASYMMETRIC CARBON ATOM. A carbon *atom* in a *molecule* of an *organic compound* with four different atoms or groups attached to its four *valencies*. Such a grouping permits of two different arrangements in space, leading to the existence of optical isomers. See *stereoisomerism*.

ASYMPTOTE. A line approaching a curve, but never reaching it within a finite distance.

-ATE. Suffix used in the naming of chemical *compounds*; in the case of *salts*, denoting a salt of the corresponding -*ic* acid; e.g. *sulphate* from *sulphuric acid*.

ATHERMANCY. Property of being opaque to *radiant heat*; i.e. of absorbing heat radiations.

ATMOLYSIS. Separation of a *mixture* of *gases* through the walls of a porous vessel by taking advantage of the different rates of *diffusion* of the constituents.

ATMOSPHERE. Gaseous envelope surrounding the *Earth* (or other heavenly body). The composition of the Earth's atmosphere varies very slightly in different localities and according to altitude. Volume composition of dry air at sea-level (average values): nitrogen, 78·08%; oxygen, 20·95%; argon, 0·93%; *carbon dioxide*, 0·03%; neon, 0·0018%; helium, 0·0005%; krypton, 0·0001%; xenon, 0·00001%. Air generally contains, in addition to the above, *water vapour, hydrocarbons, hydrogen peroxide*, sulphur *compounds*, and dust particles in small and very variable amounts. See also *upper atmosphere*.

ATMOSPHERE, the normal or standard. Unit of *pressure*. The pressure which will support a column of mercury 760 mm. high (29·92 inches) at 0° C., sea-level and latitude 45°. 1 normal atmosphere = 1·0132 bars = 14·72 lb./sq. in. (approx.). Atmospheric pressure fluctuates about this value from day to day.

ATMOSPHERICS. Electrical discharges which take place in the atmosphere, causing crackling sounds in *radio* receivers.

ATOM. Smallest portion of an *element* which can take part in a *chemical reaction*. See *atom, structure of*; *atomic theory*.

ATOM SMASHER. A popular name for an *accelerator*.

ATOM, STRUCTURE OF. The *atom* consists of a positively charged central core, the *nucleus*, surrounded by one or more negatively charged planetary *electrons*. The openness of atomic structure is indicated by the following approximate dimensions:

> Effective radius of atom 10^{-8} cm.
> Effective radius of nucleus 10^{-12} cm.
> Effective radius of electron 10^{-13} cm.

Almost all the *mass* of the atom resides in the nucleus, which is composed of two different types of stable particle of almost equal mass, the *proton* which is positively charged, and the *neutron* which is electrically neutral. The mass of the electron is 1/1836th of that of the proton, and although its charge is opposite in sign, it is numerically equal to that of the proton. The number of planetary electrons in the electrically neutral atom is therefore equal to the number of protons in the nucleus. The chemical behaviour of an atom is determined by its number of planetary electrons (characterized by the *atomic number*), chemical combination between atoms taking place by the transfer or sharing of outer electrons between combining atoms. See *valency, electronic theory of*.

According to the *Bohr theory*, the planetary electrons of an atom were to be thought of as moving in well defined *orbits* about the nucleus, corresponding to specific *energy levels* – the emission or absorption of a *photon* of *electromagnetic radiation* occurring when an electron made a *quantum* jump from one permitted orbit, or energy level, to another. In the more modern *wave mechanics* the electrons are regarded as having a dual wave/particle existence which is expressed mathematically by a *wave function*. The precise position of the electron in the Bohr model of the atom is therefore replaced in the wave mechanical model, by a *probability* that a particular planetary electron, visualized as a particle, may be found at a particular point in the path of a wave. Thus, in this model the atom is visualized as a central nucleus surrounded by a distribution of probabilities that individual electrons will exist at certain points at certain instants of time.

Atoms of an *element* which have the same number of protons, p, in their nuclei, but a different number of neutrons, n, are called *isotopes* of that element. When a particular isotope is being considered the following notation is used: to the chemical *symbol* of the element, the *mass number* (n+p) of the isotope is added as a superscript. The atomic number of the element may also be added as a subscript; e.g. $^1_1H, ^{12}_6C, ^{197}_{79}Au$, are the most abundant isotopes of hydrogen, carbon, and gold.

ATOMIC BOMB. See *nuclear weapons*.

ATOMIC CLOCK. A very accurate form of clock in which the basis of the time scale is derived from the vibrations of *atoms* or *molecules*. e.g. caesium clock, ammonia clock.

ATOMIC CONSTANTS. Electronic charge, $e = 4\cdot80298 \times 10^{-10}$ e.s.u.

Electronic *rest mass*, $m = 0\cdot91091 \times 10^{-27}$ gm.

Planck's constant, $h = 6\cdot6256 \times 10^{-27}$ erg. sec.

Velocity of *light*, $c = 2\cdot9979 \times 10^{10}$ cm./sec.

ATOMIC ENERGY. See *nuclear energy*.

ATOMIC HEAT. The numerical product of the *atomic weight* and the specific heat (see *heat, specific*) of an *element*. *Dulong and Petit's law* states that the atomic heat of all *solid* elements is approx. 6 *calories* per *gram-atom* per degree. The law is obeyed by many elements at ordinary *temperatures*, but at lower temperatures the atomic heat of all elements falls below this value, tending to zero as *absolute zero* of temperature is approached.

ATOMIC MASS UNIT. Unit used for expressing the masses of individual *isotopes* of *elements*: approximately equal to $1\cdot66 \times 10^{-24}$ gm. Formerly defined so that the most abundant isotope of oxygen, $^{16}_8O$, had a mass of 16 atomic mass units. In 1961 a unified scale of atomic masses based upon the isotope of carbon, $^{12}_6C$, was adopted by the International Union of Pure and Applied Physics and the International Union of Pure and Applied Chemistry. *Atomic weights* given in this dictionary are based upon this scale. See Table 1, pages 330–2.

ATOMIC NUCLEUS. See *nucleus, atomic*.

ATOMIC NUMBER. The number of *electrons* rotating round the *nucleus* of the neutral *atom* of an *element*, or the number of *protons* in the nucleus. (See *atom, structure of* and Table 1, pages 331–3.)

ATOMIC ORBITAL. The volume containing all the points within a free *atom* at which the *wave function* of an *electron* has an appreciable magnitude.

ATOMIC PILE. The original name for a *nuclear reactor*.

ATOMIC THEORY. Hypothesis as to the structure of *matter*, fore-shadowed by Democritus, put forward as a formal explanation of chemical facts and laws by Dalton in the beginning of the nineteenth century. Assumes that matter is made up of small indivisible particles called *atoms*; the atoms of any one *element* are identical in all respects, but differ from those of other elements at least in *weight*. Chemical *compounds* are formed by the union of atoms of different elements in simple numerical proportions. Modern views on the structure of the atom (see *atom, structure of*) diverge considerably from Dalton's hypothesis, but it is still of value in affording a simple explanation of the laws of *chemical combination*.

ATOMIC WEIGHT. The mean weight of the *atoms* of a given specimen of an *element*, expressed in *atomic mass units*. The atomic weights of the elements are given in Table 1, pages 330–2.

ATP. See *adenosine triphosphate*.

ATROPINE. $C_{17}H_{23}NO_3$. Member of the *alkaloids*. Colourless crystalline *insoluble* substance, m.p. 115° C.; extremely poisonous, has a powerful effect upon the nervous system, used in medicine to dilate the pupil of the eye. Occurs in the deadly nightshade and henbane.

ATTENUATION (phys.). The loss of *power* suffered by *radiation* as it passes through *matter*.

ATTO-. Prefix denoting one million million millionth; 10^{-18}.

AUDIBILITY, LIMITS OF. The limits of *frequency* of *sound*-waves which are audible as sound to the human ear. The lowest is about 30 vibrations per sec., corresponding to a very deep vibrating rumble, and the highest in the region of 20,000, corresponding to a shrill hiss.

AUDIO-FREQUENCY. A *frequency* between 30 and about 20,000 *cycles* per second, which in the case of *sound* waves would be audible.

AUDIOMETER. An instrument for measuring the level of human hearing.

AUER METAL. *Pyrophoric alloy* of 65% *misch metal* (a mixture of cerium and other metals) and 35% iron. Used as 'flint' in lighters.

AUGER EFFECT. The emission of an *electron* by an *atom*, without the emission of *X*- or *γ-radiation*, as a result of a change from an excited state (see *excitation*) to a lower energy state.

AURIFEROUS. Gold-bearing.

AURORA BOREALIS, Northern lights. A display of coloured light streamers and glows, mainly red and green, visible in the regions of the North and South Poles. Probably caused by streams of electrified particles from the *Sun*; most prominent when large *sun-spots* are observed. See *solar corpuscular streams*.

AUSTENITE. *Solid solution* of carbon or of iron carbide in the *gamma* form of iron; normally stable only at high *temperatures*, but may be preserved at normal temperatures by certain alloying *elements* or by rapid cooling.

AUTOCLAVE. Thick-walled vessel with a tightly fitting lid, in which substances may be heated above 100° C.

AUTOLYSIS. The self-destruction of biological *cells* after death, as a result of the action of their own *enzymes*.

AUTOMATION. The application of mechanical, or more commonly *electronic*, techniques to minimize the use of manpower in any process.

AUTORADIOGRAPH. Image obtained by placing a thin biological or other specimen, containing a *radioactive isotope*, in contact with a photographic plate, exposing for a suitable period and *developing*. The image shows the distribution of the radioactive *element* in the specimen.

AUXINS, phytamins, plant hormones. Substances promoting or directing the growth of plants.

AVALANCHE (phys.). A *shower* of particles caused by the collision of a high *energy* particle (e.g. a *cosmic ray*) with any other form of *matter*.

AVOGADRO'S LAW. Avogadro's hypothesis. Equal *volumes* of all *gases* contain equal numbers of *molecules* under the same conditions of *temperature* and *pressure*.

AVOGADRO'S NUMBER. The number of *molecules* in a *gram-molecule* or of *atoms* in a *gram-atom* of a substance; $6 \cdot 02252 \times 10^{23}$.

AVOIRDUPOIS WEIGHTS. System of *weights* used in the English-speaking countries. See *weight, British units of*.

AXIS. An imaginary line about which a given body or system is considered to rotate.

AXIS OF MIRROR. See *mirrors, spherical*.

AXIS OF SYMMETRY. Line about which a given figure is symmetrical; e.g. the diameter of a *circle*.

AXON. A long nerve fibre which carries impulses away from the body of a *neuron*.

AZEOTROPIC MIXTURE, constant boiling mixture. A mixture of two or more *liquids* which distils at a given constant *temperature* and has a constant composition, at a given *pressure*.

AZIMUTH (astr.). The *angular distance* from the north or south point of the horizon to the foot of the vertical circle through a heavenly body. The azimuth of a horizontal direction is its deviation from the north or south.

AZO-DYES. Class of organic *dyes*, mainly red or yellow, derived from azo-benzene, $C_6H_5N : NC_6H_5$.

AZO GROUP. The *bivalent* group —N : N—.

AZOTE. Former name for *nitrogen*.

AZURITE. Natural *basic* copper carbonate, blue in colour. $2CuCO_3.Cu(OH)_2$.

B

BABBITT METAL. A class of *alloys* with a high proportion of tin, and small amounts of copper and antimony. Part of the tin may be replaced by lead. Used for bearings.

BABO'S LAW. The addition of a non-volatile *solid* to a *liquid* in which it is *soluble* lowers the *vapour pressure* of the *solvent* in proportion to the amount of substance dissolved.

BACILLUS. In general, a rod-shaped *bacterium*. In particular, a genus of spore producing bacteria.

BACK E.M.F. OF CELL. When the poles of a *cell* become polarized (see *polarization, electrolytic*) a back *E.M.F.* is set up opposing the natural E.M.F. of the cell.

BACK E.M.F. OF ELECTRIC MOTOR. *E.M.F.* set up in the coil of an *electric motor*, opposing the current flowing through the coil, when the *armature* rotates.

BACKGROUND (phys.). The counting rate of a *counter tube* caused by sources other than the one being measured. Due primarily to natural *radioactivity* in the soil, and *cosmic rays*.

BACTERICIDE. Substance which kills *bacteria*.

BACTERIOLOGY. The study of *bacteria*.

BACTERIOPHAGE. Phage. A *virus* which requires a *bacterium* in which to replicate.

BACTERIUM. A cellular *micro-organism* incapable of *photosynthesis*. Usually single celled and usually reproduced by *mitosis* although there are exceptions. Bacteria are the causes of many diseases, most of which can now be treated by the use of *antibiotics*. However, bacteria also perform an indispensable function in nature by bringing about the decay of plant and animal debris in the soil. Bacteria are broadly classified by their shape into three main groups: the spherical or *coccus* form, the spiral-shaped organism called a *spirillum*, and the rod-shaped or *bacillus* type.

BAKELITE*. Trade name for various synthetic *resins* of which *phenol-formaldehyde resins* are amongst the most widely known.

BAKING POWDER. Mixture which produces *carbon dioxide* gas, CO_2, on wetting or heating, thus causing the formation of bubbles in the dough and making it 'rise'. Usually contains *sodium bicarbonate*, $NaHCO_3$, and tartaric acid or *cream of tartar*.

BAKING SODA. *Sodium bicarbonate*, $NaHCO_3$.

BALANCE. Apparatus for weighing. In principle consists of a lever with two equal arms, with a pan suspended from the end of each arm. Masses placed in the pans are subject to pulls of gravity; when these *forces* are equal, as indicated by the beam being horizontal, the masses themselves must be equal. Sensitive balances have beam and pans poised on knife-edges of *agate* resting on agate surfaces. An accurate balance will weigh to the nearest ·0001 gm. More sensitive balances have been designed for special work, for example, microbalances have been made which are capable of detecting differences in weight of only $0·25 \times 10^{-6}$ *milligrams* in a load of 250 milligrams.

BALANCED REACTION. See *chemical equilibrium*.

BALATA. A natural *rubber*-like material very similar to *gutta-percha*.

BALLISTIC GALVANOMETER. Instrument for measuring the total quantity of *electricity* passing through a circuit due to a momentary current. Any *galvanometer* may be used ballistically provided that its period of oscillation is long compared with the time during which the current flows.

BALLISTIC MISSILE. A ground-to-ground missile with a parabolic flight path.

BALLISTICS. The study of the flight path of *projectiles*.

BALMER SERIES. The visible *spectrum* of hydrogen. Consists of a series of sharp distinct lines, the *wave-lengths*, λ, of which may be represented by the formula $\frac{1}{\lambda} = A\left(\frac{1}{2^2} - \frac{1}{n^2}\right)$; $n = 3, 4, 5$, etc., A is a constant.

BAND SPECTRUM. *Emission* or *absorption spectrum* which consists of a number of fluted bands each having one sharp edge. Each band is composed of a large number of closely spaced lines. Band spectra arise from *molecules*.

BAR. Unit of *pressure* in the *C.G.S. system*; a pressure of 10^6 *dynes* per sq. cm. Equivalent to a pressure of 76 cm. of mercury.

BARBITURATES. Class of *organic compounds* derived from barbituric acid (malonyl urea), $CO(NH . CO)_2CH_2$. Many of these compounds have a powerful and sometimes dangerous soporific effect. Used in medicine.

BARFF PROCESS. Prevention of rusting of iron by the action of *steam* upon the surface of the red-hot metal, resulting in a surface coating of black oxide of iron, Fe_3O_4.

BARIUM. Ba. Element. A.W. 137·34. At. No. 56. Silvery-white soft *metal*, tarnishes readily in air. S.G. 3·5, m.p. 850° C. Occurs as *barytes*, $BaSO_4$, and as the carbonate, $BaCO_3$. *Compounds* resemble those of calcium but are poisonous. Compounds are used in the manufacture of *paints*, *glass*, and fireworks.

BARIUM TITANATE. $BaTiO_3$. A substance with good *ferroelectric* and *piezo-electric* properties used in *transducers*.

BARKHAUSEN EFFECT. Effect observed when a *ferromagnetic substance* is magnetized by a slowly increasing *magnetic field*; the magnetization does not take place continuously, but in a series of small steps. The effect is due to orientation of *magnetic domains* present in the substance.

BARN. Unit of area for measuring the *cross-section* of *nuclei*. 1 Barn equals 10^{-24} sq. cm.

BAROGRAPH. Instrument used in *meteorology* for recording on paper the variations in atmospheric pressure over a period of time.

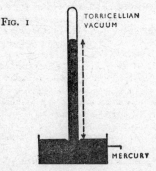

FIG. 1

TORRICELLIAN VACUUM

MERCURY

BAROMETER. (See also *aneroid* barometer.) Instrument for measuring atmospheric pressure. Consists of a long tube closed at the upper end filled with mercury and inverted in a vessel containing mercury; the vertical height of the mercury column which the atmospheric pressure is able at any time to support being taken as the atmospheric pressure at that time. See Fig. 1.

BARRIER-LAYER RECTIFIER. A *rectifier* which consists of a *semiconductor* between rectifying and non-rectifying metal *electrodes*.

BARYE. Unit of pressure in the *C.G.S. system*, equal to one *dyne* per sq. cm.

BARYON. A collective name for *nucleons* and *hyperons*. The number of baryons minus the number of corresponding anti-baryons taking part in a process is called the baryon number – a quantity which appears to be conserved in all processes. See *fermions*.

BARYTA. Barium oxide. BaO. White powder.

BARYTES, heavy spar. Natural barium sulphate, $BaSO_4$. White *insoluble solid*.

BASALT. Rock of volcanic origin, chemically resembling *felspar*.

BASE (chem.). Substance which reacts with an *acid* to form a *salt* and *water* only; substance which has a tendency to accept *protons*; substance which yields *hydroxyl ions* if dissolved in water. See also *organic base*.

BASE (phys.). The part of a *transistor* which separates the *emitter* from the *collector*.

BASE EXCHANGE, CATION EXCHANGE. See *ion exchange*.

BASE METALS. In contradistinction to the *noble metals*, metals which corrode, tarnish, or oxidize on exposure to air, moisture or heat.

BASIC (chem.). Of the nature of a *base*; opposite to *acidic*; reacting chemically with *acids* to form *salts*.

BASIC DYES. Group of *dyes* which are *salts* of *organic bases*, and are used for dyeing wool and natural silk, especially if specially bright shades are needed. Also used for staining *nucleic acids* in *biochemistry*.

BASIC SALT. *Salt* which has been formed by the partial neutralization of a *base*; consists of the normal salt combined with a definite molecular proportion of the base. E.g. *white lead*, basic lead carbonate, $2PbCO_3.Pb(OH)$.

BASIC SLAG. An impure *mixture* of tetracalcium phosphate, $Ca_4P_2O_9$, calcium silicate, $CaSiO_3$, *lime*, CaO, and *ferric oxide*, Fe_2O_3. By-product of *steel* manufacture; its high phosphorus content makes it a valuable *fertilizer*.

BATH SALTS. The main constituent is generally sodium sesquicarbonate, $Na_2CO_3.NaHCO_3.2H_2O$, or some other *soluble* sodium *salt* to soften the *water*. See *hard water*.

BATHYMETRY. Measurement of depth, especially of the sea.

BATTERY. A number of *primary* or *secondary cells* arranged in series or parallel. In series, they give a multiple of the *E.M.F.* of the cell; in parallel, they give the same E.M.F. as the cell, but have a greater capacity, i.e. a given current can be supplied for a longer period. The common 'dry batteries' usually consist of *Leclanché cells*.

BAUMÉ SCALE. A scale of *specific gravity* of *liquids*.

$$\text{Degrees Baumé} = \frac{144 \cdot 3 (\text{S.G.} - 1)}{\text{S.G.}}; \quad \text{S.G.} = \frac{144 \cdot 3}{144 \cdot 3 - \text{Degrees Baumé}}$$

BAUXITE. Natural *hydrated* aluminium oxide, $Al_2O_3.xH_2O$. The most important ore of aluminium.

BAUXITE CEMENT, ciment fondu. A rapid-hardening cement consisting mainly of calcium aluminate; made from *bauxite* and *lime* in an electric furnace.

BEAM (phys.). *Radiation* travelling in a particular direction.

BEAM HOLE. A hole made in the shield, and usually through the *reflector*, of a *nuclear reactor* to permit the escape of a beam of radiation, particularly *neutrons*, for experimental purposes.

BEAM TRANSMISSION. *Radio* transmission in which the *electromagnetic waves* are sent in a particular direction in a *beam* instead of being radiated in all directions.

BEARING (math.). The direction of a point B from a fixed point A; stated either in terms of the angle the line AB makes with the line running due North and South through A (e.g. 20° East of North); or in terms of the angle the line AB makes with the line running due North through A, considered in a clockwise direction.

BEAT FREQUENCY. The difference *frequency* resulting from the inter-action between *radio frequency* signals of different *wave-lengths*.

BEATS (phys.). A periodic increase and decrease in loudness which is heard when two notes of nearly the same *frequency* are sounded simultaneously. Caused by *interference* of *sound*-waves, the number of beats produced per second is equal to the difference in frequencies of the two notes.

BECKMANN THERMOMETER. Sensitive *thermometer* for measuring small differences or changes in *temperature*. The quantity of mercury in the bulb can be varied by causing it to overflow into a reservoir at the top, thus enabling the thermometer to be used over various ranges of temperature. The scale covers 6–7 degrees and is graduated to ·01 degree.

BEESWAX. A whitish *wax* consisting of a *mixture* of *compounds*, secreted by bees for the purpose of building their honeycombs. Used in polishes and cosmetics.

BEET SUGAR, sucrose. $C_{12}H_{22}O_{11}$. Obtained from the sugar beet; chemically identical with *cane sugar*.

BEL. Ten *decibels*

BELL, ELECTRIC. Simple device making use of the magnetic effect of an *electric current*. Closing the switch (see Fig. 2) causes a current, provided by a *Leclanché cell*, to flow through a small *electromagnet*. This then attracts a piece of soft iron attached to a hammer, causing the latter to strike the gong of the bell. The movement of the iron breaks the circuit; the current ceases to flow through the electromagnet, and the iron and attached hammer spring back into their original position, thus closing the circuit again; this process continues as long as the switch is closed.

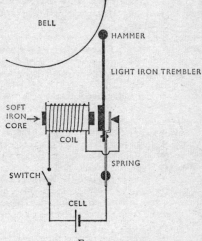

FIG. 2.

BELL METAL. *Alloy* of copper (60%–85%) and tin.

BENDING MOMENT. The bending moment about any point in a loaded beam is the *algebraic sum* of the *moments* of all the vertical *forces* to one side of that point.

BENTONITE. A clay-like material similar to *fuller's earth*.

BENZEDRINE. Amphetamine. $C_6H_5CH_2CH(CH_3)NH_2$. *Organic compound* used as a stimulant and for relieving catarrhal conditions.

BENZENE, benzol. C_6H_6. *Aromatic hydrocarbon* found in *coal-tar*. Colourless *liquid*, b.p. $80·1°$ C. Used as a *solvent*, in motor fuel, and in the manufacture of numerous *organic compounds*.

BENZIDINE. $NH_2C_6H_4C_6H_4NH_2$. An *aromatic* base, m.p. $128°$ C., of importance in the dyestuff industry.

BENZINE. Mixture of *hydrocarbons* of the *paraffin* series, boiling $50°–65°$ C. Used for dry cleaning and as a *solvent*.

BENZOIC ACID. C_6H_5COOH. The simplest of the *carboxylic acids* of the *aromatic* series, m.p. $122°$ C. Used as a food preservative, because it inhibits the growth of *yeasts* and moulds. Also used for this purpose in the form of its sodium *salt* which is highly water *soluble*.

BENZOL, benzole. See *benzene*.

BENZYL. The *univalent radical* $C_6H_5.CH_2$—.

BENZYL CELLULOSE. A *benzyl ether* of *cellulose*, possessing good electrical insulating properties, which forms the basis of a *plastic* material.

BERGIUS PROCESS. A process for the manufacture of *oil* from *coal*. Coal, made into a paste with heavy oil, is heated with hydrogen under a pressure of 250 *atmospheres* to a *temperature* of 450°–470° C., in the presence of a *catalyst*. The carbon of the coal reacts with the hydrogen to give a mixture of various *hydrocarbons*.

BERKELIUM. Bk. *Transuranic element*. At. No. 97. Member of the *actinide* series. Most stable *isotope*, $^{247}_{97}$Bk, has a *half-life* of about 7000 years.

BERNOULLI'S THEOREM. At any point in a tube through which a *liquid* is flowing, the sum of pressure energy, *potential energy*, and *kinetic energy* is constant.

BERTHOLLIDE COMPOUNDS. Chemical *compounds* the composition of which does not conform to a simple ratio of *atoms* in the *molecule*.

BERYL. Natural beryllium silicate, $3BeO.Al_2O_3.6SiO_2$.

BERYLLIUM, glucinum. Be. Element. A.W. 9·0122, At. No. 4. Hard white *metal*, S.G. 1·85, m.p. 1280° C. Occurs as *beryl*, from which it is obtained by *electrolysis*. Used for light, corrosion-resisting *alloys*.

BESSEMER PROCESS. A process for making *steel* from *cast iron*. Molten iron from the *blast furnace* is run into the Bessemer converter, a large egg-shaped vessel with holes below. Through these, air is blown into the molten metal, and the carbon is oxidized. The requisite amount of *spiegel* is then added to introduce the correct amount of carbon for the type of steel required.

BETA PARTICLE. An *electron* or *positron* emitted by a *radioactive nucleus*. The emission of an electron involves the change of a *neutron* into a *proton* within the nucleus, while the emission of a positron involves the change of a proton into a neutron. Beta particles do not exist within the nucleus, but are created at the instant of emission. See *neutrino*.

BETA RAYS, β-rays. Stream of *beta particles*; possess greater penetrating power than *alpha rays* and are emitted with velocities in some cases exceeding 98% of the *velocity* of light.

BETA TRANSFORMATION. Beta process. The transformation of a *nucleus* caused by the emission of a *beta particle*. A beta transformation involves a unit change of *atomic number* but no change of *mass number*.

BETATRON. A cyclic *accelerator* for accelerating a continuous beam of *electrons* to high speeds by means of the *electric field* produced by a changing magnetic flux. The electrons move in stable circular orbits in an evacuated *torus*-shaped chamber.

BEVATRON. A cyclic *accelerator* for accelerating *protons* and other particles to very high *energies*.

BI-. Prefix denoting two; in chemical nomenclature indicating an *acid salt* of a *dibasic acid*. E.g. sodium bisulphate, $NaHSO_4$.

BICARBONATE. *Acid salt* of *carbonic acid*, H_2CO_3; carbonic acid in which half the *acidic hydrogen* has been replaced by a *metal*. E.g. *sodium bicarbonate*, $NaHCO_3$.

BICHROMATE OF POTASH. $K_2Cr_2O_7$. See *potassium dichromate*.

BILE. Secretion of the liver of vertebrates which is important in the digestion of *fats*.

BILLION. Million million, 10^{12} (British); thousand million, 10^9 (American).

BIMETALLIC STRIP. A strip composed of two different *metals* welded together in such a way that a rise of *temperature* will cause it to buckle as a result of unequal expansion. Used in *thermostats*.

BIMORPH CELL. Two plates of *piezo-electric* material joined together so that they bend in proportion to an applied *voltage*.

BINARY CELL. An element in a *computer* which can store information by virtue of its ability to remain stable in one of two possible states.

BINARY COMPOUND. A chemical *compound* of two *elements* only. Denoted by the suffix -ide; e.g. *calcium carbide*, CaC_2.

BINARY NOTATION. Binary number system. A system of numbers which has only two different *digits*, usually 0 and 1. There are several ways of representing numbers in the binary notation, one common method is given below.

Decimal system	*Binary system*
1	0001
2	0010
3	0011
4	0100
5	0101
6	0110
7	0111
8	1000
9	1001
10	1010

BINARY STARS. Two *stars* gravitationally attracted to each other, so that they revolve around their common *centre of gravity*, thus forming a *double star*.

BINDING ENERGY (phys.). The *energy* which must be supplied to a *nucleus* in order to cause it to decompose into its constituent *neutrons* and *protons*. The binding energy of a neutron or a proton is the energy required to remove a neutron or a proton from a nucleus.

BINOCULAR. Any optical instrument designed for the simultaneous use of both eyes; e.g. binocular field-glasses.

BINOMIAL. Mathematical expression consisting of the sum or difference of two terms; e.g. $a^2 - 3b$.

BINOMIAL NOMENCLATURE (bio.). The method of naming plants and animals introduced by Linnaeus in the mid eighteenth century. Every plant or animal has two Latin names; a generic name designating its genus, and a specific name indicating the species; e.g. Felis tigris, the tiger.

BINOMIAL THEOREM. The expansion of

$$(x+y)^n = x^n + nx^{n-1}y + \frac{n(n-1)}{\lfloor 2} x^{n-2}y^2 + \ldots + y^n,$$

n being a positive *integer*. In general, for n not a positive integer, the following expression is valid if the numerical value of x is less than unity:

$$(1+x)^n = 1 + nx + \frac{n(n-1)}{\lfloor 2} x^2 + \ldots \text{ to } \infty.$$

BIOCHEMISTRY. The *chemistry* of living matter.

BIOGENESIS. The biological doctrine that only life begets life, as opposed to the unsubstantiated theory that animate matter may still be spontaneously generated from inanimate matter.

BIOLOGY. The science of life.

BIOMETRY. The application of mathematical and statistical methods to the study of *biology*.

BIOPHYSICS. The application of *physics* to the study of *biology*.

BIOTIN. A *vitamin* of the B complex group, widely distributed in nearly all living *cells* in very small quantities. Appears to be of importance in the *metabolism* of *carbohydrates*, *fats*, and *proteins*.

BI-PRISM. Optical device for obtaining *interference* fringes; consists of two acute-angled *prisms* placed base to base.

BIRKELAND AND EYDE PROCESS. Process for the fixation of atmospheric nitrogen (see *fixation of nitrogen*), becoming obsolete. Nitrogen and oxygen from the atmosphere are made to combine to form *nitric oxide*, NO, by the action of an electric *arc*.

BISECTION. Division into two equal parts.

BISECTOR. Line dividing into two equal parts.

BISMUTH. Bi. Element. A.W. 208·98. At. No. 83. White crystalline *metal* with a reddish tinge. S.G. 9·7; m.p. 271° C. Brittle, rather poor *conductor* of *heat* and *electricity*. Expands on solidifying. Occurs as the metal, or as the *oxide*, Bi_2O_3. Extracted by roasting the ore and heating with *coal*. Used in *alloys* of low *melting point* (see *Rose's metal*, *Wood's metal*); *compounds* used in medicine.

BIT. A unit of information in *information theory*. The amount of information required to specify one of two alternatives, e.g. to distinguish between 1 and 0 in the *binary notation* as used in *computers*. Also used as a unit of capacity in a storage device.

BITTERN (chem.). *Mother-liquor* remaining after the crystallization of common *salt*, NaCl, from *sea-water*. Source of *compounds* of magnesium, bromine, and iodine.

BITUMEN. Term covering numerous mixtures of *hydrocarbons*, more particularly solid or tarry, mixtures, *soluble* in *carbon disulphide*.

BITUMINOUS. Containing, or yielding upon *distillation, bitumen,* or *tar.*

BIURET. Carbamyl Urea. $NH_2CONH.CONH_2.H_2O$. *Organic compound* formed from *urea.* See *biuret reaction.*

BIURET REACTION. A *chemical reaction* in which an *alkaline* solution of *biuret* gives a purple colour on the addition of cupric sulphate. Used as a biochemical test for *protein* and *urea.*

BIVALENT, divalent. Having a *valency* of two.

BLACK ASH. Impure *sodium carbonate* obtained in the *Leblanc process.*

BLACK BODY RADIATION. Full or complete *radiation*; radiation of all *frequencies*, such as would be emitted by an ideal 'black body' which absorbs all radiations falling upon it. As the *emissivity* of a black body is one, the radiation which it emits is a function of *temperature* only.

BLACKDAMP. *Carbon dioxide* (in coal mines).

BLACKLEAD, plumbago, graphite. Natural crystalline form of carbon. Soft grey-black *solid*; used for making vessels to resist high *temperatures*, in pencils, and as a lubricant.

BLANC FIXE. Artificial barium sulphate, $BaSO_4$. Used as an *extender* in the *paint* industry.

BLANKET (phys.). A layer of *fertile* material surrounding the core of a *nuclear reactor* to act as a *reflector*, or for the purpose of breeding new fuel. See *breeder reactor.*

BLAST FURNACE. Furnace for the smelting of iron from iron oxide ores. Constructed of *refractory* bricks covered with *steel* plates. Charged from above with a mixture of the ore, *limestone* ($CaCO_3$), and *coke.* The coke is ignited at the bottom of the furnace by a blast of hot air; the *carbon monoxide* so produced reduces the iron oxide to iron, while the heat of the action decomposes the limestone into *carbon dioxide* and *lime*, CaO. The lime combines with the sand and other impurities in the ore to form a molten *slag.* The molten iron and the slag are tapped off at the bottom of the furnace. The resulting *pig-iron* or *cast iron* contains up to 4.5% carbon.

BLASTING GELATIN. Jelly-like mixture of *gun-cotton* with *nitroglycerin.* A very powerful *explosive.*

BLASTULA. A hollow ball of *cells* which forms in the very early embryonic development of animals.

BLEACHING. Removing the colour from coloured materials by chemically changing the dyestuffs into colourless substances. *Bleaching powder* and other *oxidizing agents*, or *sulphur dioxide* and other *reducing agents* are often used.

BLEACHING POWDER, chloride of lime. Whitish powder, consisting mainly of calcium oxychloride, $CaOCl_2$, with water; prepared by the action of chlorine on *slaked lime*, $Ca(OH)_2$. The action of *dilute acids* liberates chlorine which acts as an *oxidizing agent* and so bleaches the material.

BLENDE. Natural zinc sulphide, ZnS.

BLOOD. A *liquid* which circulates throughout the body of the higher animals, transporting oxygen and *cell* foods to all the component cells of the body, and removing their excretions. Blood consists of a liquid, *blood plasma*, in which *blood cells* are suspended.

BLOOD CELLS. Blood corpuscles. There are three types of blood cell: red corpuscles (*erythrocytes*), white corpuscles (*leucocytes*), and *blood platelets*. The function of the red corpuscles is the transport of oxygen throughout the body, by way of the *haemoglobin* which they contain. The function of the white cells is to combat infection.

BLOOD PLASMA. *Blood* from which all *blood cells* have been removed. Plasma is 90% water, in which the principal *solutes* are *proteins*, *salts*, *sugar*, and *urea*.

BLOOD PLATELETS. Thrombocytes. Small membrane-bounded, coin-shaped particles which circulate in the *blood*. If a blood vessel should break, the platelets clump together to form a plug to stop the bleeding. Platelets contain substantial quantities of *ATP*, and it is now known that the diphosphate causes the agglutination.

BLOWN OIL. A thickened *oil* made by blowing air through a natural vegetable or animal oil.

BLOWPIPE. Device for producing a jet of *flame* by forcing an inflammable *gas* mixed with air or oxygen through a nozzle at high pressure.

BLUE VITRIOL, bluestone. Crystalline *copper sulphate*, $CuSO_4.5H_2O$. Used for copper plating and in *solution* for spraying plants.

BLUE-PRINT, cyanotype. Device much used for reproducing electrical circuit diagrams, engineering designs, etc. Sensitive paper, coated with an organic ferric *salt* and potassium ferricyanide, $K_3Fe(CN)_6$, is used; the original drawing is placed over this and the whole exposed to *light*. The sensitive paper is then developed by washing with water; this gives an image of white lines on a blue background. The blue colour is caused by the reduction of the ferric salt to a ferrous salt by the action of light, and the interaction of the ferrous salt with the potassium ferricyanide to give *Prussian Blue*.

BLUESTONE. See *blue vitriol*.

BOARD OF TRADE UNIT, B.O.T. unit. Legal British unit of *electrical energy*, the *kilowatt-hour*. The energy obtained when a power of 1 *kilowatt* is maintained for 1 hour.

BOART. See *bort*.

BOG IRON ORE. Impure form of *hydrated* iron oxide, $Fe_2O_3.xH_2O$, found in bogs and marshes.

BOHR THEORY of hydrogen atom spectrum. Theory of the *atom* put forward by Bohr to explain the *line spectrum* observed for hydrogen (see *Balmer series*). Based on three postulates: 1. The *electrons* rotate in certain *orbits* round the *nucleus* of the atom without radiating *energy* in the form of *electromagnetic waves*. 2. These orbits are such that the *angular momentum* of the electron about the nucleus is an *integral* multiple of $h/2\pi$, where $h = Planck's constant$. 3. Emission or absorption of radiation occurs when an electron jumps from one of these so-called *stationary states* of energy E_1 to another of energy E_2, the *frequency*, v, of the emitted (or absorbed) *light* being given by $E_1 - E_2 = hv$. If E_1 is greater than E_2, light is emitted; conversely, light is absorbed. See *quantum mechanics*. This theory has now been superseded by the application of *wave mechanics*, which has shown that for the hydrogen atom spectrum, Bohr's theory is a very good approximation. Wave mechanics has the advantage of requiring no *ad hoc* assumptions and can deal more effectively with the problem of atoms with two or more electrons. (See also *Atom, structure of*.)

BOILED OIL. *Linseed oil* boiled with, or containing, a drying agent such as *litharge*, PbO. Used in *paints*.

BOILING, ebullition. The state of a *liquid* at its *boiling point* when the maximum *vapour pressure* of the liquid is equal to the external pressure to which the liquid is subject, and the liquid is freely converted into *vapour*.

BOILING POINT, b.p. of a liquid. The *temperature* at which the maximum *vapour pressure* of the *liquid* is equal to the external pressure; the temperature at which the liquid boils freely under that pressure. Boiling points are normally quoted for standard atmospheric pressure, i.e. 760 mm. of mercury.

BOILING WATER REACTOR. BWR. A *nuclear reactor* in which *water* is used as coolant and *moderator*. *Steam* is thus produced in the reactor under pressure, and can be used to drive a *turbine*.

BOLOMETER. Extremely sensitive instrument for measuring *heat radiations*. Consists essentially of two very thin, blackened platinum gratings, forming two arms of a *Wheatstone bridge* circuit. Radiant heat falling upon one of the gratings raises its electrical *resistance*, thus causing a deflection of the needle of a *galvanometer* in the circuit.

BOLTZMANN'S CONSTANT. $K = \dfrac{R}{N} = 1 \cdot 38054 \times 10^{-16}$ *erg.* deg.$^{-1}$

where $R =$ the *gas constant* $\left(\dfrac{PV}{T}$ for 1 gm.-mol. of a *perfect gas*$\right)$

$N =$ *Avogadro's number*.

BOMB CALORIMETER. Strong metal vessel used for measuring *heats of reaction*, especially *heats of combustion*; e.g. for determining the *calorific value* of a *fuel*. To do this, a known *weight* of the substance under test is burnt in the vessel, and by measuring the quantity of heat produced, the calorific value is calculated.

BOND, valency bond, linkage. Representation of a *valency* link by which one *atom* is attached to another in a chemical *compound*.

BOND ENERGY. *Energy* characterizing a chemical *bond* between two *atoms*. Measured by the energy required to separate the two atoms.

BOND LENGTH. The distance between the *nuclei* of two *atoms* joined by a chemical *bond*.

BONE ASH. *Ash* obtained by heating bones in air. Consists mainly of calcium phosphate, $Ca_3(PO_4)_2$.

BONE BLACK. See *animal charcoal*.

BONE CHAR. See *animal charcoal*.

BONE OIL, Dippel's oil. Product obtained by the *destructive distillation* of bones. Dark, oily, evil-smelling liquid; source of *pyridine*.

BOOLEAN ALGEBRA. A branch of symbolic logic used in automatic *computers*. Logical operations are performed by operators such as 'and', 'or', 'not-and' in a way analogous to mathematical signs.

BORACIC ACID. See *boric acid*.

BORAX. Sodium pyroborate, $Na_2B_4O_7.10H_2O$. White, *soluble* crystalline *salt*, occurs naturally as *tincal*. On heating, loses water and melts to a clear glass-like *solid* (see *borax bead test*). Used as an *antiseptic*, in fire-proofing, soldering, *glass*, *ceramics*, and other industries.

BORAX BEAD TEST. Chemical test for the presence of certain *metals*. A bead of *borax* fused in a wire loop will react chemically with the *salts* of a number of metals, often producing colours which help to identify the metal; e.g. manganese *compounds* give a violet bead, cobalt a deep blue.

BORDEAUX MIXTURE. Mixture of copper sulphate (*blue vitriol*, $CuSO_4$), *lime* CaO, and *water*. Used for spraying plants as a *fungicide* for plant diseases.

BORIC ACID, boracic acid. H_3BO_3. White crystalline *soluble solid*. Occurs naturally in volcanic regions; also manufactured from *borax*. Used as a mild *antiseptic* and in various industries.

BORON. B. Element. A.W. 10·811. At. No. 5. Brown *amorphous* powder or yellow *crystals*; S.G. 2·3, m.p. 2300° C. Occurs as *borax* and *boric acid*. Used for hardening *steel* and for producing *enamels* and *glasses*. As boron absorbs slow *neutrons*, it is used in steel *alloys* for making *control rods* in *nuclear reactors*.

BORON CARBIDE. B_4C. A very hard black crystalline substance, m.p. 2450° C., used as an *abrasive*.

BORON CHAMBER. An *ionization chamber* lined with boron or boron *compounds* or filled with boron trifluoride *gas*. Used in *Boron counter tubes*.

BORON COUNTER TUBES. A *counter tube* containing a *boron chamber* used for counting *neutrons*. The counting pulse results from particles emitted when *neutrons* react with the $^{10}_5B$ *isotope*.

BORT, boart. Impure or discoloured *diamond*, useless as gem, but as hard as pure diamond, and used for drills, cutting tools, etc.

BOSCH PROCESS. Industrial process for the manufacture of hydrogen. *Water gas*, a *mixture* of *carbon monoxide* and hydrogen, is mixed with *steam* and passed over a heated *catalyst*. The steam reacts chemically with the carbon monoxide to give *carbon dioxide*, CO_2, and hydrogen. The CO_2 is then removed by dissolving it in water under pressure.

BOSE-EINSTEIN STATISTICS. The branch of statistical mechanics used with systems of identical particles which have the property that the *wave function* remains unchanged if any two particles are interchanged. See *bosons*.

BOSONS. Particles which conform to *Bose-Einstein statistics*, such as *photons* and *mesons*, whose numbers are not conserved in particle interactions.

BOTANY. The scientific study of plants.

BOURDON GAUGE. *Pressure* gauge for steam boilers, etc. Depends on the tendency of a partly flattened curved tube to straighten out when under internal pressure.

BOYLE'S LAW. At a constant *temperature*, the *volume* of a given quantity of any *gas* is inversely proportional to the *pressure* upon the gas; i.e.

$V \propto \dfrac{1}{P}$, or $PV=$ constant. True for a *perfect gas*.

BRAKE HORSE-POWER. *Horse-power* of an engine measured by the degree of resistance offered by a brake; represents the useful horse-power that the engine can develop.

BRANCHING (phys.). The occurrence of more than one *radioactive disintegration* scheme for a particular *nuclide*.

BRASS. Large class of *alloys*, consisting principally of copper and zinc.

BREEDER REACTOR. A *nuclear reactor* which produces the same kind of *fissile* material as it burns. E.g. a reactor using plutonium as a fuel can produce more plutonium than it uses by conversion of Uranium-238.

BREWING. The making of beer. *Malt* is ground and mixed with water. In the resulting 'mash', chemical changes take place, the chief of which is the conversion of *starch* into *maltose*, forming a sweetish liquid known as wort. This is boiled with the addition of hops. After cooling and removal of *solids*, *yeast* is added and *fermentation* occurs.

BREWSTER'S LAW. The tangent of the angle of *polarization* is numerically equal to the *refractive index* of the reflecting medium.

BRIGHTNESS. The brightness at any point of an extended source, in a given direction, is the quotient of the *luminous intensity* of a small element of the source containing the point, and the area of the element projected on to a plane perpendicular to the given direction. Measured in *candelas* per unit area.

BRIMSTONE. Sulphur fused into blocks or rolls.

BRINELL TEST. Test for the hardness of *metals*. A ball of chrome *steel*, or other hard material, of standard size, is pressed by a heavy load into the surface of the metal, and the diameter of the depression is measured.

BRITANNIA METAL. *Alloy* of variable composition, containing 80%–90% tin, with some antimony and copper, and sometimes also zinc and lead.

BRITISH THERMAL UNIT. Quantity of *heat* required to raise the *temperature* of 1 lb. of *water* through 1° Fahrenheit, 251·98 *calories*.

BROMIDE. *Salt* of hydrobromic acid, HBr; *binary compound* with bromine. 'Bromide' of pharmacy is *potassium bromide*, KBr.

BROMIDE PAPER. Photographic paper containing *silver bromide*, AgBr.

BROMINE. Br. Element. A.W. 79·909. At. No. 35. Dark red fuming *liquid* with a choking, irritating smell, b.p. 58·8° C. Occurs as magnesium bromide, $MgBr_2$, in *bittern* from *sea-water*; in the *Stassfurt deposits*; in marine plants and animals; and in some inland lakes. Used as a *disinfectant* and in the manufacture of some *organic compounds*. Compounds used in *photography* and medicine.

BRONZE. Class of *alloys* of copper and tin; term is also sometimes applied to alloys containing no tin, e.g. *aluminium bronze*, an alloy of copper and aluminium.

BROWNIAN MOVEMENT. Erratic random movements performed by microscopic particles in a *disperse phase*; e.g. particles in suspension in a *liquid* or *smoke* particles in air. Caused by the continuous irregular bombardment of the particles by the *molecules* of the surrounding medium.

BRUNSWICK GREEN, cupric oxychloride. $CuCl_2.3Cu(OH)_2$. Used as a *pigment*.

BRUSH DISCHARGE. Discharge of *electricity* from sharp points on a *conductor*. The surface density (i.e. quantity of electricity per unit area) is greatest at sharp points; the high charge at such points causes a displacement of the charge on the air particles near the points, and hence an attraction to the points. On reaching the points, the particles acquire some of the charge on the points and are repelled. This causes a stream of charged air particles to leave the vicinity of the points.

BUBBLE CHAMBER. An instrument for making the tracks of ionizing particles visible as a row of bubbles in a *liquid*.

BUCHNER FUNNEL. Funnel, usually of *porcelain*, with a flat circular base perforated with small holes. Used for filtering by suction.

BUFFER SOLUTION. A *solution* the *hydrogen ion concentration* of which, and hence the acidity or alkalinity, is practically unchanged by dilution, and which resists a change of *pH* on the addition of *acid* or *alkali*.

BULK MODULUS. *Elastic modulus* applied to a body having uniform *stress* distributed over the whole of its surface. Its value is given by the expression $\dfrac{pV}{v}$ where p = intensity of stress, V = original *volume* of the body, and v = change in volume.

BUNSEN BURNER. Burner for *coal-gas*, used in laboratories. Consists of a metal tube with an adjustable air-valve for burning a mixture of gas and air.

BUNSEN CELL. A *primary cell* in which the *anode* consists of zinc and is immersed in dilute *sulphuric acid*, and the *cathode* consists of carbon immersed in concentrated *nitric acid*.

BUOYANCY. The upward thrust exerted upon a body immersed in a *fluid*; equal to the *weight* of the fluid displaced (See *Archimedes' Prin-*

ciple). Thus a body weighs less when weighed in water, the apparent loss in weight being equal to the weight of the water displaced. For accurate weighing of bodies in air, a small allowance has to be made to correct for the buoyancy of the body.

BURETTE. Graduated glass tube with a tap, for measuring the volume of *liquid* run out from it. Used in *volumetric analysis*.

BURNING. See *combustion*.

BURNT ALUM. White porous mass of *anhydrous* potassium aluminium sulphate, $K_2SO_4.Al_2(SO_4)_3$, obtained by heating *alum*.

BUTADIENE. $CH_2:CH.CH:CH_2$. A *gas* used in the manufacture of synthetic *rubbers*. See *styrene-butadiene rubber*, *nitrile rubber*, and *stereo-regular rubbers*.

BUTANE. C_4H_{10}. *Hydrocarbon* of the *paraffin series*. *Gas* at ordinary *temperatures*. B.p.$-0.6°C$.

BUTTER OF ANTIMONY. Antimony trichloride, $SbCl_3$. White crystalline substance, m.p. $73°C$.

BUTYL. *Univalent alkyl radical* C_4H_9—.

BUTYL RUBBER. A synthetic *rubber*; copolymer (see *polymerization*) of iso-butylene and sufficient *isoprene* ($2\%-3\%$) to enable vulcanization to be effected. Owing to its low *permeability* to *gases*, butyl rubber is used in the manufacture of tyre inner tubes.

BUZZER, electric. Device similar in principle to the electric *bell*, but without a hammer or gong. The rapid vibration of the arm produces a definite buzzing note when the current flows.

BYPASS CAPACITOR. Bypass Condenser. A *capacitor* which provides a path of low *impedance* over a certain range of *frequencies*.

BY-PRODUCT. Substance obtained incidentally during the manufacture of some other substance. Often as important as the manufactured substance itself. E.g. the by-products of *coal-gas* manufacture include *ammonia*, *coal-tar*, and *coke*.

C

CABLE, COAXIAL. Cable consisting of central conducting wire together with a concentric cylindrical *conductor*, the space between the two being filled with a *dielectric* substance, e.g. *polythene*, air, etc. The outer conductor is normally connected to earth. Its main use is to transmit *high-frequency* power from one place to another with minimum *energy* loss; e.g. from a transmitter to its *aerial*.

CADMIUM. Cd. Element. A.W. 112.40. At. No. 48. Soft silvery-white *metal*, S.G. 8.642, m.p. $320.9°C$. Occurs together with zinc. Used in the manufacture of *fusible alloys* and for *electroplating*. As cadmium is a good absorber of *neutrons* it is used in the manufacture of *control rods* for *nuclear reactors*.

CADMIUM CELL. Standard *primary cell*. See *Weston cell*.

CAESIUM, Cesium. Cs. Element. A.W. 132.905. At. No. 55. Silvery-white *metal* resembling sodium in its physical and chemical properties.

S.G. 1·87, m.p. 28·5° C. Highly reactive. *Compounds* are very rare. Used in *photo-electric cells* and as a *catalyst*.

CAFFEINE, theine. $C_8H_{10}O_2N_4$. Member of the *purine* group of *organic compounds*. White crystals, m.p. 235° C. Occurs in tea-leaves, coffeebeans, and other plant material. Has a powerful action on the heart; used in medicine.

CALAMINE. A zinc mineral, originally either zinc carbonate, $ZnCO_3$, or zinc silicate, $2Zn.SiO_3.H_2O$. In English usage calamine now refers to the carbonate but in American usage it refers to the silicate. Also used for a skin preparation consisting of zinc oxide with $\frac{1}{2}$% ferric oxide.

CALCIFEROL, vitamin D_2. $C_{28}H_{43}OH$. Formed by the action of *ultraviolet radiation* on *ergosterol*. See *vitamins*.

CALCINATION. Strong heating; conversion of *metals* into their *oxides* by heating in air.

CALCITE, calcspar. Natural crystalline *calcium carbonate*, $CaCO_3$.

CALCIUM. Ca. Element. A.W. 40·08. At. No. 20. Soft white *metal*, tarnishes rapidly in air; S.G. 1·55, m.p. 845° C. *Compounds* are very abundant, widely distributed, and essential to life. Occurs as the carbonate, $CaCO_3$ (*limestone, marble,* and *chalk*); sulphate, $CaSO_4$ (*gypsum, anhydrite*); essential constituent of bones and teeth. Compounds are of great industrial importance; e.g. *lime*.

CALCIUM CARBIDE, 'carbide'. CaC_2. Greyish solid, colourless when pure; prepared by heating *lime*, CaO, with carbon in an electric furnace. Reacts with *water* to give *acetylene*.

CALCIUM CARBONATE. $CaCO_3$. White insoluble solid; occurs naturally as *chalk, limestone, marble,* and *calcite*.

CALCIUM CYANAMIDE, 'cynamide', Nitrolime. $CaCN_2$. Artificial *fertilizer* made by heating *calcium carbide*, CaC_2, in nitrogen at 1000° C. Water in the soil converts it into *ammonia*. Also used as the starting point in the manufacture of various chemical products.

CALCIUM HYDROXIDE, *slaked lime*, $Ca(OH)_2$. See *lime*.

CALCIUM HYPOCHLORITE. Calcium oxychloride. See *bleaching powder*.

CALCIUM OXIDE, *quicklime*, CaO. See *lime*.

CALCULUS, the. Branch of mathematics, divided into two main parts, *differential* and *integral calculus*. Deals with *variable* quantities and their rates of change. Affords a powerful method of solving numerous mathematical problems.

CALIBRATION. The *graduation* of an instrument to enable measurements in definite *units* to be made with it; thus the arbitrary scale of a *galvanometer* may be calibrated in *amperes*, thereby converting the instrument into an *ammeter* for measuring *electric current*.

CALICHE. Impure natural *sodium nitrate* $NaNO_3$, found in Chile.

CALIFORNIUM. Cf. *Transuranic element*. At. No. 98. The most stable *isotope*, $^{249}_{98}Cf$, has a *half-life* of 470 years.

CALLIPERS, calipers. Instrument for measuring the distance between two points, especially on a curved surface; e.g. for measuring the internal and external diameters of tubes.

CALOMEL, mercurous chloride. Hg_2Cl_2. White *insoluble* substance used in medicine.

CALORESCENCE. Absorption of *light* radiations by a surface, their conversion into *heat*, and the consequent emission of heat *radiation*.

CALORIE. Unit of quantity of *heat*. The amount of heat required to raise the *temperature* of 1 gm. of *water* through 1° C. The 15° calorie is defined as the amount of heat required to raise the temperature of 1 gm. of water from 14·5° C. to 15·5° C.

CALORIE, LARGE, kilogram-calorie. 1000 *calories*. Written Calorie. Used for quoting energy values of foods.

CALORIE, MEAN. One-hundredth of the quantity of *heat* required to raise the *temperature* of 1 gm. of *water* from 0° C. to 100° C. Very nearly equal to the *calorie* as defined above.

CALORIFIC VALUE of a fuel. The quantity of *heat* produced by a given weight of the *fuel* on complete *combustion*. Usually given as the number of *British Thermal Units* evolved by the complete combustion of 1 lb. of the fuel. Determined by the *bomb calorimeter*.

CALORIMETER. Instrument for determining quantities of *heat* evolved, absorbed, or transferred. In its simplest form consists of an open cylindrical vessel of copper or other substance of known specific heat (see *heat, specific*).

CAMERA, PHOTOGRAPHIC. A device for obtaining photographs or exposing cinematic film, either coloured or black and white. A camera consists essentially of a *light*-proof box with a *lens* at one end and a light-sensitive film or plate at the other. An 'exposure' is made by opening a 'shutter' over the lens for a predetermined period during which an image of the object to be photographed is thrown upon the light-sensitive film. Focusing is carried out by varying the distance of the lens from the film by a suitable device. The amount of light which enters the camera, in order to obtain a correctly exposed photograph, is determined by the amount of light available (either sunlight or artificial light), the 'speed' of the film, the *aperture* of the lens, and the shutter speed. In the simplest cameras the shutter speed and aperture are fixed, so that satisfactory photographs can only be obtained in bright sunlight. In more expensive cameras the aperture can be controlled by a variable *iris* and several separate shutter speeds are provided. In some modern cameras the iris is controlled by the current from a built-in *photo-electric cell* (*exposure meter*) which measures the light available. Thus for given film and shutter speeds the camera automatically takes a correctly exposed photograph. In cinematic cameras the opening of the shutter is mechanically synchronized with the passage of the film through the camera so that, at normal speeds, between 16 and 24 frames are exposed every second. See also *photography*.

CAMERA, TELEVISION. That part of a *television* system which converts optical images into electrical signals. Consists of an optical *lens* system similar to that used in a photographic *camera*, the image from which is projected into a 'camera tube'. The camera tube comprises a *photosensitive mosaic* which is scanned by an *electron* beam housed in an evacuated glass tube. The output signals of the camera tube are usually pre-amplified within the body of the camera.

CAMPHOR. $C_{10}H_{16}O$. White crystalline *solid* with a characteristic smell. M.p. 178° C. Occurs in the camphor tree. Used in the manufacture of *celluloid* and in other industries.

CANADA BALSAM. A yellowish *liquid* derived from fir trees with a *refractive index* similar to that of *glass*. Used for mounting microscopic slides and as an adhesive for optical instruments.

CANAL RAYS. Positively charged *ions* produced during the *discharge* of electricity in gases, driven to the *cathode* by the applied *potential difference* and allowed to pass through canals bored in the cathode.

CANDELA, 'new candle'. Unit of luminous intensity. So defined that the brightness of a black body radiator (see *black body radiation*) at the *temperature* of solidification of platinum (2046° K) equals 60 candela/sq. cm. The candela now replaces the *international candle* as unit of *luminous intensity*.

CANDLEPOWER of a light source, in a given direction, is the *luminous intensity* of the source in that direction expressed in terms of the *candela*. Formerly expressed in terms of the *international candle*.

CANDLE WAX. Usually either *paraffin wax* or *stearine*.

CANE SUGAR, sucrose, saccharose. $C_{12}H_{22}O_{11}$. A *disaccharide* obtained from the sugar-cane. Chemically identical with *beet sugar*.

CANTON'S PHOSPHORUS. Impure calcium sulphide, CaS, having the property of *phosphorescence* after exposure to *light*. Used in luminous *paints*.

CAOUTCHOUC. Raw *rubber*.

CAPACITANCE. Electrical capacity. The property of a system of electrical *conductors* and *insulators* which enables it to store *electric charge* when a *potential difference* exists between the conductors. Measured by the charge which must be communicated to such a system to raise its potential by one unit. The practical unit of capacitance is the *farad* which is defined so that a system having a capacitance of one farad requires a charge of one *coulomb* to raise its potential by one *volt*. 1 farad = 8.99×10^{11} *electrostatic units*.

CAPACITOR. Electrical condenser. A system of electrical *conductors* and *insulators* the principal characteristic of which is its *capacitance*. The simplest form consists of two parallel *metal* plates separated by a layer of air or some other insulating material, such as *mica* (see *dielectric*). The capacitance, C, of such a parallel plate capacitor is given by:

$$C = \frac{AK}{4\pi d}$$

where K is the *dielectric constant*, A the area of plate, and d the distance between them.

CAPACITY, THERMAL; heat capacity. The quantity of *heat* required to raise the *temperature* of a body 1° C. Product of the *mass* of the body in grams and its *specific heat*.

CAPILLARY ACTION. General term for phenomena observed in *liquids* due to unbalanced inter-molecular attraction at the liquid boundary; e.g. the rise or depression of liquids in narrow tubes, the formation of films, drops, bubbles, etc.

CAPILLARY TUBE. Tube of small internal diameter.

CAPTURE. A process by which an atomic or nuclear system acquires an additional particle, e.g. the capture of *electrons* by *ions* or of *neutrons* by *nuclei*. 'Radiative capture' is a nuclear capture process which results in the emission of *gamma rays* only.

CARAMEL (chem.). Brown substance of complex composition, formed by the action of *heat* on *sugar*.

CARAT. 1. Measure of weight of *diamonds* and other gems; formerly 3·17 grains (0·2053 gm.), now standardized as the international carat, 0·200 gm. 2. Measure of *fineness* of gold, expressed as parts of gold in 24 parts of the *alloy*. Thus, 24 carat gold is pure gold, 18 carat gold contains 18 parts in 24 or has a fineness of 750.

CARBAMIDE. See *urea*.

CARBIDE. *Binary compound* of carbon; loose term for *calcium carbide*.

CARBOCYCLIC COMPOUNDS. *Organic compounds* containing a closed ring of carbon *atoms* within the *molecule*. E.g. *benzene*, C_6H_6, has a molecule of six carbon atoms joined in a ring, with a hydrogen atom attached to each.

CARBOHYDRATE. Large group of *organic compounds* composed of carbon, hydrogen, and oxygen only, with the general formula $C_x(H_2O)_y$. Comprises *monosaccharides*, *disaccharides* (both *sugars*), and *polysaccharides* (*starch* and *cellulose*). Carbohydrates play an essential part in the *metabolism* of all living *organisms*, starch being the principal form in which *energy* is stored and cellulose being the principal structural material of plants.

CARBON. C. Element. A.W. 12·011, At. No. 6, m.p. 3550° C. Occurs in several allotropic forms (see *allotropy*) including *diamond* (S.G. 3·51) and *graphite* (S.G. 2·25); and as *amorphous* carbon (S.G. 1·8–2·1) in the forms of *lamp-black*, *gas carbon*, etc. *Compounds* occur as the metallic *carbonates*, *carbon dioxide* in the air, and an enormous number of *organic compounds*. Owing to its *valency* of four, carbon *atoms* are able to unite with each other to form the very large *molecules* upon which life is based. See *carbon cycle* (bio.). Animals obtain their energy by the *oxidation* of carbon compounds eaten as food.

CARBON BLACK. Finely divided form of pure carbon, obtained by the incomplete *combustion* of *natural gas*. Used in the manufacture of *inks*, *rubber* products, and some *plastics*.

CARBON CYCLE (bio.). The circulation of carbon (as *carbon dioxide*) between living *organisms* and the *atmosphere*. Carbon dioxide is built into complex carbon *compounds* by plants during *photosynthesis*; animals obtain their carbon *atoms* by feeding on plants or other animals; during *respiration*, and by decay after death, some of this carbon is returned to the atmosphere in the form of carbon dioxide.

CARBON CYCLE (phys.). A cycle of six consecutive *nuclear reactions* resulting in the formation of a *helium* nucleus from four *protons*. The carbon nuclei with which the cycle starts are reformed at the end and therefore act as a *catalyst*. The *energy* liberated by the carbon cycle is thought to be the main source of energy in a large class of *stars*.

CARBON DIOXIDE, carbonic acid gas. CO_2. Colourless *gas* with faint tingling smell and taste. Occurs in the *atmosphere*; formed by the *oxidation* of carbon and carbon *compounds*. Utilized by plants. See *photosynthesis* and *carbon cycle* (*bio.*). Forms a solid at $-78 \cdot 5°$ C. at atmospheric pressure, and is used as a refrigerant in this form as *dry-ice*, for the preservation of frozen foods, etc. As carbon dioxide gas is heavier than air and does not support *combustion*, it is used in *fire extinguishers*.

CARBON DISULPHIDE, carbon bisulphide, CS_2. Colourless inflammable *liquid*, b.p. 46° C., with a high *refractive index*. Made by heating carbon with sulphur in a *retort*. Used as a *solvent* in the vulcanization of *rubber*, in the manufacture of viscose *rayon* and for killing pests.

CARBON MONOXIDE. CO. Colourless, almost odourless *gas*. Very poisonous when breathed, combines with the *haemoglobin* of the *blood* to form bright red carboxyhaemoglobin. This is chemically stable, and thus the haemoglobin is no longer available to carry oxygen. Burns with a bright blue *flame* to form *carbon dioxide*. Formed during the incomplete *combustion* of *coke*, *charcoal*, and other carbonaceous *fuels*. Occurs in *coal-gas* and in the exhaust fumes of motor engines.

CARBON TETRACHLORIDE. CCl_4. Heavy colourless *liquid* with a sweetish smell, b.p. $76 \cdot 8°$ C. Used as a non-inflammable *solvent* and in *fire extinguishers* (*pyrene*).

CARBONADÓ. Black, discoloured, or impure variety of *diamond*, useless as a gem but very hard and used for drills, etc.

CARBONATE. *Salt* of *carbonic acid*, H_2CO_3.

CARBONIC ACID. H_2CO_3. Very weak *acid* probably formed in small amounts when *carbon dioxide* dissolves in *water*. Term often applied to carbon dioxide itself. Never obtained pure; breaks up almost completely into carbon dioxide and water when obtained in a chemical reaction. Gives rise to two series of *salts*, the *carbonates* and *bicarbonates*.

CARBONIZATION. See *destructive distillation*.

CARBONYL CHLORIDE. See *phosgene*.

CARBONYL GROUP. The *divalent* group — CO.

CARBONYLS. *Compounds* of *metals* with *carbon monoxide*; e.g. nickel carbonyl, $Ni(CO)_4$.

CARBORUNDUM, silicon carbide, SiC. Dark crystalline *solid*, nearly as hard as *diamond*, used as an *abrasive* and as a *refractory* material. Made by heating *silica*, SiO_2, with carbon in an electric furnace.

CARBOXYL GROUP. The *univalent* group —COOH, characteristic of the organic *carboxylic acids*.

CARBOXYLIC ACID. An *acidic organic compound* which contains one or more *carboxyl groups*.

CARBURETTOR. Device in the *internal-combustion* petrol engine for mixing air with *petrol vapour* preliminary to explosion.

CARCINOGEN. A substance capable of producing cancer (carcinoma).

CARNALLITE. Natural potassium magnesium chloride,
$$KCl.MgCl_2.6H_2O,$$
found in the *Stassfurt deposits*. Important source of potassium *salts*.

CARNOTITE. Uranium potassium vanadate of variable composition. Ore of uranium.

CARNOT'S CYCLE. An ideal reversible cycle of operations for the working substance of a heat engine. The four steps in the cycle are: (a) *isothermal* expansion, the substance taking in *heat* and doing *work*; (b) *adiabatic* expansion, without heat change, external work done; (c) isothermal compression, heat given out, work done on the substance by external forces; (d) adiabatic compression, no heat change, work done on the substance.

CARNOT'S PRINCIPLE. The *efficiency* of any reversible heat engine depends only on the *temperature* range through which it works and not upon the properties of any material substance. If all the heat is taken up at *absolute temperature* T_1 and all given out at absolute temperature T_2 (as in *Carnot's cycle*), the efficiency is $\dfrac{T_1 - T_2}{T_1}$.

CARO'S ACID, permonosulphuric acid. H_2SO_5.

CAROTENE. $C_{40}H_{56}$. Yellow *unsaturated hydrocarbon* present in carrots and butter. Converted into vitamin A (see *vitamins*) in the animal *organism*. Carotene acts as a photosynthetic pigment (see *photosynthesis*) in plant *cells* which lack *chlorophyll*.

CARRIER (chem.). Substance assisting a *chemical reaction* by combining with part or all of the *molecule* of one of the reacting substances to form a *compound* which is then easily decomposed again by the other reacting substance; the carrier is thus left unchanged. See *catalyst*.

CARRIER (phys.). In a *semiconductor*, the mobile *electrons* or *holes* which carry charges are called carriers.

CARRIER WAVE. A continuous *electromagnetic radiation*, of constant *amplitude* and *frequency*, emitted by a *radio* transmitter. By *modulation* of the carrier wave, oscillating *electric currents* caused by *sounds* at the transmitting end are conveyed by it to the receiver.

CARRON OIL. Mixture of vegetable *oil* (olive or cotton-seed) with *lime-water*. Used as an application for burns.

CASCADE LIQUEFIER. Apparatus used for liquefying air, oxygen, etc. A *gas* cannot be liquefied until it is brought to a *temperature* below its *critical temperature*. In the cascade liquefier the critical temperature of the gas is reached step by step, using a series of gases having successively lower *boiling points*. The first of these, which can be liquefied by compression at ordinary temperatures, is allowed to evaporate under reduced *pressure*; this produces a temperature below the critical temperature of the second gas, which can then be liquefied. This is similarly allowed to evaporate, and the step is repeated until finally the desired liquefaction is reached.

CASCADE PROCESS. A process used in the separation of *isotopes*. Consists of a series of stages connected so that the separation produced by one stage is multiplied in subsequent stages. In a 'simple cascade' the enriched fraction is fed to the succeeding stage and the depleted fraction to the preceding stage.

CASCADE SHOWER. See *shower*.

CASEIN. Main *protein* of milk. Pale yellow *solid* obtained from milk by the addition of *acid* ('acid casein'), by controlled souring ('self-soured casein'), or by curdling with *rennet* ('rennet casein'). Used in paper-coating, *paints*, *adhesives*, *plastics*, and for making artificial textile fibres.

CASEINOGEN. British term for *casein* before precipitation. The American terms are casein before precipitation, and para-casein after.

CASSIOPEIUM. See *lutetium*.

CASSITERITE. SnO_2. Natural tin oxide. Principal ore of tin.

CAST IRON, pig-iron. Impure, brittle form of iron, such as produced in the *blast furnace*. Contains from 2%–$4\cdot5\%$ carbon in the form of *cementite* and usually also some manganese, phosphorus, silicon and sulphur. Generally not used direct, but converted into *steel* or *wrought iron*.

CASTOR OIL. A vegetable *oil* extracted from the seed of the castor plant, consisting of glyceryl *esters* of *fatty acids*; the predominant acid (about 85%) being ricinoleic acid, $C_{17}H_{32}(OH).COOH$. Used in the *paint* and varnish industry as well as medically as a laxative.

CATABOLISM, katabolism. Part of *metabolism* dealing with the chemical *decomposition* of complex substances into simple ones, with a release of *energy*.

CATALASE. An *enzyme* which decomposes *hydrogen peroxide*.

CATALYSIS. The alteration of the rate at which a *chemical reaction* proceeds, by the introduction of a substance (*catalyst*) which remains unchanged at the end of the reaction. Small quantities of the catalyst are usually sufficient to bring the action about or to produce a vast increase in its speed.

CATALYST. Substance which alters the rate at which a *chemical reaction* occurs, but is itself unchanged at the end of the reaction. Catalysts are widely used in the chemical industry; *metals* in a finely divided state, and *oxides* of metals, are frequently used. The *enzymes* are organic catalysts produced by living *cells*.

CATALYTIC CRACKING. The use of a *catalyst* to bring about the *cracking* of high boiling mineral *oils*.

CATAPHORESIS. See *electrophoresis*.

CATENARY. Curve formed by a chain or string hanging from two fixed points.

CATHETOMETER. *Telescope* mounted on a graduated vertical pillar along which it can move. The instrument is used for measuring lengths and displacements at a distance of a few feet.

CATHODE, kathode. Negative *electrode*. Negatively charged *conductor* in *electrolysis* and in *vacuum tubes*. See *discharge in gases*.

CATHODE RAY OSCILLOSCOPE. CRO. An instrument based upon a *cathode ray tube*, which provides a visible image of one or more rapidly varying electrical quantities. Also used as an indicator in a *radar* system.

CATHODE RAY TUBE. CRT. A vacuum tube which allows the direct observation of the behaviour of *cathode rays*. Consists essentially of an *electron gun* producing a beam of *electrons* which, after passing between horizontal and vertical deflection plates, falls upon a luminescent screen: the position of the beam can be observed by the *luminescence* produced upon the screen. *Electric potentials* applied to the deflection plates are used to control the position of the beam, and its movement across the screen, in any desired manner. Used as the picture tube in *television* receivers and in *cathode ray oscilloscopes*.

CATHODE RAYS. Stream of *electrons* emitted from the negatively charged *electrode* or *cathode* when an electric discharge takes place in a vacuum tube, i.e. a tube containing a gas at very low pressure. See *discharge in gases*.

CATION, kation. Positively charged *ion*; ion which, during *electrolysis*, is attracted towards the negatively charged *cathode*.

CAUSALITY. The relating of causes to the effects which they produce. Many contemporary physicists believe that no coherent causal description can be given of events which occur on the atomic scale.

CAUSTIC. Corrosive towards organic matter (but term is not applied to *acids*). E.g. *caustic soda*.

CAUSTIC (phys.). Parallel rays of *light* falling on a *concave* spherical mirror do not form a point image at the *focus* (see *mirrors, spherical*). Instead, there is a region of maximum concentration of the rays forming a curve or surface of revolution, called a caustic, the apex or cusp of which is at the focus of the mirror. A similar caustic occurs in the image formed by a *convex lens* receiving parallel light. Such a curve may be seen on the surface of a liquid in a cup, formed by the reflection of light upon the curved wall of the cup.

CAUSTIC ALKALI. *Sodium* or *potassium hydroxide*.

CAUSTIC POTASH. *Potassium hydroxide*, KOH.

CAUSTIC SODA. *Sodium hydroxide*, NaOH.

CELESTIAL EQUATOR (astr.). Circle in which the *plane* of the Earth's *equator* meets the *celestial sphere.*

CELESTIAL SPHERE (astr.). The imaginary *sphere* to the inner surface of which the heavenly bodies appear to be attached; the observer is situated at the centre of the sphere.

CELL (bio.). The unit of life. All living *organisms* are composed of discrete, membrane-bounded units, which usually comprise two distinct forms of *protoplasm*; the *nucleus* and the *cytoplasm*. The former contains the *nucleic acids* responsible for organizing the synthesis of the cell's *enzymes* and for controlling the characteristics of its progeny, while the latter contains the enzyme systems which control the cell's *metabolism* and manufacture its constituents. Many *micro-organisms* (e.g. *bacteria*, protozoa, etc.) consist of only one cell, whereas a man consists of some million million cells.

CELL (phys.). Device for producing an *electric current* by chemical action. See *accumulator, primary cell.*

CELLULOID. A *thermoplastic* material made from *cellulose nitrate* and *camphor.*

CELLULOSE. $(C_6H_{10}O_5)_n$. Complex *polysaccharide carbohydrate* consisting of parallel unbranched chains of *glucose* units condensed together into strong fibrous structures. Found in nature as the *cell* walls of plants. Obtained from wood pulp, cotton, and other green plants; used in the manufacture of *paper, rayon, plastics*, and *explosives.*

CELLULOSE ACETATE. *Ester* obtained by the action of acetic *anhydride* on *cellulose*. A white *solid*, used in the manufacture of *rayon* and *plastics.*

CELLULOSE NITRATE, nitrocellulose. *Nitric acid ester* of *cellulose*. Range of *compounds* formed by treatment of cellulose with a mixture of nitric and *sulphuric acids*; properties depend on the extent to which the *hydroxyl groups* of the cellulose are esterified (see *esterification*). Used in the manufacture of *plastics*, lacquers, and *explosives.*

CELSIUS TEMPERATURE SCALE. The same as the *centigrade scale of temperature.*

CELTIUM. See *hafnium.*

CEMENT. Powder which, after mixing with *water*, sets to a hard mass. Portland cement is made by heating a mixture of *limestone* and *clay* and grinding the product. Consists of calcium silicates and aluminates; complex chemical changes occur during setting.

CEMENTATION. Early process for *steel* manufacture. Bars of *wrought iron* were heated for several days in *charcoal* at red heat.

CEMENTITE, iron carbide. Fe_3C. Hard, brittle *compound* which is responsible for the brittleness of *cast iron*. Present in *steel.*

CENTI-. Prefix denoting one-hundredth of, in metric units. E.g. centimetre, one-hundredth of a metre.

CENTIGRADE DEGREE. One-hundredth of the difference between the *temperature* of melting *ice* and *water* boiling under standard atmospheric pressure (760 mm.).

CENTIGRADE SCALE of temperature. *Temperature* scale in which the m.p. of *ice* is taken as zero, and the b.p. of *water* as 100° C. Used in scientific work, and is almost universal for all purposes except in the English-speaking countries.

CENTRE OF CURVATURE of a spherical mirror. The centre of the sphere of which the *mirror* forms a part.

CENTRE OF GRAVITY of a body is the fixed point through which the *resultant force* due to the Earth's attraction upon it always passes, irrespective of the position of the body.

CENTRIFUGAL FORCE. The outward *force* acting on a body rotating in a *circle* round a central point. The centripetal force is the radial force imposed by the constraining system, necessary to keep the body moving in its circular path. The centrifugal and centripetal forces are equal and opposite.

CENTRIFUGE. Apparatus for separating particles from a *suspension*. Balanced tubes containing the suspension are attached to the opposite ends of arms rotating rapidly about a central point; by *centrifugal force* the suspended particles are forced outwards, and collect at the bottoms of the tubes. See also *ultra-centrifuge*.

CENTRIPETAL FORCE. See *centrifugal force*.

CERAMIC. Pertaining to products or industries involving the use of *clay* or other *silicates*.

CERARGYRITE. See *horn silver*.

CERENKOV (CHERENKOV) RADIATION. *Light* emitted when charged particles pass through a transparent medium at a *velocity* greater than the velocity of light in that medium. See *light, velocity of*.

CERESIN. Hard, brittle *paraffin wax* with a *melting point* in the range of 70°–100° C. Used as a substitute for *beeswax* in *paints* and polishes.

CERIUM. Ce. Element. A.W. 140·12. At. No. 58. Steel-grey soft *metal*, S.G. 6·7, m.p. 804° C. Occurs in several rare minerals, e.g. *monazite* sand. Use in *pyrophoric alloys* for lighter 'flints'; *compounds* are used in the manufacture of *gas mantles*.

C.G.S. system, centimetre-gram-second system. A system of physical *units* derived from the centimetre, *gram* mass and the *second*. E.g. *velocities* in C.G.S. units may be measured in centimetres per second.

CHABASITE. A natural *zeolite*, calcium aluminium silicate. See *ion exchange*.

CHAIN REACTION: In general, any self-sustaining molecular or *nuclear reaction*, the products of which contribute to the propagation of the reaction. In particular a fission chain reaction is a process in which one nuclear transformation is capable of initiating a chain of similar transformations. For example, when *nuclear fission* occurs in a uranium-235 *nucleus*, between 2 and 3 *neutrons* are emitted, each of which are capable of causing the fission of further uranium-235 nuclei. The chain reaction so created is the basis of the atomic bomb (see *nuclear weapons*) and the *nuclear reactor*. If the average number of *transformations* directly caused by one transformation is less than one, the reaction is said to be convergent or *sub-critical*; if it is equal to one, the reaction is self-sustained or critical; if it exceeds one, the reaction is divergent or *super-critical*.

CHALCEDONY. Variety of natural impure *silica*, SiO_2. Has a fibrous structure and a waxy lustre. Used for ornaments.

CHALK. Natural *calcium carbonate*, $CaCO_3$, formed from the shells of minute marine *organisms*. Blackboard chalk sticks are calcium sulphate, $CaSO_4$.

CHALYBEATE, chalybite. Natural ferrous carbonate, $FeCO_3$.

CHANGE OF STATE (phys.). The conversion of a substance from one of the *physical states* of matter (*solid*, *liquid*, or *gas*) into another. E.g. the melting of *ice*.

CHANNEL. In *telecommunications*, a path for the transmission of electrical signals, often specified by its *frequency band*. In *information theory*, a path or route along which information may flow or be stored.

CHANNEL CAPACITY. The number of signals per second which can be transmitted through a *channel*. Also, in *information theory*, the hypothetical limiting rate at which information could be communicated by a given channel, with the frequency of errors tending to zero.

CHARACTERISTIC (math.). The *integral* or whole-number part of a *logarithm*.

CHARCOAL. General name for numerous varieties of *carbon*, usually impure; generally made by heating vegetable or animal substances with exclusion of air. Many forms are very porous and adsorb various materials readily. See *activated carbon*.

CHARGE, ELECTRIC. See *electric charge*.

CHARLES' LAW. See *gas laws*.

CHEDDITE. Class of *explosives* containing sodium or potassium chlorate with dinitrotoluene and other organic substances.

CHELATING AGENTS. See *chelation*.

CHELATION. The formation of a closed ring of *atoms* by the attachment of *compounds* or *radicals* to a central poly-valent *metal ion* (occasionally non-metallic); usually due to the sharing of a *lone pair of electrons*, from oxygen or nitrogen atoms in the compounds or radicals, with the central ion. e.g. two *molecules* of ethylene diamine ($NH_2CH_2CH_2NH_2$) form a 'chelate ring' with a cupric ion thus:

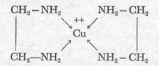

Chelating agents are used for 'locking up' unwanted metal ions; for instance they are added to shampoos with the object of softening the water by locking up ferric, calcium, and magnesium ions. Many tests for identifying metal ions depend on the formation of coloured *insoluble* chelates. *Chlorophyll* and *haemoglobin* are naturally occurring chelate compounds in which the central ions are magnesium and iron respectively.

CHEMICAL AFFINITY. See *affinity* and *free energy*.

CHEMICAL CHANGE. Change in a substance involving an alteration in its chemical composition, due to an increase, decrease, or re-arrangement of *atoms* within its *molecules*. See *equation, chemical; molecule*.

CHEMICAL COMBINATION, LAWS OF:

Law of constant composition. A definite chemical *compound* always contains the same *elements* chemically combined in the same proportions by *weight*.

Law of multiple proportions. When two *elements* unite in more than one proportion, for a fixed *weight* of one element there is always a simple relationship with the weight of the other element present.

Law of combining weights (also termed the law of reciprocal proportions, law of equivalents). *Elements* combine in the ratio of their combining weights or *chemical equivalents*; or in some simple multiple or submultiple of that ratio.

CHEMICAL ENERGY. That part of the *energy* stored within an *atom* or *molecule* which can be released by a *chemical reaction*.

CHEMICAL ENGINEERING. The design, operation, and manufacture of plant or machinery used in industrial chemical processes.

CHEMICAL EQUILIBRIUM. Many *chemical reactions* do not go to completion; in such cases a state of equilibrium or balance is reached when the original substances are reacting at the same rate as the new substances are reacting with each other to form the original substances. Thus, if two substances A and B react to form C and D, the state at equilibrium is denoted by the balanced equation $A + B \leftrightarrows C + D$. If one of the substances is removed, the system readjusts the equilibrium; thus, if C is constantly removed as soon as formed, more A and B react until the action is completed. An equilibrium reaction which could thus be made to complete itself in either direction is termed a *reversible reaction*. E.g. if *steam* is passed over red-hot iron, iron oxide and hydrogen are formed, the latter being constantly removed by more steam which passes through; the reaction thus goes to completion according to the equation $4H_2O + 3Fe = Fe_3O_4 + 4H_2$. If, however, hydrogen is passed over red-hot iron oxide, the reverse action takes place, $Fe_3O_4 + 4H_2 = 4H_2O + 3Fe$. If the reaction is allowed to proceed in an enclosed space, a state of equilibrium is reached, all four substances being present. See also *equilibrium constant*.

CHEMICAL EQUIVALENTS, combining weights. Combining proportions of substances by *weight*, relative to hydrogen as a standard. Equivalent of an *element* is the number of grams of that element which will combine with or replace 1 gm. of hydrogen or 8 gm. of oxygen. Gram-equivalent, equivalent weight, is the equivalent expressed in grams. Equivalent weight of an *acid* is the weight of the acid containing unit weight of replaceable *acidic hydrogen*. Equivalent weight of a *base* is the weight of the base required to neutralize the equivalent weight of an acid. The combining proportions of substances by weight are in the ratio of their equivalents, or in some simple multiple or sub-multiple of that ratio. For an element, the *atomic weight* is equal to the product of its equivalent and its *valency*.

CHEMICAL REACTION. The interaction of two or more substances resulting in *chemical changes* in them.

CHEMILUMINESCENCE. Cold *flame*; evolution of *light* accompanied by little *heat* during a *chemical reaction*.

CHEMISTRY. Study of the composition of substances, and of their effect upon one another.

CHERT. A natural form of *silica*, SiO_2, resembling flint.

CHILE SALTPETRE. Impure *sodium nitrate*, $NaNO_3$. Occurs in huge deposits in Chile.

CHINA CLAY, kaolin. Pure natural form of *hydrated* aluminium silicate, $Al_2Si_2O_5(OH)_4$. On heating loses *water* and changes chemical composition. Used for making *porcelain*.

CHINESE WHITE. *Zinc oxide*, ZnO.

CHITIN. Complex organic substances, related to the *carbohydrates* but containing nitrogen. Forms an essential part of the shells of crustaceans and insects. Also found in some fungi.

CHLORAL. $CCl_3.CHO$. Pungent-smelling, colourless oily *liquid*, b.p. $97.7°$ C.

CHLORAL HYDRATE. $CCl_3CH(OH)_2$. White crystalline *solid*, m.p. $57°$ C. Prepared from *chloral* by the action of *water*. Used in medicine as a soporific.

CHLORARGYRITE. See *horn silver*.

CHLORIDE. *Binary compound* with chlorine; *salt* of *hydrochloric acid*, HCl.

CHLORIDE OF LIME. Calcium oxychloride, $CaOCl_2$. See *bleaching powder*.

CHLORINE. Cl. Element. A.W. 35·453. At. No. 17. Greenish-yellow *gas* with a choking irritating smell. Poisonous; first poison gas to be used in warfare (by Germany, Ypres, 1915). *Compounds* occur as common salt (*sodium chloride*), NaCl, in *sea-water* and as *rock salt*; and as chlorides of other *metals*. Manufactured almost entirely by the *electrolysis* of brine. Used in the manufacture of *bleaching powder*, *disinfectants*, *hydrochloric acid*. Also used as a *germicide* in drinking-water.

CHLOROFORM. $CHCl_3$. *Volatile* colourless heavy *liquid* with a powerful sweet smell, b.p. $61°$ C. Made from *acetone*, *acetaldehyde*, or *ethyl alcohol* by the action of *bleaching powder*, or by the action of chlorine on *methane*, CH_4. Used as an *anaesthetic* and industrial *solvent*.

CHLOROPHYLL. Green *pigment* found in plants, which absorbs *energy* from sunlight, enabling them to build up *carbohydrates* from atmospheric *carbon dioxide* and *water* by *photosynthesis*. Consists of a mixture of two pigments, chlorophyll-a $(C_{55}H_{72}O_5N_4Mg)$ and chlorophyll-b $(C_{55}H_{70}O_6N_4Mg)$.

CHLOROPICRIN. CCl_3NO_2. Oily *liquid*, b.p. 112° C. Highly poisonous and chemically active. Used as a *disinfectant* and *fungicide*.

CHLOROPRENE. $CH_2CH:CCl.CH_2$. Colourless *liquid* used in the manufacture of *neoprene* synthetic *rubber*.

CHOKE, choking coil. A coil of low *resistance* and high *inductance* used in electrical circuits to pass *direct currents* whilst suppressing *alternating currents*.

CHOKE-DAMP. See *after-damp*.

CHOLESTEROL. $C_{27}H_{45}OH$. *Organic compound* belonging to the *sterol* group. White waxy substance present in the tissues of the human body, in which it performs a number of vital functions. Its excessive production in man is suspected of being a contributory cause of coronary thrombosis.

CHOLINE. $OH.C_2H_4N(CH_3)_3OH$. An *organic base* which is a constituent of some *fats* and of egg yolk. Member of *vitamin* B complex.

CHORD (math.). Straight line joining two points on a curve. See *circle*.

CHROMATIC ABERRATION. See *aberration, chromatic*.

CHROMATOGRAPHY. Method of chemical analysis developed from the fact that if a *liquid mixture* is allowed to trickle through a column of adsorbing material (e.g. *chalk*) the components of the mixture may be adsorbed in separate layers in the column. See also *gas chromatography* and *paper chromatography*.

CHROMATRON. Chromoscope. A type of *cathode ray tube* which has four screens; used as a colour picture-tube in *television*.

CHROME ALUM. Chromium potassium sulphate,
$$K_2SO_4.Cr_2(SO_4)_3.24H_2O.$$
Dark purple crystalline *soluble salt*; used in dyeing, calico-printing, *tanning*.

CHROME IRON ORE, chrome ironstone, chromite. Ferrous chromite, $FeO.Cr_2O_3$. Source of chromium *metal* and its *compounds*.

CHROME RED. *Basic* lead chromate, $PbO.PbCrO_4$. Used as a *pigment* in *paints*.

CHROME YELLOW. Lead chromate, $PbCrO_4$. Used as a *pigment*.

CHROMITE. See *chrome iron ore*.

CHROMIUM. Cr. Element. A.W. 51·996. At. No. 24. Hard white *metal* resembling iron; S.G. 6·92, m.p. 1890° C. Occurs as *chrome iron ore*. Extracted by reducing the *oxide* with aluminium (see *Goldschmidt process*). Used in the manufacture of *stainless steel* and for *chromium plating*.

CHROMIUM PLATING. Deposition of a thin, resistant film of chromium *metal* by *electrolysis* from a bath containing a *solution* of chromic acid, CrO_3.

CHROMIUM STEEL. *Steel* containing varying amounts of chromium; strong and tough, used for tools, etc.

CHROMOSOMES. Thread-like bodies which occur in the *nuclei* of living *cells*, the *molecules* of which carry the *genetic code*. Consist of *nucleoproteins*, the *nucleic acid* being *DNA*. The unit of genetic information is the *gene* (see also *cistron*) and each chromosome may be regarded as comprising a number of genes. Chromosomes occur in pairs in *somatic* cells, each species being characterized by the different number of chromosomes which its cells contain (Man has 46 chromosomes per cell).

CHROMOSPHERE. Layer of the Sun's atmosphere surrounding the *photosphere*, which is visible during a total *eclipse*. The chromosphere is several thousand miles thick and has an estimated temperature of 20,000° K.

CHRONOGRAPH. Accurate time-recording instrument.

CHRONOMETER. Accurate clock; term now applied mainly to instruments used in navigation.

CHRONOTRON. A device which measures the time between two events, by measuring the positions on a transmission line of pulses initiated by the events.

CIMENT FONDU. See *bauxite cement*.

CINNABAR. Natural mercuric sulphide, HgS. Bright red crystalline *solid*, S.G. 8·1. Ore of mercury.

CIRCLE (math.). Plane figure contained by a line, called the circumference, which is everywhere equidistant from a fixed point within it, called the centre. Distance from the centre to the circumference is the radius; a straight line joining any two points on the circumference is a *chord*; a chord passing through the centre, equal in length to twice the radius, is a diameter; any portion of the circumference is an arc; a portion cut off by a chord is a segment; a portion cut off by two radii is a sector. Ratio of circumference to diameter, denoted by π ('pi') $=3\cdot14159$ ... (approx. $3\frac{1}{7}$). Length of circumference $=2\pi r$; area $=\pi r^2$, where $r=$radius.

CIRCUIT, ELECTRICAL. The complete path traversed by an *electric current*.

CIRCULAR MEASURE of angles. Measurement of *angles* in *radians*; the size of an angle stated as the ratio of the length of arc cut off by the angle at the centre of a *circle* to the radius of the circle. Thus

$$180° = \pi \text{ radians}; \quad 1 \text{ radian} = \frac{180}{\pi}\text{degrees} = 57° \ 17\cdot7'.$$

CIRCULAR MIL. A unit of area. The area of a *circle* whose diameter is 0·001 inches, i.e. $0\cdot785 \times 10^{-6}$ sq. in. Used in measuring the cross-section of fine wire.

CIRCULARLY POLARIZED LIGHT. *Light* which can be resolved into two vibrations lying in *planes* at right angles, of equal *amplitude* and *frequency* and differing in *phase* by 90°. The electric *vector* of the wave describes, at any point in the path of the wave, a *circle* about the direction of propagation of the light as axis. See also *polarization of light*.

CIRCUMFERENCE. See *circle*.

CIS-FORM. See *cis-trans isomerism*.

CIS-TRANS ISOMERISM. Form of *isomerism* associated with *compounds* containing a *double bond*. Like groups in such compounds may be either on the same side of the plane of the double bond (*cis*-form) or on opposite sides (*trans*-form). E.g. H—C—COOH, maleic acid, and

$$H—C—COOH$$
H—C—COOH, fumaric acid, are respectively *cis*- and
$$HOOC—C—H$$

trans-forms. See also *stereoisomerism*.

CISTRON. The functional unit of genetic information, taking into account the distribution of abnormal (mutant) *genes* among pairs of *chromosomes*, and the way in which an abnormal gene in one chromosome may be compensated for by a normal gene either in the same chromosome (cis-configuration) or its pair (trans-configuration.)

CITRATE. *Salt* of citric acid.

CITRIC ACID. $C_6H_8O_7$. White crystalline *soluble* organic *tribasic acid*, m.p. 153° C. Has a sour taste, occurs as the free acid in lemons (6%) and other sour fruits. Used in the preparation of effervescent salts.

CITRIC ACID CYCLE. Krebs cycle. A complex cycle of *enzyme*-controlled biochemical reactions, which occur within living *cells*, as a result of which *pyruvic acid* is broken down into *carbon dioxide* and *energy*. The citric acid cycle is a most important clearing-house of metabolic intermediates, since it deals with the final stages of the *oxidation* of *carbohydrates* and *fats* and is also involved in the synthesis of some *amino acids*.

CLADDING (phys.). The covering of a *fuel element* in a *nuclear reactor* by a thin layer of another *metal*, to prevent corrosion by the coolant and the escape of *fission products*.

CLARK CELL. Standard *primary cell*, used as a standard of *EMF*; produces 1·4328 *volts* at 15° C. Consists of a zinc *amalgam anode* and a mercury *cathode*, both immersed in a *saturated solution* of zinc sulphate.

CLASSICAL PHYSICS. *Physics* prior to the *quantum theory* (or in some senses prior to the theory of *relativity*).

CLATHRATE COMPOUNDS. Chemical *compounds* formed not by the action of *valency bonds*, but by 'molecular imprisonment', the combined *molecules* being held together mechanically by virtue of their configuration in space.

CLAY. A class of complex *silicates*, e.g. kaolinite or *china clay*.

CLEAVAGE. Manner of breaking of a crystalline substance.

CLINICAL THERMOMETER. See *thermometer, clinical*.

CLOTTING. Formation of *solid* deposits or clots in *liquids*, often due to the *coagulation* of *soluble proteins* dissolved in the liquid. E.g. the clotting of *blood*.

CLOUD CHAMBER (phys.). An apparatus for making the tracks of ionizing particles visible as a row of droplets which condense from a super-saturated *vapour*. Depends on the fact that *water vapour* condenses more readily on charged *ions* than on uncharged *molecules*.

CLUSTER (astr.). An aggregation of *stars* which move together. A *globular cluster* is an aggregation of stars in a roughly spherical arrangement.

COAGULATION OF PROTEINS. When *solutions* of water-soluble *proteins* (*albumens*) are heated, the protein becomes 'denatured' at a definite *temperature*; it then becomes *insoluble* and either remains in *suspension* or is precipitated as a clot or curd. Other types of proteins, e.g. *globulins* may be denatured and coagulated by *heat*, or by the addition of *acids* or *alkalis*. A denatured protein cannot be easily reconverted into the original *compound* (see *denature*).

COAL. Material, occurring in large underground deposits, consisting of carbon and various carbon *compounds*. Formed by the *decomposition* of vegetable matter during periods of many millions of years. The main types of coal are: *peat, lignite*, ordinary or *bituminous* coal, and *anthracite*.

COAL-GAS. Fuel *gas* manufactured by the *destructive distillation* of *coal* in closed iron *retorts*; often supplemented with *water-gas*. Composition by *volume* (average values): hydrogen 50%, *methane*, CH_4, 30%, *carbon monoxide*, CO, 8%, other *hydrocarbons* 4%, nitrogen, *carbon dioxide*, and oxygen 8%.

COAL-GAS BY-PRODUCTS. Amongst the valuable substances obtained during the manufacture of *coal gas* are *coke, coal-tar, ammonia, sulphuric acid*, and *pitch*.

COAL-TAR. Thick black oily *liquid* obtained as a by-product of *coal-gas* manufacture. *Distillation* and purification yields, amongst other valuable products: *benzene*, C_6H_6; *toluene*, $C_6H_5CH_3$; *xylene*, $C_6H_4(CH_3)_2$; *phenol*, C_6H_5OH; *naphthalene*, $C_{10}H_8$; *cresol*, $CH_3C_6H_4OH$, and *anthracene*, $C_{14}H_{10}$. *Pitch* is left as a residue.

COAL-TAR DYES. *Organic compounds*, used as dyestuffs, prepared or derived from substances such as *benzene* occurring in *coal-tar*.

COAXIAL. Having a common axis.

COBALAMINE. Vitamin B12. Cobalt containing *vitamin* required by many *organisms*.

COBALT. Co. Element. A.W. 58.9332. At. No. 27. Hard silvery-white magnetic *metal* resembling iron. S.G. 8.9, m.p. $1480°$ C. Occurs combined with sulphur and with arsenic. Extracted by converting the ore into the *oxide* and reducing with aluminium, or with carbon in an electric furnace. Used in many *alloys*; compounds used to produce a blue colour in *glass* and *ceramics*.

COBALT STEEL. *Steel* containing cobalt, and often other *metals* such as wolfram (tungsten), chromium, and vanadium. The addition of cobalt results in greater hardness and brittleness, improves the cutting power of *high-speed steel* tools, and alters the magnetic properties.

COCAINE. $C_{17}H_{21}O_4N$. Member of the *alkaloids*; occurs in the coca plant. White *solid*, m.p. 98° C. Powerful *anaesthetic*. A dangerous habit-forming drug.

COCCUS. A globular or spherical-shaped *bacterium*.

COCHINEAL. Natural red dyestuff obtained from the dried body of the Coccus cacti insect.

COCKROFT-WALTON GENERATOR or ACCELERATOR. A high voltage *direct current accelerator* used for accelerating nuclear particles (particularly *protons*). The DC voltage is obtained by multiplying a low AC voltage by an arrangement of *rectifiers* and *capacitors*.

CODEINE. $C_{18}H_{21}O_3N$, Member of the *alkaloids* chemically closely related to *morphine*, but is not a powerful *narcotic*. Occurs in *opium*; used in the treatment of coughs.

COEFFICIENT (math.). A number or other known *factor* written in front of an algebraic expression. E.g. in the expression $3x^4$, 3 is the coefficient of x^4.

COEFFICIENT (phys.). *Factor* or multiplier which measures some specified property of a given substance, and is constant for that substance under given conditions. E.g. coefficient of expansion. (See *expansion, coefficient of.*)

COENZYME. A substance which plays an essential part in some reactions catalysed by *enzymes*, often acts as a temporary *carrier* of an intermediate product of the reaction.

COERCIVE FORCE of a substance. The strength of the *magnetic field* to which a *ferromagnetic substance* undergoing an *hysteresis cycle* must be subjected in order to *demagnetize* the substance completely. If the substance is magnetized to saturation during the cycle, the coercive force is called the *coercivity*.

COERCIVITY. See *coercive force*.

COFFEY STILL. Apparatus for the *fractional distillation* of *solutions* of *ethyl alcohol* as obtained by *fermentation* on an industrial scale; the product is known as rectified spirit.

COHERENT. A beam of *light*, or other *electromagnetic radiation*, is said to be coherent if its waves are in *phase*. See *laser*.

COHESION. Holding together; *force* holding a *solid* or *liquid* together owing to attraction between the *molecules*. Decreases with rise in *temperature*.

COINAGE METALS. The *metals* copper, silver, gold.

COINCIDENCE CIRCUIT. Coincidence gate. An *electronic* circuit which produces an output only when two or more input signals arrive simultaneously, or within a specified time interval.

COKE. Greyish, porous brittle *solid* containing about 80% carbon.

Obtained as a residue in the manufacture of *coal-gas* ('gas coke'); also made specially in coke ovens, in which the *coal* is treated at lower *temperatures* than in gas manufacture.

COLCHICINE. $C_{22}H_{25}NO_6$. A yellow crystalline *alkaloid*, obtained from the autumn crocus, which interferes with the process of *mitosis* in such a way that it causes an increase in the number of *chromosomes* in a *cell*. Used as an artificial method of obtaining new agricultural and horticultural varieties.

COLCOTHAR, rouge, red iron oxide. *Ferric oxide*, Fe_2O_3. Used as a *pigment* and for polishing.

COLLAGEN. A *protein* which is the major fibrous constituent of skin, tendon, ligament, and bone: it is, therefore, probably the most abundant protein in the animal kingdom. Collagen owes its unique properties not only to its chemical composition, but also to the physical arrangement of its individual *molecules*. The basic molecular *polypeptide* chain forms a left-handed *helix*, and three such helices are wrapped around each other to form a right-handed super-helix. On boiling with *water* collagen gives rise to *gelatin*.

COLLARGOL. Powder containing *protein* material and finely divided silver; with *water* forms a *colloidal solution* of silver.

COLLECTOR. The *electrode* in a *transistor* through which a primary flow of *carriers* leaves the inter-electrode region.

COLLIGATIVE PROPERTIES. Those properties of a substance (e.g. a *solution*) which depend only on the *concentration* of particles (*molecules* or *ions*) present and not upon their nature; e.g. *osmotic pressure*.

COLLIMATOR. Tube containing a *convex achromatic lens* at one end and an adjustable slit at the other, the slit being at the focus of the lens. *Light* rays entering the slit thus leave the collimator as a parallel *beam*. Also used in *radiology* to mean an arrangement of absorbers for limiting a beam of *radiation* to the required dimensions and angular spread.

COLLISION DENSITY. The number of collisions per unit volume per unit time which a given *neutron* flux makes when passing through *matter*.

COLLODION. *Solution* of *cellulose nitrate* in a mixture of *alcohol* and *ether*.

COLLOID. Substance present in *solution* in the *colloidal state*. The original division, made by Graham, of all substances into *crystalloids* and colloids according to the ability of their solutions to pass through a *semipermeable membrane* is not generally accepted now, since most substances can be brought into the colloidal state by suitable means.

COLLOIDAL METALS. *Colloidal solutions* or *suspensions* of *metals*, the metal being distributed in the *solvent* in the form of very small electrically charged particles. May be prepared by striking an electric *arc* between poles made of the metal, under water; or by the chemical *reduction* of a *solution* of a *salt* of the metal. Used in medicine.

COLLOIDAL SOLUTION, sol. A *solution* in which the *solute* is present in the *colloidal state*. Common examples include solutions of *starch*, *albumen, colloidal metals,* etc. The *solvent* is termed the *dispersion medium* and the dissolved substance the *disperse phase.* Several types of colloid solution are possible, depending upon whether the dispersion medium and the disperse phase are respectively *liquid* and *solid* (suspensoid sols), liquid and liquid (emulsoid sols), *gas* and solid, etc. If the disperse phase, when removed from solution by *evaporation* or coagulation, returns to the colloidal state on merely mixing with the dispersion medium, it is termed a reversible or *lyophilic colloid,* and the solution a reversible sol. If the disperse phase does not return to the colloidal state on simple mixing, it is termed an irreversible or *lyophobic colloid.*

COLLOIDAL STATE. A system of particles in a *dispersion medium,* with properties distinct from that of a true *solution* because of the larger size of the particles. The presence of these particles, which are approximately 10^{-5} to 10^{-7} cm. across, can often be detected by means of the *ultramicroscope.* As a result of the grouping of the *molecules,* a *solute* in the colloidal state cannot pass through a suitable *semi-permeable membrane* and gives rise to negligible *osmotic pressure, depression of freezing point,* and *elevation of boiling point* effects. The molecular groups or particles of the solute carry a resultant *electric charge,* generally of the same sign for all the particles.

COLOPHONY. See *rosin.*

COLORIMETER. Apparatus used in *colorimetric analysis* for comparing intensities of *colour.*

COLORIMETRIC ANALYSIS. Determination of the amounts of substances by comparing the intensity of *colour* produced by them with specific *reagents,* with the intensity of colour produced by a standard amount of the substance.

COLOUR. The sensation of colour is the result of the interpretation by the human central nervous system of the effect produced upon the eye by *electromagnetic radiation* of a particular *wave length.*

COLOUR TEMPERATURE. The *temperature* of a full radiator (see *black-body radiation*) which would emit visible *radiation* of the same spectral distribution as the radiation from the *light* source under consideration.

COLOUR VISION. White *light,* such as daylight, consists of a mixture of *electromagnetic radiations* of various *wave-lengths.* A surface which reflects all of these will appear white; some surfaces, however, have the property of absorbing some of the radiations they receive, and reflecting the rest. Thus, a surface which absorbs all light radiations excepting those corresponding to green, will appear green by reflecting only those radiations. In the cases of colour seen by transmitted light, as in coloured *glass,* the glass absorbs all the radiations except those which are visible, and which pass through. See *surface colour; pigment colour.*

COLOURTRON. A type of *cathode ray tube,* used as a colour picture-tube in *television,* which has three *electron guns,* one for each *primary colour.*

COLUMBIUM, Cb. See *niobium.*

COLZA OIL, rapeseed oil. Yellow oil obtained from the seeds of various Brassica plants. Used as an edible oil, illuminant, lubricant, and in the *quenching of steel*. 'Mineral colza' oil is a mixture of *paraffin hydrocarbons* with a boiling range of 250°–350° C.

COMBINATION, LAWS OF CHEMICAL. See *chemical combinations, laws of*.

COMBINATION (math.). A selection of a specified number of different objects from some larger specified number. The number of combinations of r different objects selected from n objects (i.e. the number of combinations of n objects taken r at a time) is denoted by the expression

$^{n}C_{r}$, and is equal to $\dfrac{\lfloor n}{\lfloor r . \lfloor n-r}$. (See *factorial*.)

COMBUSTION. Burning. A *chemical reaction*, or complex of chemical reactions, in which a substance combines with oxygen producing *heat*, *light*, and *flame*. The combustion reactions which supply most of the *energy* required by human civilization involve the oxidation of *fossil fuels* in which carbon is converted into *carbon dioxide* and hydrogen is converted into *water* (*steam*).

COMET. Heavenly body, moving under the attraction of the *Sun*. Consists of a hazy gaseous cloud containing a brighter nucleus and a fainter tail.

COMMUNICATION SATELLITE. See *satellite, artificial*.

COMMUTATOR. Device for altering or reversing the direction of an *electric current*; used in the *dynamo* to convert the *alternating current* into a direct one if required. Consists of a cylindrical assembly of insulated *conductors* each of which are connected to sections of the winding. Spring mounted carbon brushes make contact with the conductors and thus carry the current to external circuits.

COMPASS, MAGNETIC. In its simplest form consists of a magnetized needle pivoted at its centre so that it is free to move in a horizontal plane. The effect of the Earth's *magnetic field* is to cause the needle to set along the *magnetic meridian*. The needle is usually placed at the centre of a circular scale marked with the points of the compass. As such a compass is also affected by magnetic fields other than that of the Earth, for navigation the *gyro-compass* is used.

COMPLEMENTARITY. A term introduced into *quantum theory* by Niels Bohr, implying that evidence relating to atomic systems which has been obtained under different experimental conditions cannot necessarily be comprehended by one single model. Thus, for example, the wave model of the *electron* is complementary to the particle model.

COMPLEMENTARY ANGLES. *Angles* together totalling 90° or one right angle.

COMPLEMENTARY COLOURS. Pairs of *colours* which, when combined, give the effect of white. See *colour vision*.

COMPLETE RADIATION. See *black body radiation*.

COMPLEX NUMBER. A complex number consists of two parts, 'real' and 'imaginary', and can be expressed in the form $x+iy$, where both x and y are real quantities and i is the square root of -1, i.e. $i^2 = -1$. The real part of the complex number is 'x' and the imaginary part 'iy'. Such numbers obey the ordinary laws of *algebra* except that in *equations* containing them the real and imaginary parts are equated separately.

COMPONENT (chem.). Term in the *phase rule*. The number of components in a system is the least number of substances from which every *phase* of the system may be constituted. E.g. each of the phases *ice*, *water*, *water vapour* in equilibrium is composed of one component, H_2O.

COMPONENT FORCES AND VELOCITIES. Two or more *forces* or *velocities* which produce the same effect upon a body as a single force or velocity, known as the *resultant*.

COMPOUND (chem.). Substance consisting of two or more *elements* chemically united in definite proportions by *weight*.

COMPOUND, INTERSTITIAL. A *compound* of a *metal* and certain *metalloids* in which the metalloid *atoms* occupy the interstices between the atoms of the metal *lattice*.

COMPRESSIBILITY. The coefficient of compressibility (*isothermal*) of a substance is given by $c = -\dfrac{1}{V} \cdot \dfrac{\delta V}{\delta p}$, where δV is the change in the *volume* V of the substance resulting from a change of *pressure* δp, the *temperature* remaining constant.

COMPTON EFFECT. The reduction in the *energy* of a *photon*, as a result of its interaction with a free *electron*. Part of the photon's energy is transferred to the electron (Compton or recoil electron) and part is redirected as a photon of reduced energy (Compton scatter).

COMPUTER. An *electronic* device which can accept data, apply a series of logical processes to it, and supply the results of these processes as information. The two main types are the *analogue computer* and the *digital computer*.

CONCAVE. Curving inwards; thus, a concave (or bi-concave) *lens* is thinner at the centre than at the edges.

CONCENTRATED (chem.). As applied to *reagents*, containing the minimum of *water* or other *solvent*; the opposite of *dilute*.

CONCENTRATION of any substance in a given *space*, or in another substance, is the amount of it present per definite amount of space or of the other substance. Concentration of *aqueous solutions* is usually expressed in *grams*, *gram-molecules*, or *gram-equivalents* per *litre*.

CONCENTRATION CELL. A *primary cell* whose *EMF* is due to a difference in *concentration* between different parts of the *electrolyte*.

CONCENTRIC. Having the same centre. E.g. two concentric tubes would appear, in cross-section, as two concentric *circles*.

CONCHOIDAL FRACTURE. Type of break or fracture characteristic of an *amorphous solid*; an irregular break with a curved face exhibiting concentric rings.

CONCRETE. Building material composed of stone, sand, *cement*, and *water*.

CONDENSATION (chem.). Chemical change in which two or more *molecules* react with the elimination of *water* or of some other simple substance. E.g. acetic anhydride, $(CH_3CO)_2O$, may be regarded as a condensation product of *acetic acid*, CH_3COOH, a molecule of the *anhydride* being formed when two molecules of the acid combine with the elimination of one molecule of water. See also *polymerization*.

CONDENSATION OF VAPOUR. Change of *vapour* into *liquid*. Takes place when the *pressure* of the vapour becomes equal to the maximum *vapour pressure* of the liquid at that *temperature*.

CONDENSATION PUMP. Diffusion Pump. Apparatus used to obtain high vacua, i.e. *pressures* of the order of 10^{-6} mm. mercury. Mercury or oil *vapour* issuing as a jet through the orifice O exhausts the system attached to the tube A. *Gas molecules* in A diffuse through the layer of mercury vapour around the orifice and are carried down with the vapour stream by molecular bombardment. The mercury vapour is cooled at the jet causing it to condense, so preventing it from diffusing back into the system which is being exhausted. See Fig. 3.

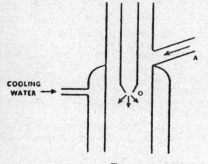

FIG. 3

CONDENSER (chem.). Liebig condenser. Apparatus for converting *vapour* into *liquid* during *distillation*. In its simplest form consists of a tube along which the vapour passes and is cooled, usually by cold water flowing through an outer jacket surrounding the tube.

CONDENSER, ELECTRICAL. See *capacitor*.

CONDENSER MICROPHONE. *Microphone* consisting essentially of an electrical *condenser*, one plate of which is fixed and the other plate forms the diaphragm upon which the *sound* waves fall. The vibrations of the diaphragm vary the *capacitance* of the condenser, which in turn alters the *potential* across a high *resistance*. This varying potential is then amplified in the normal way.

CONDENSER, OPTICAL. Device used in optical instruments to converge rays of *light*; e.g. in the *microscope* a condenser *lens* is used to converge upon the object to be viewed.

CONDUCTANCE. The conductance of a *direct current* circuit is the *reciprocal* of its *resistance*. The conductance of an *alternating current* circuit is its resistance divided by the square of its *impedance*. Measured in both cases by 'reciprocal ohms' or *mhos*.

CONDUCTION BAND. The range of energies (see *energy bands*) in a *semiconductor* corresponding to states in which the *electrons* can be made to flow by an applied *electric field*.

CONDUCTION, THERMAL. The transmission of *heat* from places of higher to places of lower *temperature* in a substance, by the interaction of *atoms* or *molecules* possessing greater *kinetic energy* with those possessing less. In *gases* the heat energy is transmitted by collision of the gaseous molecules, those possessing the greater kinetic energy imparting, on collision, some of their energy to molecules having less. Conduction in *liquids* is mainly due to the same process. In solid electrical *conductors*, the chief contribution to thermal conduction arises from a similar process taking place between the free *electrons* present. The interaction of the molecules responsible for thermal conduction in solid electrical *insulators* arises from the elastic binding *forces* between the molecules, which are effectively fixed in space.

CONDUCTIVITY, ELECTRICAL. The *reciprocal* of the *resistivity* or specific resistance of a *conductor*. Measured in 'reciprocal ohms' or *mhos* per centimetre cube.

CONDUCTIVITY, THERMAL; heat conductivity. Rate of transfer of *heat* along a body by *conduction*. Measured in *calories* flowing per second across a centimetre cube of the substance, having a *temperature* difference of $1°$ C. on opposite faces.

CONDUCTOR, ELECTRICAL. Body capable of carrying an *electrical current*; a body which, if given an *electric charge*, will distribute that charge over itself.

CONDUCTOR, THERMAL; conductor of heat. A body which will permit *heat* to flow through it by *conduction*.

CONDY'S FLUID. *Solution* of sodium or calcium (or sometimes aluminium) permanganate, $NaMnO_4$ or $Ca (MnO_4)_2$. Used as a *disinfectant*.

CONE (math.). Solid figure traced by a straight line passing through a fixed point, the vertex, and moving along a fixed *circle*. For a cone of vertical height h, slant height s, and radius of base r, the *volume* is given by $V = \frac{1}{3}\pi r^2 h$, and the area of the curved surface $A = \pi r s$.

CONGRUENT FIGURES. Geometrical figures equal in all respects.

CONIC SECTIONS. Curves obtained by the intersection of a *plane* with a *cone*; include the *circle*, *ellipse*, *parabola*, and *hyperbola*.

CONJUGATE POINTS of a lens. Points on either side of the *lens*, such that an object placed at either will produce an image at the other.

CONJUGATED DOUBLE BOND. In an *unsaturated organic compound* two *double bonds* separated by a single bond are said to be conjugated, e.g. *butadiene*, $CH_2:CH.CH:CH_2$.

CONJUNCTION (astr.). A *planet* (or other heavenly body) is said to be in superior conjunction when it is in a straight line with the *Sun* and the *Earth*; a planet with its orbit inside that of the Earth is in inferior conjunction when it is between the Sun and the Earth and in line with them.

CONSERVATION OF MASS AND ENERGY. A principal, resulting from Einstein's special theory of *relativity*, which combines the separate laws of the conservation of *energy* and of *mass*. The law of the conservation of energy states that in any system energy cannot be created or destroyed, and the law of the conservation of mass (or *matter*) states that in any system matter cannot be created or destroyed. These laws are now seen to be approximations which can only be applied to systems not involving *nuclear reactions* or *velocities* approaching the velocity of *light*. The general principle of the conservation of mass and energy, which is of universal applicability, and which is based upon the *mass-energy equation*, states that in any system the sum of the mass and energy remains constant.

CONSERVATION OF MOMENTUM, principle of. The total *momentum* of two colliding bodies before impact is equal to their total momentum after impact. When *velocities* comparable to the speed of *light* are being considered, the variation of *mass* with velocity (see *relativity, theory of*) must be taken into account, and the expression for the momentum becomes

$$\text{Momentum} = mv = \frac{m_0}{\sqrt{1 - \dfrac{v^2}{c^2}}} \times v, \text{ where}$$

$m_0 = $ *rest mass* and
$v = $ velocity of the body.

CONSTANT (math., phys.). Any quantity which does not vary; e.g. π ('pi'), the ratio of the circumference to the diameter of any *circle*.

CONSTANT BOILING MIXTURE. See *azeotropic mixture*.

CONSTANT COMPOSITION, LAW OF. See *chemical combination, laws of*.

CONSTANTAN. *Alloy* of copper containing 10%–55% nickel; electrical *resistance* does not vary with *temperature*; used in electrical equipment.

CONTACT ANGLE, for solid-liquid interface. The *angle* included between the tangent plane to the surface of a *liquid* and the tangent plane to the surface of a *solid* at any point along their line of contact.

CONTACT POTENTIAL DIFFERENCE. If two dissimilar *metals*, *a* and *b*, are in contact (see Fig. 4, page 69), then in general a *potential difference* exists between point *A*, just outside *conductor a*, and a point *B*, just outside conductor *b*. This is the contact potential difference of the two conductors.

FIG. 4

CONTACT PROCESS. Industrial process for the manufacture of *sulphuric acid*, H_2SO_4. *Sulphur dioxide*, SO_2, is made to combine with oxygen by passing over a heated *catalyst*, usually platinum or platinized asbestos. The *sulphur trioxide*, SO_3, which is formed is combined with *water* to give sulphuric acid.

CONTAINMENT. Confinement. In a controlled *thermonuclear reaction*, the process of preventing the *plasma* from coming into contact with the walls of the containing vessel is referred to as containment or confinement. The approximate period for which the *ions* remain trapped by the containing field is referred to as the 'containment time' or the 'confinement time'.

CONTINUOUS SPECTRUM. See *spectrum*.

CONTINUOUS WAVE. CW. *Radio* or *radar* transmissions which are generated continuously and not in short *pulses*.

CONTINUUM. A continuous series of component parts passing into one another; e.g. the three *space* dimensions and the time dimension are considered to form a four-dimensional continuum.

CONTROL GRID. An *electrode* placed between the *cathode* and the *anode* of a *thermionic valve* for controlling the flow of *electrons* through the valve.

CONTROL ROD. Part of the control system of a *nuclear reactor* which directly affects the rate of reaction therein. Usually a rod or tube, which can be moved up or down its *axis*, made of steel or aluminium containing boron, cadmium, or some other strong absorber of *neutrons*.

CONTROLLED THERMONUCLEAR REACTION. CTR. See *thermonuclear reaction*.

CONVECTION. Transference of *heat* through a *liquid* or *gas* by the actual movement of the *fluid*. Portions in contact with the source of heat become hotter, expand, become less dense and rise; their place is taken by colder portions, thus setting up convection currents.

CONVERGENCE. Coming to a point.

CONVERGING LENS. *Lens* capable of bringing to a point a *beam* of *light* passing through it; a *convex* lens.

CONVERSE. The transposition of a statement consisting of a fact or datum and a consequent conclusion. Thus the converse of the proposition 'equal chords of a *circle* are equidistant from the centre' is 'chords which are equidistant from the centre of a circle are equal.' The converse of a statement is not necessarily true.

69

CONVERSION. The process in a *nuclear reactor* as a result of which *fertile* material is transformed into *fissile* material, e.g. the conversion of thorium-232 into uranium-233. The 'conversion factor' is the number of fissile *atoms* produced from the fertile material per fissile atom destroyed in the fuel.

CONVERSION ELECTRON. An *orbital electron* ejected from an *atom* as a result of the *energy* it acquires from a transition of the *nucleus* from one energy state to another in the absence of *gamma-ray* emission.

CONVERTER REACTOR. A *nuclear reactor* which produces *fissile* material from *fertile* material by *conversion*.

CONVEX. Curving outwards; e.g. a convex *lens*, one thicker at the centre than at the edges.

CO-ORDINATE BOND. Dative Bond. See *valency, electronic theory of*.

CO-ORDINATE GEOMETRY. See *analytical geometry*.

CO-ORDINATES, CARTESIAN. The two distances of any point, *P*, from two axes in its *plane* which intersect (generally at right angles) at a point *O*, called the *origin*. The distance from the horizontal or *x*-axis (measured along the vertical or *y*-axis) is termed the *ordinate* of *P*; the distance from the *y*-axis is the *abscissa*. See Fig. 5.

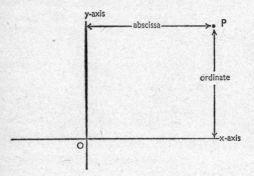

FIG. 5

COPAL. Natural *resin* obtained from certain trees. Used in varnishes.

CO-PLANAR (math.). In the same *plane*.

CO-POLYMERIZATION. See *polymerization*.

COPPER. Cu. Element. A.W. 63·54. At. No. 29. Red *metal*, m.p. 1084° C., S.G. 8·95. Very malleable and ductile; after silver, the best *conductor* of electricity. Unaffected by *water* or *steam*. Occurs as the free metal, and as cuprite or ruby ore, Cu_2O; copper glance, Cu_2S; copper pyrites, $CuFeS_2$. Extracted from *sulphide* ores by alternate roasting and fusing with sand, thus removing iron and *volatile* impurities, and leaving a mixture of *cuprous oxide* and sulphide. This is then heated in a *reverbera-tory furnace*, giving impure copper, which is then refined by various methods. Used for steam boilers, electrical wire and apparatus in *electrotyping*, and in numerous *alloys*, e.g. *bronze, brass, speculum metal, gun metal, bell metal, Dutch metal, manganin, constantan, nickel silver, German silver*, etc.

COPPER SULPHATE, cupric sulphate, *blue vitriol*. $CuSO_4.5H_2O$. Blue crystalline *soluble salt*, used in plant spraying.

COPPERAS, *green vitriol, ferrous sulphate*. $FeSO_4.7H_2O$.

CORAL. Deposit of impure *calcium carbonate*, $CaCO_3$, formed of the hard skeletons of various marine *organisms*.

CORDITE. *Explosive* prepared from *nitrocellulose* and *nitroglycerine*.

CORONA. White irregular halo surrounding the *Sun*, visible during a total *eclipse*.

CORONA DISCHARGE. A luminous discharge which appears round the surface of a *conductor* due to *ionization* of the air (or other *gas* surround-ing it), caused by the *voltage* gradient exceeding a critical value, but not being sufficient to cause sparking.

CORPUSCLE. See *blood cell*.

CORPUSCULAR THEORY. Theory that *light* consists of minute cor-puscles in rapid motion. The original corpuscular theory was aban-doned in the middle of the nineteenth century in favour of the *wave theory of light*, first put forward by Huygens in 1678. Later research has shown that light phenomena must be interpreted in terms of *photons* and waves, as the two descriptions are merely two different ways of viewing one and the same reality.

CORROSION. Surface chemical action, especially on *metals*, by the action of moisture, air, or chemicals.

CORROSIVE SUBLIMATE, mercuric chloride. $HgCl_2$. White crystalline *soluble salt*, m.p. 275° C. Very poisonous; used as a *germicide*.

CORTISONE. 17-hydroxy-11-dehydrocorticosterone. A *steroid hormone* secreted by the cortex of the adrenal gland. Produces healing responses and reduces local inflammation, used in the treatment of rheumatic conditions.

CORUBIN. Crystalline aluminium oxide, Al_2O_3. Obtained as a *by-product* of the *thermit* process.

CORUNDUM. Natural aluminium oxide, Al_2O_3. Crystalline substance nearly as hard as *diamond*, used as an *abrasive*.

COSECANT. See *trigonometrical ratios*.

COSINE. See *trigonometrical ratios*.

COSMIC DUST. Small particles of *matter*, probably ranging in size from one-hundredth to one ten-thousandth of a *millimetre*, distributed throughout *space*.

COSMIC RAY SHOWER. Cascade shower. See *shower*.

COSMIC RAYS. Very energetic *radiation* falling upon the Earth from outer *space*, and consisting chiefly, if not entirely, of charged particles. The majority of these are most probably *protons*, although *electrons* and *alpha particles* are also present. There is also evidence that a small component (about 2%) of the primary radiation consists of heavy atomic *nuclei*. The primary particles, when incident upon our atmosphere, cause several secondary processes. Proton-*neutron* collisions in the top tenth of the atmosphere give rise to *mesons*, several different types of which are now known. High-energy electrons are created in the atmosphere by meson *decay*, by interaction of high energy protons with nuclei, by *knock-on* collisions of mesons with electrons, etc. These high-energy electrons give rise to *cosmic ray showers* resulting in the creation of *photons, positrons*, and further electrons. Energies as high as 10^{19} *electron-volts* have been observed with cosmic ray particles. The origin of cosmic rays is not known with certainty although some appear to emanate from the *Sun*. See also *east-west asymmetry*.

COSMOGONY. The science of the nature of the heavenly bodies, with particular reference to the formation of *planets, stars*, and *galaxies*.

COSMOLOGY. The science of the nature, origin, and history of the Universe. A more general and widely used term than *cosmogony* when referring to the Universe as a whole.

COSMOTRON. A *proton accelerator* containing a very large ring-shaped *electromagnet*.

COTANGENT. See *trigonometrical ratios*.

COULOMB, THE. Unit of quantity of *electricity*; quantity of electricity transferred by 1 *ampere* in one second. *Absolute coulomb* = 1 absolute ampere in one second; 10^{-1} *electromagnetic units*; 3×10^9 *electrostatic units*.

COULOMB SCATTERING. The *scattering* of sub-atomic particles caused by the *electrostatic* (coulomb) *field* surrounding an atomic *nucleus*.

COULOMB'S LAW. The *force* of attraction or repulsion between two charged bodies (whose charges behave as though they were concentrated at a point) is proportional to the magnitude of the charges and inversely proportional to the square of the distance between them.

COULOMETER. Coulombmeter. See *voltameter*.

COUMARONE. Benzofuran. $C_6H_4\overline{OCH:CH}$. *Organic compound* which polymerizes into a synthetic *resin*; used in the *paint* and varnish industry.

COUNTER TUBE. A device for counting individual ionizing events. See *Geiger counter, scintillation counter*, and *crystal counter*.

COUPLE (phys.), torque. Two equal and opposite parallel, but not co-linear, *forces* acting upon a body. The *moment* of a couple is the product of either force and the perpendicular distance between the line of action of the forces.

COVALENT BOND. See *valency, electronic theory of*.

COVALENT CRYSTAL. A *crystal* in which the *atoms* are held in the *lattice* by covalent bonds (see *valency, electronic theory of*). Typical examples are *diamond*, silicon, and most organic crystals. See also *semiconductors*.

CRACKING (chem.), pyrolysis. *Decomposition* of a chemical substance by *heat*; especially the conversion of *mineral oils* of high *boiling point* into more *volatile* oils suitable for petrol engines, by 'cracking' the larger *molecules* of the heavy oils into smaller ones.

CREAM OF TARTAR. Potassium hydrogen tartrate. $C_4O_6H_5K$. Sparingly *soluble* white *solid*, obtained from *argol* (tartar).

CREEP. A permanent change in the physical dimensions of a *metal* caused by the application of a continuous *stress*.

CREOSOTE. A *distillation* product obtained from *tar*; term often restricted to the product from the tar obtained by the *destructive distillation* of wood. Oily, transparent *liquid* containing *phenol* and *cresol*. Used for preserving timber.

CRESOL. Hydroxy toluene. $CH_3C_6H_4OH$. *Liquid aromatic organic compound* obtained from *coal-tar*. Consists of three *isomers* which boil in the range 191°–203° C. Used in the *plastics, explosive*, and *dye* industries, and as a *disinfectant*. See *lysol*.

CRITH. *Weight* of 1 litre of hydrogen at 0° C. and a pressure of 760 mm.; approximately ·09 gm.

CRITICAL ANGLE of a medium (phys.). The least angle of *incidence* at which *total internal reflection* occurs. When a ray of *light* passing from a denser to a less dense medium, e.g. *glass* to air, meets the surface, a portion of the light does not emerge, but is internally reflected. As the angle of incidence increases, the intensity of the internally reflected beam also increases until an angle is reached when the whole beam is thrown back, total internal reflection taking place.

CRITICAL DAMPING. A measuring instrument is said to be critically damped when it takes up its *equilibrium* deflection in the shortest possible time, the oscillations of the indicator (needle) about the equilibrium position being quickly damped out. *Galvanometers* are normally used critically damped.

CRITICAL MASS. The minimum amount of *fissile* material required in a *nuclear reactor* or a *nuclear weapon* to sustain a *chain reaction*.

CRITICAL POTENTIAL. The minimum *energy* required to raise the *energy level* of an *orbital electron* (see *excitation*) or to remove it from the atom. See *ionization potential* and *radiation potential*.

CRITICAL PRESSURE. The *pressure* of the *saturated vapour* of a substance at the *critical temperature*.

CRITICAL REACTION. See *chain reaction*.

CRITICAL TEMPERATURE of a *gas*. The *temperature* above which the gas cannot be liquefied by *pressure* alone.

CRITICAL VELOCITY. The *velocity* at which the flow of a *liquid* ceases to be *streamline* and becomes *turbulent*.

CRITICAL VOLUME of a substance is the *volume* occupied by 1 gm. of the substance at the *critical temperature* and under the *critical pressure*.

CROSS-LINKAGE (chem.). The joining of polymer *molecules* (see *polymerization*) to each other by *valency bonds*. A polymer may be imagined, in the simplest case, to consist of very long chain-like *molecules*; cross-linkage would have the effect of joining adjacent chains by lateral links.

CROSS-SECTION. Term used in *nuclear physics* to represent the effective area, which has to be attributed to a particular *atom* or *nucleus*, to account geometrically for its interaction with an incident *beam* of *radiation*. The 'total' (or 'collision') cross-section, which accounts for all interactions, is subdivided into the 'elastic cross-section' and the 'inelastic cross-section'. The elastic cross-section accounts for all elastic *scattering* in which the incident radiation suffers no loss of *energy* to the atom or nuclei. The inelastic cross-section accounts for all other interactions and may be further subdivided to account for specific interactions, e.g. 'capture cross-section', 'fission cross-section', 'ionization cross-section', etc.

CROWN GLASS. Variety of *glass* containing potassium or barium in place of sodium; less fusible than ordinary *soda glass*; used in optical instruments.

CRUCIBLE. Vessel of heat-resisting material used for containing high-temperature *chemical reactions*.

CRYOGEN. *Freezing mixture.*

CRYOGENICS. The study of materials and phenomena at *temperatures* close to *absolute zero*.

CRYOHYDRATES. Crystalline substances, containing the *solute* with a definite molecular proportion of *water*, which crystallize out from *solutions* cooled below the *freezing point* of pure water.

CRYOLITE. Natural sodium aluminium fluoride, Na_3AlF_6. Used in the manufacture of *aluminium*.

CRYOPHORUS. Apparatus used to demonstrate the cooling effect of *evaporation*.

CRYOSCOPIC METHOD for the determination of *molecular weights*; freezing-point method. The determination of the molecular weight of a dissolved substance by noting the *depression of freezing point* produced by a known *concentration*.

CRYOSTAT. Vessel in which a specified low *temperature* may be maintained.

CRYOTRON. A switch based on *super-conductivity*. Simplest form consists of a coil of wire of one super-conducting material wound round a length of wire of another super-conductor, all immersed in a bath of liquid helium. A control current passed through the coil produces a *magnetic field* strong enough to destroy the super-conductivity of the central wire but not of the coil. Thus the current in the coil controls the *resistance* of the wire, switching it from zero to a finite value.

CRYSTAL. Substance solidified in a definite geometrical form. Most *solid* substances, when pure, are obtainable in a definite crystalline form. Solids which do not form crystals are said to be *amorphous*. Crystals are classified according to the structure of their *lattices*, or according to the type of *bond* which holds them together, i.e. *electrovalent* (or *ionic crystals*), *covalent crystals*, or *metallic crystals*.

CRYSTAL COUNTER. A *counter tube* which depends upon a *crystal* in which the electrical *conductivity* is momentarily increased by an ionizing event.

CRYSTAL DETECTOR. See *detector*. Consists of a fine wire ('cat's whisker') in contact with a crystal of *galena* (PbS) or other suitable *semiconductor*. This arrangement is a good conductor of *electricity* in one direction, and suppresses most of the flow of electricity in the other direction.

CRYSTAL OSCILLATOR. A source of electrical oscillation of very constant *frequency* determined by the physical characteristics of a *quartz crystal*. See *quartz clock*.

CRYSTAL RECTIFIER. A *semiconductor* used as a *rectifier*, usually in a manner similar to a *diode* valve; also called a semiconductor diode.

CRYSTALLOGRAPHY. Study of the geometrical form of *crystals*. See *X-ray crystallography*.

CRYSTALLOIDS. Substances which, in *solution*, are able to pass through a *semi-permeable membrane*; substances which do not usually form *colloidal solutions*.

CUBE. 1. A regular hexahedron; regular solid figure with six square faces. 2. The third power of a number. E.g. 8 is the cube of 2, 2^3.

CUBE ROOT, $\sqrt[3]{}$, of a number A is the quantity which, when 'cubed' (i.e. raised to the third power), gives A. Thus 2 is the cube root of 8.

CUBIC CENTIMETRE. c.c. Metric unit of volume. 1000 c.c. = 1 *litre* very nearly. Term used synonymously with *millilitre*, ml., one-thousandth of a litre.

CULTURE MEDIUM. A preparation used for growing and cultivating *micro-organisms* for experimental purposes.

CUPEL. Dish used in the extraction of the *noble metals* by *cupellation*.

CUPELLATION. Separation of silver, gold, and other *noble metals* from impurities which are oxidized by hot air. The impure metal is placed in a *cupel*, a flat dish made of porous *refractory* material, and a blast of hot air is directed upon it in a special furnace. The impurities are oxidized by the air and are partly swept away by the blast and partly absorbed by the cupel.

CUPRIC. *Compound* of *bivalent* copper. Most of the commoner copper compounds are cupric *salts*.

CUPROUS. *Compound* of *univalent* copper.

CUPROUS OXIDE, red copper oxide, Cu_2O. Red *insoluble* powder, formed when *Fehling's solution* is reduced.

75

CURARE. Very poisonous material, containing certain *alkaloids*. Obtained from various South American trees.

CURIE, the. Measure of the *activity* of a *radioactive* substance (see *radioactivity*). Originally defined as the quantity of *radon* in radioactive equilibrium with 1 gm. of radium. Now extended to cover all radioactive *isotopes* and defined as that quantity of a radioactive isotope which decays at the rate of $3 \cdot 7 \times 10^{10}$ *disintegrations* per second.

CURIE POINT, Curie temperature. The temperature for a given *ferromagnetic* substance above which it becomes merely *paramagnetic*.

CURIUM. Cm. *Transuranic element*, At. No. 96. Radioactive *actinide* whose most stable *isotope*, $^{248}_{96}Cm$, has a *half-life* of $4 \cdot 7 \times 10^5$ years.

CURRENT, electric. See *electric current*.

CURRENT BALANCE. Instrument for the determination of an *electric current* in absolute *electromagnetic units*. Consists of two similar coils attached to the extremities of a balance arm. Above and below each of these coils is a fixed coil. The six coils are connected in series in such a way that when the current is allowed to pass through them, the beam experiences maximum *torque*. The beam is restored to its horizontal *equilibrium* position by means of a known torque supplied by a rider sliding along the arm. From the known torque and the geometry of the system the current can be calculated.

CURRENT DENSITY, in *electrolysis*. Current per unit area of *electrode*.

CURSOR. Transparent slider with a fine hair-line; used in *slide-rules*.

CYANAMIDE. NH_2CN. Colourless *crystals*, m.p. $44°$ C. Name often applied to *calcium cyanamide*.

CYANIDE. *Salt* of *hydrocyanic acid*, HCN. All cyanides are intensely poisonous.

CYANIDE PROCESS for gold. Extraction of gold from its ores by dissolving the gold in a *solution* of potassium cyanide, KCN, reducing the resulting potassium aurocyanide, $KAu(CN)_2$, with zinc, filtering off, melting down, and cupelling (see *cupellation*) the metal.

CYANOGEN. C_2N_2. Colourless, very poisonous *gas* with a smell of bitter almonds. In its chemical properties resembles the *halogens*, forming *cyanides* analogous to the *chlorides*, etc.

CYANOTYPE. See *blueprint*.

CYBERNETICS. The theory of communication and control mechanisms in living beings and machines.

CYCLE (phys.). Any series of changes or operations performed by or on a system, which brings it back to its original state. E.g. the *frequency* of an *alternating current* is measured in cycles per second.

CYCLIC FIGURE (math.). Figure through all the vertices or corners of which a *circle* may be drawn; figure inscribed in a circle.

CYCLIC HYDROCARBONS. *Organic compounds* of carbon and hydrogen only, some or all of the carbon *atoms* in the *molecule* being linked in a closed ring structure; e.g. *benzene*.

CYCLIC QUADRILATERAL. Four-sided plane *rectilinear* figure through the vertices of which a *circle* may be drawn. The pairs of opposite angles are *supplementary* (i.e. total 180°).

CYCLOID. Figure traced out in space by a point on the circumference of a *circle* which rolls without slipping along a fixed straight line.

CYCLONITE, hexogen, R.D.X.*, $(CH_2N.NO_2)_3$. A very powerful *explosive* made from *hexamine*.

CYCLOTRON. An *accelerator* for imparting to charged particles of atomic magnitudes, *energies* of several million *electron-volts*. The *ions* or charged particles are caused to traverse a spiral path between two hollow semi-circular *electrodes*, called dees, by means of a suitable *magnetic field* applied perpendicularly to the plane of the dees. At each half-revolution the particles receive an energy increase of some tens of thousands of electron-volts from an oscillating *voltage* applied between the dees.

CYLINDER. Solid figure traced out by a rectangle rotating round one side as *axis*. For a cylinder having vertical height h and radius of base r, the volume is $\pi r^2 h$ and the total surface area $2\pi r(h+r)$.

CYTOCHROME. A respiratory *pigment* widely distributed in *aerobic organisms*. Consists of *proteins* with an iron *prosthetic group* similar to that of *haemoglobin*. The *oxidation* of cytochrome by molecular oxygen, and its subsequent *reduction* in the cell, is the principal route by which atmospheric oxygen enters into cellular *metabolism*.

CYTOLOGY. The study of the structure and function of living *cells*.

CYTOLYSIS. The dissolution of *cells*, particularly by the destruction of their surface membranes.

CYTOPLASM. The *protoplasm* of a living *cell* outside its *nucleus*.

CYTOSINE. Aminopyrimidone. $C_4H_5N_3O$. One of the *pyrimidine* bases which occur in the *nucleotides* of the *nucleic acids* and which play a part in the formulation of the *genetic code*.

D

DAILY VARIATION of the Earth's magnetic field (See *magnetism, terrestrial*). Small variation of the *horizontal intensity*, *magnetic declination*, and *dip* recurring over a period of a day.

DALTON'S ATOMIC THEORY. See *atomic theory*.

DAMPING. Decrease in the *amplitude* of an oscillation or *wave motion* with time.

DANIELL CELL. *Primary cell* having a negative pole of amalgamated zinc, standing in a porous pot containing dilute *sulphuric acid*. This pot stands in *copper sulphate solution*, which also contains the positive pole, a copper plate. On completion of the external circuit, a current flows and the following reactions take place: at the negative pole, zinc is dissolved, zinc sulphate being formed; at the positive pole, copper is deposited. The *E.M.F.* is $1 \cdot 1$ *volts*.

DARAF. The practical unit of *elastance*; *reciprocal* of the *farad*.

DARK GROUND ILLUMINATION. Device used in microscopy, whereby transparent or unstained objects are made to appear as bright particles on a black background.

DASH-POT. Mechanical damping device. Depends upon the fact that when a body moves through a *fluid* medium, viscous *forces* are set up which damp the motion of the body. Usually consists of a piston, attached to the part whose movements are to be damped, fitting loosely into a cylinder containing either air or oil.

DATING. The determination of the age of *mineral*, *fossil*, or wooden objects by measuring their *radioactivity*. See also *radiocarbon dating* and *radioactive age*.

DATIVE BOND. Co-ordinate bond. A *covalent type* of *bond* in which both *electrons* forming the bond are donated by one *atom*. See *valency*, *electronic theory of*.

DAVY LAMP. See *safety lamp*.

D.D.T. DichloroDiphenylTrichloroethane. $(C_6H_4Cl)_2.CH.CCl_3$. White powder, m.p. 107° C., with a fruity smell. Used as a contact *insecticide*.

DEAMINATION. The removal of *amino groups* from a *compound*.

DEAN AND STARK METHOD. A method of estimating the quantity of *water* in an *oil* or other *liquid* substance. The liquid under examination is distilled into a special *reflux condenser* so constructed that the water is prevented from running back into the distillation flask. The *volume* of water so collected is measured and thus the water content of a known *weight* of initial liquid can be calculated.

DE BROGLIE WAVE-LENGTH. A moving particle, whatever its nature, has wave properties associated with it. For a particle of *mass m* moving with *velocity v*, the *wave-length* of the associated de Broglie wave is given by $\lambda = \dfrac{h}{mv}$, where h is *Planck's constant*.

DEBYE AND HUCKEL'S THEORY of electrolysis. An explanation of the phenomena of *electrolysis* put forward to overcome certain difficulties which arise in the interpretation of the phenomena on the classical theory of *electrolytic dissociation*. It is assumed that strong *electrolytes* are completely dissociated, and that the increase in equivalent *conductivity* which is observed with dilution is due not to an increase in the fraction ionized, but to an increase in the mobility of *the ions*, due to the decrease of *electrostatic forces*.

DEBYE UNIT. A unit of molecular *dipole* moment equal to 1×10^{-18} *electrostatic units*.

DECANTATION. Separation of a *solid* from a *liquid* by allowing the former to settle and pouring off the latter.

DECAY. Term used in relation to the *disintegration* of a *radioactive atom*; the *transformation* of a radioactive substance into its decay (or daughter) products. (See *radioactivity*.) Also used in relation to the transformation of particles into more stable particles.

DECAY CONSTANT. See *disintegration constant*.

DECAY, PERIOD OF. See *half-life*.

DECI-. Prefix used in the *metric system* to mean one tenth.

DECIBEL. One tenth of a *bel*. A unit which compares levels of *power*. Two power levels, P_1 and P_2, are said to differ by n decibels when:

$$n = 10 \log_{10} \frac{P_2}{P_1}$$

This unit is often used to express *sound* intensities. In this case, P_2 is the intensity of the sound under consideration and P_1 is the intensity of some reference level, often the intensity of the lowest audible note of the same *frequency*.

DECINORMAL SOLUTION. A *solution* containing one-tenth of a *gram-equivalent* per *litre*.

DECLINATION (astr.). The *angular distance* of a heavenly body from the *celestial equator*.

DECLINATION, MAGNETIC. See *magnetic declination*.

DECOMPOSITION (chem.). Breaking up of a chemical *compound*. E.g. mercuric oxide, HgO, decomposes on heating into mercury and oxygen. Also used in relation to the breaking up of organic materials as a result of the action of *bacteria*, *fungi*, or chemicals.

DECREPITATION. Bursting or cracking of *crystals* of certain substances on heating, mainly due to expansion of water within the crystals.

DEFECT. A discontinuity in the pattern of *atoms*, *ions*, or *electrons* in a *crystal*. A 'point defect' consists of a *vacancy* or an *interstitial*. A 'line defect' is caused by a *dislocation*. In a *semiconductor*, 'defect conduction' is a result of *hole* conduction in the *valence band*.

DEFICIENCY DISEASES. Diseases produced by lack of a particular *vitamin* or other essential food factor in the diet; e.g. scurvy, caused by the deficiency of vitamin C.

DEFORMATION. Alteration in the size or shape of a body.

DEFORMATION POTENTIAL. The *electric potential* which acts on a *free electron* in a *conductor* or *semiconductor* as a result of *deformation* of the *crystal lattice*.

DEGAUSSING. *Demagnetization* of a magnetized substance. Achieved by surrounding the substance with a coil carrying an *alternating current* of ever-decreasing magnitude.

DEGENERATE GAS. A state of *matter* in which *electrons* and atomic *nuclei* are packed too closely together for the evolution of *nuclear energy*; occurs in *stars* of the *white dwarf* class.

DEGREE. Subdivision of an interval in a scale of measurement; e.g. the Centigrade degree.

DEGREE, measure of angle. See *angle*.

DEGREES OF FREEDOM (chem.). 1. Term used in the *phase rule*; the least number of independent variables defining the state of a system (e.g. the *temperature* and *pressure* in the case of a *gas*) which must be given definite values before this state is completely determined. 2. The number of independent ways in which a *molecule* may possess translational, vibrational, or rotational *energies*.

DEGREES OF LATITUDE AND LONGITUDE. See *latitude, longitude*.

DEHYDRATION. Elimination or removal of *water*; term usually applied to the removal of chemically combined water. E.g. concentrated *sulphuric acid*, H_2SO_4, acts as a dehydrating agent on substances which contain hydrogen and oxygen in the proportions in which they occur in water.

DEHYDROGENASE. An *enzyme* which catalyses *oxidation* reactions by the removal of hydrogen from the *substrate*.

DEKA-. Prefix denoting ten times, in the *metric system*.

DEKATRON. A gas-filled emission tube with a central *anode* usually surrounded by ten *cathodes* and associated transfer *electrodes*. Incoming pulses cause a *glow discharge* to be transferred from one cathode to the next so that the tube may be used for counting or switching.

DELAY LINE. A component or circuit designed to introduce a calculated delay in the transmission of a signal.

DELAYED NEUTRONS. *Neutrons* resulting from *nuclear fission* which are emitted with a measurable time delay. Only a small proportion of neutrons are delayed, but the average delay period must be taken into account in the control of *nuclear reactors*. See *prompt neutrons*.

DELIQUESCENT. Having the property of picking up moisture from the air to such an extent as to dissolve in it; becoming *liquid* on exposure to air.

DELTA CONNEXION. A method of connecting the three windings of a three-*phase* electrical system. The windings are connected in series, the three-phase supply being taken from, or put into, the three junctions.

DELTA METAL. *Alloy* of copper (55%) and zinc (43%) with small amounts of iron and other *metals*.

DELTA RAY. An *electron* ejected from an *atom* by a fast moving ionizing particle.

DEMAGNETIZATION. The process of depriving a body of its magnetic properties. The 'demagnetization energy' is the *energy* which would be released when a body is completely demagnetized.

DEMODULATION. The process, in a *radio* or *radar* receiver, of separating information from a *modulated carrier wave*. The equipment used is called a demodulator or a *detector*.

DENATURE. 1. To denature *ethyl alcohol* is to add some poisonous substance to it to make it unfit for human consumption, e.g. *methylated spirits*. 2. To denature a *fissile* material is to add another *isotope* to it to render it unsuitable for use in a *nuclear weapon*. 3. To denature a *soluble*, or globular, *protein* is to produce a structural change in it, either chemically or by heating, so that it loses most of its solubility. Usually involves an unfolding of the *polypeptide* chain.

DENDRITE. 1. (chem.) a many-branched *crystal*. 2. (bio.) Branching processes of a *neuron* which carry impulses into the *cell* body, and which form *synapses* with the *axons* of other neurons.

DENITRIFYING BACTERIA. *Bacteria* in the *soil* which, in the absence of oxygen, break down *nitrates* and *nitrites* with the evolution of free nitrogen.

DENOMINATOR (math.). The number below the line in a vulgar fraction e.g. 4 in $\frac{3}{4}$.

DENSITOMETER. Instrument for the measurement of the density of an image produced by *light*, *X-rays*, *gamma rays*, etc., on a photographic plate.

DENSITY. The *mass* of unit *volume* of a substance. Expressed in such units as grams per c.c. or lb. per cu. ft. The density of *water* is one gram per c.c. and therefore in these units density is numerically equal to *specific gravity*.

DENSITY, OPTICAL. If one medium has a greater *refractive index* than another for *light* of a given *wave-length*, then it has the greater optical density for that wave-length.

DEOXYRIBONUCLEIC (DESOXYRIBOSENUCLEIC) ACID. DNA. Long thread-like *molecules* found in *chromosomes* and *viruses*, consisting of two interwound helical chains of *polynucleotides*. The *sugar* of all the *nucleotides* is 2-deoxy-D-*ribose*, but each nucleotide is characterized by one of the four following nitrogenous bases: *adenine*, *cytosine*, *guanine*, and *thymine*. DNA molecules are responsible for storing the *genetic code* by the order of the arrangement of their nitrogenous bases, three bases coding for one *amino acid*. The structure of a DNA molecule has been likened to a twisted rope-ladder, the sides of which consist of sugar-phosphate chains, the rungs of linked nitrogenous bases.

DEPILATORY. Substance used for removing hair.

DEPLETED MATERIAL. In general, a material which contains less of a particular *isotope* than it normally possesses. In particular, applied to *nuclear fuel*, a material which contains less *fissile* isotopes than natural uranium, e.g. the residue from an *isotope separation* plant or a *nuclear reactor*.

DEPLETION LAYER. The region of a *semiconductor* in which the density of mobile *carriers* is too low to neutralize the fixed charge density of *donors* and *acceptors*.

DEPOLARIZATION. Prevention of electrical *polarization* in a *cell*. In the *Leclanché cell* polarization is reduced by surrounding the positive carbon pole with *manganese dioxide*, MnO_2. This oxidizes the hydrogen liberated at the pole, the chief cause of polarization.

DEPRESSION, ANGLE OF. If B is a point below the level of another point A, the angle of depression of B from A is the *angle* which AB makes with the horizontal *plane AX* through A. See Fig. 6 on page 82.

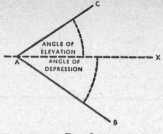

FIG. 6.

DEPRESSION OF FREEZING POINT. Lowering of the *freezing point* of a *liquid* when a *solid* is dissolved in it. With certain exceptions, the depression is proportional to the number of *molecules* or *ions* present, and the depression produced by the same *molecular concentration* of any substance is a constant for a given *solvent*. This gives rise to the *cryoscopic method* for the determination of *molecular weights*.

DERIVATIVE (chem.). Substance derived or prepared from some other substance, usually retaining the general structure of the parent substance, E.g. *nitrobenzene*, $C_6H_5NO_2$, is a derivative of *benzene*, one of the hydrogen *atoms* in every *molecule* of the latter being replaced by a nitro group, NO_2.

DERIVATIVE (math.). Derived function; result of *differentiation* of a mathematical function. See Table 4, page 334.

DERIVED FUNCTION. See *derivative*.

DERIVED UNITS. *Units* of physical measurement, other than the *fundamental units* of length, mass, and time, but derived from these. E.g. the unit for *velocity* is derived from the units for length and time, velocity being expressed as length per unit time, e.g. feet per second.

DESICCATION. Drying; removal of moisture.

DESICCATOR. Apparatus used in laboratories for drying substances and for preventing *hygroscopic* substances from picking up moisture. Consists of a glass vessel, with a close-fitting ground lid, which contains some hygroscopic substance, e.g. *phosphorus pentoxide*, P_2O_5.

DESTRUCTIVE DISTILLATION. Carbonization. Heating a complex substance to produce chemical changes in it, and distilling off the *volatile* substances so formed. E.g. the destructive distillation of *coal* produces *coal-gas* and many other valuable products.

DETECTOR. That part of a *radio* receiver in which the information is separated from the *modulated carrier wave*. Now more usually called a demodulator. See *demodulation*, also *crystal detector*.

DETERGENT. A cleaning agent; term usually restricted to substances used in *solution* for cleaning a solid surface by action other than simple dissolution; e.g. by using a *surface-active agent*.

DETINNING. Recovery of metallic tin from scrap tin-plate by the action of chlorine, which combines with the tin to form *volatile* stannic chloride, $SnCl_4$.

DETONATING GAS. Mixture of hydrogen and oxygen in a *volume* ratio of 2:1; i.e. in the volume ratio required to form *water*. Extremely explosive when lit or sparked.

DETONATION. Extremely rapid *combustion* which takes place within a high velocity *shock wave*. Also used loosely, but incorrectly, to describe the combustion reactions which occur during *knocking* or 'pinking' in an *internal-combustion engine*.

DEUTERIUM. D. $^2_1$H. *Isotope* of hydrogen with *mass number* 2, and *atomic mass* 2·0147. The *abundance* of deuterium in natural hydrogen is 0·0156%. Occurs in *water* as the oxide, D_2O (see *heavy water*), from which it is obtained by fractional *electrolysis*.

DEUTERON. *Nucleus* of *deuterium atom*.

DEVARDA'S ALLOY. *Alloy* of 50% copper, 45% aluminium, 5% zinc.

DEVELOPING, PHOTOGRAPHIC. The action of certain chemicals, usually organic *reducing agents*, on an exposed photographic plate or film in order to bring out the latent image. The developer reduces those areas of the silver *salts* which had been exposed to *light* to metallic silver. This remains as a black deposit. See *photography*.

DEVITRIFICATION of glass. Crystallization of *glass*, which is normally an *amorphous* mixture in a *metastable* state; when crystallization takes place, the glass loses its characteristic state of clear transparency.

DEW. Liquid *water* produced by *condensation* of *water vapour* in the air when the *temperature* falls sufficiently for the vapour to reach saturation.

DEW POINT. The *temperature* at which the *water vapour* present in the air saturates the air and begins to condense, i.e. *dew* begins to form.

DEWAR FLASK. Glass vessel used for keeping *liquids* at *temperatures* differing from that of the surrounding air. This is done by reducing to a minimum the transfer of *heat* between the liquid and the air. Consists of a double-walled flask with the space between the two walls exhausted to a very high *vacuum*, to minimize transfer of heat by *convection* and *conduction*. The inner surfaces of the walls are silvered to reduce transfer of heat by *radiation*; areas of contact between the two walls are kept at a minimum to keep down conduction of heat. See Fig. 7, page 84.

DEXTRIN. British gum, starch gum. Mixture of gummy *polysaccharide carbohydrates* obtained by the partial *hydrolysis* of *starch*.

DEXTROROTATORY. Rotating or deviating the plane of vibration of polarized light to the right (observer looking against the oncoming light). See *polarization of light*.

DEXTROSE. See *glucose*.

DIAGONAL. Line joining the intersections of two pairs of sides of a *rectilinear* figure.

DIALYSIS. Separation of *colloids* in *solution* from other dissolved substances (*crystalloids*) by selective *diffusion* through a *semi-permeable membrane.* Such a membrane is slightly permeable to the *molecules* of the crystalloids, but not to the larger molecules or groups of molecules in the colloidal state.

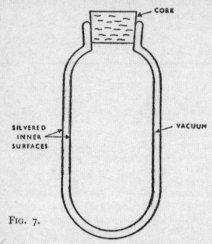

FIG. 7.

DIALYZED IRON. A *colloidal solution* of ferric hydroxide, $Fe(OH)_3$. Deep red liquid, used in medicine.

DIALYZER. Arrangement for effecting *dialysis.* The *solution* to be dialyzed is placed in a vessel in which it is separated from *water* by a *semi-permeable membrane*; this is not permeable to the substance in the *colloidal state,* which will eventually remain as a pure solution on its side of the membrane.

DIAMAGNETISM. The property of a substance which has a small negative *magnetic susceptibility.* This type of magnetism is due to a change in the orbital motion of the *electrons* in the *atoms* of the substance consequent on the application of an external *magnetic field.* The phenomenon occurs in all substances, although the resulting diamagnetism is often masked by the much greater effects due to *paramagnetism* or *ferro-magnetism.*

DIAMETER. See *circle.*

DIAMOND. Natural crystalline allotropic form (see *allotropy*) of carbon. Colourless when pure, sometimes coloured by traces of impurities. Has a very high *refractive index* and *dispersive power.* Hardest substance known. Transparent to *X-rays* (imitations are not). Used for cutting tools and drills, and as a gem.

DIASTASE. *Enzyme* contained in *malt.* Converts *starch* into *maltose* during *brewing.* See also *amylase.*

DIATHERMANCY. Property of being able to transmit *heat radiation*; similar to transparency with respect to *light*.

DIATHERMY. Method of medical treatment by heating the body-tissues by the passage of a *high-frequency* electric discharge.

DIATOMACEOUS EARTH. See *kieselguhr*.

DIATOMIC (chem.). Consisting of two *atoms* in a *molecule*; e.g. hydrogen *gas*, H_2.

DIAZO COMPOUNDS. *Organic compounds* of the general formula RN:NR'. Many are important in the manufacture of *dyes*.

DIBASIC ACID. *Acid* containing two *atoms* of *acidic hydrogen* in a *molecule*; acid giving rise to two series of *salts*, normal and acid salts; e.g. *sulphuric acid*, H_2SO_4, which gives rise to normal sulphates and bisulphates.

DICHROMATE CELL, bichromate cell. *Primary cell* having a positive pole of carbon and a negative pole of zinc in a *liquid* consisting of a *solution* of *sulphuric acid*, H_2SO_4, and *potassium dichromate*, $K_2Cr_2O_7$, the latter acting as a depolarizing agent (see *depolarization*) by its oxidizing action. The *EMF* is 2·03 *volts*.

DICHROMATE OF POTASH. See *potassium dichromate*.

DICHROMATISM. A form of colour blindness in which only two *colours* of the *spectrum* can be distinguished.

DIELECTRIC. Non-conductor of electricity, insulator. Substance in which an *electric field* gives rise to no net flow of *electric charge* but only to a displacement of charge.

DIELECTRIC CONSTANT. Relative Permittivity. Specific Inductive Capacity. The ratio of the *capacitance* of a *capacitor* with the given substance as *dielectric*, to the capacitance of the same capacitor with air (or a *vacuum*) as the dielectric. The dielectric constant, K, is also given by:

$$K = \frac{Q_1 Q_2}{Fr^2}$$

where F is the *force* between two charges Q_1 and Q_2, which are separated by a distance r.

DIELECTRIC HEATING. A form of heating in which electrically insulating material is heated by being subjected to an alternating *electric field*. Results from *energy* being lost by the field to *electrons* within the *atoms* and *molecules* of the material. In industrial dielectric heating the material to be heated is placed between the plates of a *capacitor* connected to a *high frequency* power source.

DIELECTROPHORESIS. The motion of electrically polarized (see *electric polarization*) particles in a non-uniform *electric field*.

DIENE. *Unsaturated hydrocarbon* containing two *double bonds*, e.g. *butadiene*.

DIESEL ENGINE. Type of *internal-combustion engine* which burns heavy oil. Air which is mixed with the oil is compressed and thereby heated to the *ignition temperature* of the oil.

DIFFERENTIAL CALCULUS. A branch of mathematics which deals with continuously varying quantities. It is based upon the *differential coefficient* of one quantity with respect to another of which it is a *function*. Used for solving problems involving the rates at which processes occur and for obtaining maximum and minimum values for continuously varying quantities.

DIFFERENTIAL COEFFICIENT, derived function. See *differentiation* and Table 4, page 334.

DIFFERENTIAL EQUATION. An equation which involves *differential coefficients*. An ordinary differential equation is one in which only one independent variable is involved. The 'order' of a differential equation is the same as that of the *derivative* of the highest order appearing in it; the 'degree' is given by the largest *exponent*.

DIFFERENTIATION (bio.). 1. The development of *cells* so that they are capable of performing specialized functions in the organs and tissues of the *organisms* to which they belong. 2. In microscopic specimens, the removal of the excess stain from certain parts to show up the structure of the whole.

DIFFERENTIATION (math.). Operation, used in the *calculus*, of obtaining the *differential coefficient*; if $y = x^n$, the differential coefficient, $\frac{dy}{dx} = nx^{n-1}$. See Table 4, page 334.

DIFFRACTION. When a beam of *light* passes through an *aperture* or past the edge of an opaque obstacle and is allowed to fall upon a screen patterns of light and dark bands (with *monochromatic light*) or coloured bands (with *white light*) are observed near the edges of the beam, and extend into the geometrical shadow. This phenomenon, which is a particular case of *interference* is due to the wave nature of light, and is known as diffraction. The phenomenon is common to all *wave motions*. See also *electron diffraction*.

DIFFRACTION GRATING. Device used to disperse a beam of *light*, *X-rays*, or other *electromagnetic radiation* into its constituent *wavelengths*, i.e. for producing its *spectrum*. It may consist of any device which acts upon an incident *wave front* in a manner similar to that of a regular array of parallel slits where the slit width is of the same order as the wave-length of the incident radiation. Such gratings may be prepared by ruling equidistant parallel lines on to a *glass* (transmission grating) or *metal* surface (reflection grating). The grating may be plane or *concave*, the latter having self-focusing properties.

DIFFUSION OF GASES. *Molecules* of all *gases* move freely and tend to distribute themselves equally within the limits of the vessel enclosing the gas; thus all gases diffuse within the limits of any enclosing walls, and are all perfectly miscible with one another. The rates of diffusion of gases through porous bodies are inversely proportional to the square roots of their *densities*. (See *Graham's law*.)

DIFFUSION OF LIGHT. *Scattering* or alteration of direction of *light* rays, such as is produced by transmission through frosted glass, fog, etc., or by irregular reflections at matt surfaces such as blotting paper.

DIFFUSION OF PARTICLES. In *nuclear physics*, the passage of *elementary particles* through *matter* in such a way that the *probability* of *scattering* is large compared to that of *capture*.

DIFFUSION OF SOLUTIONS. *Molecules* or *ions* of a dissolved substance move freely through the *solvent*, the *solution* becoming uniform in *concentration*; the phenomenon is similar to *diffusion of gases*.

DIFFUSION PLANT. A plant for separating *isotopes*, based on their different rates of *diffusion* in the gaseous state through a membrane.

DIFFUSION PUMP. See *condensation pump*.

DIGIT (astr.). One-twelfth of the diameter of the *Sun* or *Moon*; used to denote the extent of an *eclipse*.

DIGIT (math.). Single figure or numeral; e.g. 325 is a number of 3 digits.

DIGITAL COMPUTER. A *computer* which operates on data in the form of *digits*, rather than the physical quantities used in *analogue computers*. Originally mechanical devices employing cogs, gears, and levers, now depend upon *electronic* techniques which allow computers to be constructed capable of dealing automatically with a very wide range of problems at very high speeds.

DIGITALIS. A mixture of *glucosides* of vegetable origin (e.g. digitonin, digitoxin), used in the treatment of certain heart conditions.

DILATION, dilatation (phys.). Change in *volume*.

DILATOMETER. Apparatus used for measuring *volume* changes of substances. Generally consists of a bulb with a graduated stem.

DILUTE. Containing a large amount of *solvent*, generally *water*. 'Dilute' laboratory solutions of *reagents* are generally of twice normal strength, containing 2 *gram-equivalents* per *litre*. See *normality*.

DILUTION. 1. Further addition of *water* or other *solvent* to a *solution*. 2. The *reciprocal* of *concentration*; the *volume* of *solvent* in which unit quantity of *solute* is dissolved.

DIMENSIONS OF UNITS. The dimensions of a physical quantity are the *powers* to which the *fundamental units* (length l, mass m, time t, etc.) expressing that quantity are raised. E.g. *volume*, l^3, is of dimensions three in length; *velocity*, i.e. length per unit time, l/t, is of dimensions one in length and -1 in time.

DIMER. A substance composed of *molecules* each of which comprise two molecules of a *monomer*.

DIMORPHISM. Existence of a substance in two different crystalline forms.

DIMORPHOUS. Existing in two different crystalline forms.

DI-NEUTRON. An unstable system comprising two *neutrons*.

DIODE. *Thermionic valve* containing two *electrodes*, *anode* and *cathode*. The diode is used chiefly for *rectification* and *demodulation*.

DIOPTRE. Unit of power of a *lens*; the power of a lens in dioptres is the *reciprocal* of its *focal length* in metres. The power of a *converging lens* is usually taken to be positive, that of a *diverging lens* negative.

DIP, magnetic. See *magnetic dip*.

DIP CIRCLE. Instrument for measuring the *angle* of *magnetic dip*. Consists of a magnetized needle mounted to rotate in a vertical plane, the angle being measured on a circular scale, marked in degrees.

DIPLOID. A *cell* in which the *nucleus* contains *chromosomes* in pairs, is said to be diploid. Characteristic of nearly all animal cells except *gametes*. See *haploid*.

DIPOLE. Two equal point *electric charges* (electric dipole) or *magnetic poles* (magnetic dipole) of opposite sign, separated by a small distance. The dipole moment is the product of either charge (or pole) and the distance between the two. May also be expressed as the *couple* which would be required to maintain the dipole at right angles to a *field* (electric or magnetic) of unit intensity. *Molecules* in which the centres of positive and negative *charge* are separated constitute dipoles, the dipole moments of which are measured in *Debye units*. Dipole moments can often provide evidence as to the shape of molecules, e.g. *water* has a dipole moment of $1 \cdot 85$ Debye units, which indicates that it is triangular in shape with an angle of $105°$ between the two O-H bonds.

DIPOLE MOMENT. See *dipole*.

DIPPEL'S OIL. See *bone oil*.

DI-PROTON. An unstable system comprising two *protons*.

DIRECT CURRENT. An *electric current* flowing always in the same direction.

DIRECT DYES, cotton dyes, substantive dyes. Group of *dyes* which dye cotton, viscose *rayon*, and other *cellulose* fibres direct, without the use of *mordants*. Generally used with 'assistants' such as common *salt* or *sodium sulphate*, which assist absorption by the fibre.

DIRECT VISION SPECTROSCOPE. *Spectroscope* designed for compactness and portability. In this instrument, the middle portion of the *spectrum* (the yellow) remains undeviated. The eye thus looks in the direction of the source when observing the spectrum.

DISACCHARIDES. Group of *sugars* the *molecules* of which are derived by the *condensation* of two *monosaccharide* molecules with the elimination of a molecule of *water*. On *hydrolysis* disaccharides yield the corresponding monosaccharides. E.g. *cane-sugar*, sucrose, $C_{12}H_{22}O_{11}$, is a disaccharide which, on hydrolysis with dilute *acids*, gives a *mixture* of *glucose* and *fructose*, both monosaccharides having the formula $C_6H_{12}O_6$. (See *inversion of cane-sugar*.) Other important disaccharides are *lactose* and *maltose*.

DISCHARGE, ELECTRICAL. 1. The release of the *electric charge* stored in a *capacitor* through an external circuit. 2. The conversion of the *chemical energy* stored in an electric *cell* into *electrical energy*.

DISCHARGE IN GASES. The passage of *electricity* through a tube containing a *gas* at low pressure. *Electrons* and *ions* present in the tube are accelerated towards their respective *electrodes* by the applied *potential difference*, the net transfer of *electric charge* constituting the current. The electrons are accelerated sufficiently to produce ions by collision with the gas *molecules*. Re-combination of oppositely charged ions gives rise to luminous glows at certain parts of the tube. The study of this pheno- menon has led to many important results, including the discovery of the electron and of *isotopes*.

DISCRIMINATOR. An *electronic* circuit which converts *frequency* or *phase modulation* into *amplitude modulation*.

DISINFECTANT. Substance capable of destroying disease *bacteria*.

DISINTEGRATION (phys.). Any process in which the *nucleus* of an *atom* emits one or more particles or *photons*, either due to spontaneous *radioactivity* or as the result of a collision.

DISINTEGRATION CONSTANT. Decay Constant. Transformation Con- stant. The *probability* of the *decay* of an atomic *nucleus* per unit time which characterizes a *radioactive isotope*. It determines the exponential decrease with time, t, of the *activity*, a, given by:

$$a = a_0 e^{-\lambda t}$$

where a_0 is the activity when $t = 0$, and λ is the disintegration constant.

DISLOCATION. A line *defect* in a *crystal*, the result of a slip along a surface of one or more *lattice* constants.

DISORDERING. The displacement of *atoms* from their position in a *crystal lattice* (e.g. as a result of the effect of *ionizing radiation*) to positions which are not part of the lattice.

DISPERSE PHASE. The dissolved or suspended substance in a *colloidal solution* or *suspension*.

DISPERSION MEDIUM. Medium in which a substance in the *colloidal state* is dispersed; the *solvent* in a *colloidal solution*.

DISPERSION OF LIGHT. The splitting of *light* of mixed *wave-lengths* into a *spectrum*. A beam of ordinary *white light*, e.g. sunlight, on passing through an optical *prism* or a *diffraction grating*, is divided up or dis- persed into light of the different wave-lengths of which it is composed; if the beam which emerges after dispersion is allowed to fall upon a screen, a coloured band or spectrum is observed. Dispersion by a prism is due to the fact that light-waves of different wave-lengths are refracted (see *refraction*) or bent through different angles on passing through the prism, and are thus separated.

DISPERSIVE POWER of a medium. A measure of the *dispersion of light* produced by a *prism* or a particular medium with respect to light of two specified *wave-lengths* ('1' and '2'); given by the ratio $\dfrac{\mu_1 - \mu_2}{\mu - 1}$, where μ_1 is the *refractive index* of the medium for wave-length 1, μ_2 that for wave-length 2, and μ is the average of μ_1 and μ_2. When considering the dispersive power of media for ordinary *white light*, the dispersive power is often defined as $\dfrac{\mu_b - \mu_r}{\mu_y - 1}$ where μ_b, μ_r, and μ_y are the refractive indices for blue, red, and yellow light respectively.

DISSOCIATION (chem.). A temporary, reversible *decomposition* of the *molecules* of a *compound*, which occurs under some particular conditions. In *electrolytic dissociation*, the molecules are split into *ions* (see *ionic hypothesis*). In *thermal dissociation*, the effect of *heat* is to decompose a definite fraction of the molecules; e.g. *ammonium chloride*, NH_4Cl, dissociates into *ammonia*, NH_3, and *hydrogen chloride*, HCl, on heating. The products re-combine on cooling, and the degree of dissociation depends on the *temperature*. The ratio of the product of the *active masses* of the molecules resulting from the dissociation, to the active mass of the undissociated molecules, when *chemical equilibrium* has been reached under a particular set of physical conditions, is called the 'dissociation constant'.

DISTILLATE. *Liquid* obtained by *condensation* of *vapour* in *distillation*.

DISTILLATION. Process of converting a *liquid* into *vapour*, condensing the vapour, and collecting the condensed liquid or *distillate*. Used for separating *mixtures* of liquids of different *boiling points* or for separating a pure liquid from a non-*volatile* constituent. (See *fractional distillation*.) Also used in the separation of *isotopes*. See *isotopes, separation of*.

DISTILLED WATER. *Water* which has been purified of the substances dissolved in it by *distillation*.

DIURNAL. Daily; performed or completed once every 24 hours.

DIVALENT, bivalent. Having a *valency* of two.

DIVERGENT. Going away in different directions from a common path or point.

DIVERGING LENS. *Lens* which causes a parallel *beam* of *light* passing through it to diverge or spread out; *concave* lens.

DIVISION. An arithmetic operation in which a dividend is divided by a divisor to give a quotient and a remainder.

DNA. See *deoxyribonucleic acid*.

DOLOMITE, pearl spar. Natural double *carbonate* of magnesium and calcium, $MgCO_3.CaCO_3$. Whitish solid; occurs naturally in vast amounts, comprising whole mountain ranges.

DONOR. An imperfection in a *semiconductor* which causes *electron* conduction.

DOPING. The addition of a small quantity of impurity to a *semiconductor* to achieve a particular characteristic.

DOPPLER BROADENING. The broadening of spectral emission or absorption lines (see *spectrum*) due to random motion of the emitting or absorbing *molecules*, *atoms* or *nuclei*.

DOPPLER EFFECT. Doppler shift. Doppler's principle. The apparent change in the *frequency* of sound or *electromagnetic radiation* due to relative motion between the source and the observer. The *pitch* (*frequency*) of the sound emitted by a moving object (e.g. the whistle of a moving train) appears to a stationary observer to increase as the object approaches him and to decrease as it recedes from him. The *light* emitted by a moving object appears more red (red light being of lower frequency than the other colours) when it is receding from the observer (or the observer receding from it). Thus the fact that the light emitted by the *stars* of distant *galaxies* suffers a *red shift*, when observed from the Earth, is taken to mean that these distant galaxies are receding from our *Galaxy*. This is the principle evidence for the widely accepted hypothesis concerning the *expansion of the Universe*. The Doppler effect is also used in *radar*, to distinguish between stationary and moving targets and to provide information concerning their *velocity*, by measuring the frequency shift between the emitted and the reflected radiation.

DOSE (phys.). The 'absorbed dose' is the *energy* imparted by *ionizing radiation* to unit *mass* of irradiated *matter*. Measured in *rads* (i.e. 100 *ergs* per gram). The 'maximum permissible dose (or level)' is the recommended upper limit for the absorbed dose which a person should receive during a specified period.

DOUBLE BOND (chem.). Two *valency bonds* linking two *atoms* in a chemical *compound*; characteristic of an *unsaturated compound*.

DOUBLE DECOMPOSITION (chem.). Metathesis. *Chemical reaction* between two *compounds* in which each of the original compounds is decomposed and two new compounds are formed. E.g. the action of *sodium chloride* on *silver nitrate* according to the equation $NaCl + AgNO_3 = AgCl + NaNO_3$.

DOUBLE REFRACTION. Formation of two refracted rays of *light* (see *refraction*) from a single incident ray; property of certain *crystals*, notably *calcite*.

DOUBLE STAR. Two *stars* which are held very close to each other as a result of their mutual gravitational attraction, and which move through *space* together giving the appearance, to the naked eye, of being one star.

DOUBLET. A pair of associated lines in a *spectrum* characteristic of the *alkali metals*.

DRACHM, FLUID. British unit of *volume*; 60 *minims*; 3·55 c.c.

DRUG. Chemical substance used in medicine; term often loosely applied to substances which form a 'habit' by causing a craving for further doses.

DRY CELL, dry battery. Type of small *Leclanché cell* containing no free *liquid*. The *electrolyte* of *ammonium chloride* is in the form of a paste, and the negative zinc pole forms the outer container of the cell. Used for torch batteries, *radio* batteries, etc.

DRY ICE. Solid *carbon dioxide*, CO_2, used in refrigeration.

DRYING OIL. An animal or vegetable *oil* which will harden to a tough film when a thin layer is exposed to the air. The hardening is due to *oxidation* or *polymerization* of the *unsaturated fatty acids* of which these oils partially consist. Used in *paints* and varnishes (e.g. *linseed oil*, dehydrated *castor oil* and certain fish oils).

DUCTILITY. Property, especially of *metals*, of being capable of being drawn out into a wire.

DUCTLESS GLANDS, endocrine glands. Glands or organs producing *hormones* in the body.

DULONG AND PETIT'S LAW. For a *solid element*, the product of the *atomic weight* and the *specific heat*, i.e. the *atomic heat*, is a constant, approximately equal to 6·4 *calories* per *gram-atom*. For validity of this law, see *atomic heat*.

DUPLET. A pair of *electrons* shared between two *atoms* forming a single covalent bond. See *valency, electronic theory of*.

DURALUMIN*. Light hard aluminium *alloy* containing about 4% copper, and small amounts of magnesium, manganese and silicon.

DUST CORE. A core for magnetic devices made of powdered *metal* (often molybdenum) held together with a suitable binder. Particularly suitable for *high frequency* equipment.

DUTCH LIQUID. See *ethylene dichloride*.

DUTCH METAL. *Alloy* of copper and zinc; variety of *brass*.

DWARF STAR. *Star* of low luminosity. See also *white dwarf star*.

DYAD (chem.). *Element* having a *valency* of two.

DYES. Coloured substances which can be fixed firmly to a material to be dyed, so at to be more or less 'fast' to *water, light*, and *soap*. Usually *organic compounds*; some which were originally extracted from plants are now made artificially from *coal-tar by-products*; most modern dyes are entirely artificial and do not occur in Nature. See *acid dyes, azo dyes, direct dyes, mordants, vat dyes*.

DYNAMIC EQUILIBRIUM. If two opposing processes are going on at the same rate in a system, thus keeping the system unchanged, the system is said to be in dynamic equilibrium. E.g. a *liquid* in equilibrium with its *saturated vapour*; the rate of *evaporation* from the liquid surface is equal to the rate of *condensation* of the *vapour*.

DYNAMICS. Branch of *mechanics*; the mathematical and physical study of the behaviour of bodies under the action of *forces* which produce changes of motion in them.

DYNAMITE. *Explosive* consisting of *nitroglycerine* absorbed in *kieselguhr*.

DYNAMO. Device for converting *mechanical energy* into *electrical energy*. Depends on the fact that if an electrical *conductor* moves across a *magnetic field*, an *electric current* flows in the conductor. (See *induction*.) The simplest form of dynamo consists of a powerful *electromagnet*, termed the *field magnet*, between the *poles* of which a suitable conductor, usually in the form of a coil or coils, termed the *armature*, is rotated. The mechanical energy of the rotation is thus converted into electrical energy in the form of a current in the armature.

DYNAMOMETER. Any instrument designed for the measurement of *power*.

DYNATRON OSCILLATOR. Oscillator, using a *tetrode* (screen grid valve) in such a way that the *anode* current increases as the anode *voltage* is reduced.

DYNE. *Absolute unit* of *force*; the force which, acting upon a *mass* of 1 gm., will impart to it an *acceleration* of 1 cm. per second per second.

DYSPROSIUM. Dy. Element. A.W. 162·50. At. No. 66. See *lanthanides*.

DYSTETIC MIXTURE. A *mixture* which has a constant maximum *melting point*.

E

EARTH, THE. *Planet* having its *orbit* between those of *Venus* and *Mars*. Sphere, slightly flattened towards the poles (i.e. approximating to an oblate *spheroid* in shape). Equatorial radius 3963·18 miles; polar radius 3949·89 miles. Mean *density* 5·52 gm. per c.c.; mass $5·976 \times 10^{24}$ kilogm.

EARTHING a conductor. Making an electrical connexion between the *conductor* and the Earth; the Earth is assumed to have zero *potential*.

EARTH'S CRUST, lithosphere. Consists of an outer layer of surface soil of varying thickness lying upon a mass of hard rock several miles thick. The approximate estimated percentages by *weight* of the chief chemical *elements* composing the Earth's crust are: oxygen 47%, silicon 28%, aluminium 8%, iron 4·5%, calcium 3·5%, sodium and potassium 2·5% each, magnesium 2·2%, titanium 0·5%, hydrogen 0·2%, carbon 0·2%, phosphorus and sulphur 0·1% each.

EARTH'S MAGNETISM. See *magnetism, terrestrial*.

EAST-WEST ASYMMETRY OF COSMIC RAYS. The observed intensity of *cosmic ray* particles coming from the West is greater than that coming from the East at any given *latitude*. This asymmetry is due to the deflection of the primary charged cosmic ray particles by the *magnetic field* of the Earth, and indicates a preponderance of positively charged particles in the incoming radiation.

EAU DE JAVELLE. See *Javelle water*.

EBONITE, vulcanite. Hard black insulating material made by vulcanizing *rubber* with high proportions of sulphur. Contains about 30% combined sulphur.

EBULLITION. See *boiling*.

ECHELON (phys.). Type of grating which replaces the ordinary *diffraction grating* in spectroscopy when very high resolution is required. Consists essentially of a pile of plates of exactly equal thickness arranged in stepwise formation with a constant offset. The echelon can be used either as a transmission or as a reflection grating.

ECHO. Effect produced when *sound* is reflected or thrown back on meeting a solid obstacle.

ECHO SOUNDER. A device for estimating the depth of the sea beneath a ship by measuring the time taken for a *sound* pulse to reach the sea bed and for its *echo* to return.

ECLIPSE. The passage of a non-luminous body into the *shadow* of another. An 'eclipse of the *Moon*', or lunar eclipse, occurs when the *Sun*, the *Earth*, and the Moon are in line so that the shadow of the Earth falls upon the Moon. An 'eclipse of the Sun', or solar eclipse, is said to occur when the shadow of the Moon falls on the Earth. See Fig. 8, which also illustrates the areas of partial and total eclipse.

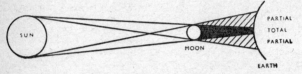

FIG. 8.

ECLIPTIC. The *Sun*'s apparent path in the sky relative to the *stars*; the circle described by the Sun on the *celestial sphere* in the course of a year.

ECOLOGY. The study of the relation of plants and animals to their environment.

ECTOPLASM. The outer layer of the *cytoplasm* of a living *cell*. Usually a semi-solid *gel* containing relatively few granules.

EDDY CURRENT HEATING. See *induction heating*.

EDDY CURRENTS, electrical, Foucault currents. Induced (see *induction*) *electric currents* set up in the iron cores of *electromagnets* and other electrical apparatus. These currents cause considerable waste of *energy* in the cores of *armatures* of *dynamos* and in *transformers*.

EDISON ACCUMULATOR*. A nickel-iron *accumulator*.

EFFECTIVE RESISTANCE. The *resistance* of a *conductor* of electricity to *alternating currents*; in addition to the *direct current* resistance it includes the effect of any losses caused by the current (e.g. *eddy currents*). Measured by the ratio of the total loss to the square of the *root mean square* of the current.

EFFERVESCENCE. The escape of small *gas* bubbles from a *liquid*, usually as the result of chemical action.

EFFICIENCY OF A MACHINE. The ratio of the output *energy* to the input energy. The efficiency of a machine can never be greater than unity. Often expressed as a percentage.

EFFLORESCENCE (chem.). Property of some crystalline *salts* of losing a part of their *water of crystallization*, becoming powdery on the surface. E.g. crystals of *washing-soda*, $Na_2CO_3.10H_2O$.

EFFUSION (chem.) of gases. The passage of *gases* through small apertures under pressure. The relative rates of effusion of different gases under the same conditions are inversely proportional to the square roots of their *densities*.

EINSTEIN SHIFT. A slight displacement towards the red of the lines of the solar *spectrum* due to the *Sun's gravitational field*. Predicted by Einstein's general theory of *relativity* and subsequently verified experimentally.

EINSTEINIUM. Es. *Transuranic element*, At. No. 99. Most stable *isotope* $^{254}_{99}$Es has a *half-life* of 320 days.

ELASTANCE. The *reciprocal* of *capacitance*; measured in reciprocal *farads* or *darafs*.

ELASTIC COLLISION. A collision between bodies under ideal conditions, such that their total *kinetic energy* before collision equals their total kinetic energy after collision. Referred to *nuclear physics*, an elastic collision is one in which an incoming particle is scattered without causing the *excitation* or breaking up of the struck *nucleus*.

ELASTIC CROSS-SECTION. See *cross-section*.

ELASTIC LIMIT of a material. The limit of *stress* within which the *strain* in a material completely disappears when the stress is removed.

ELASTIC MODULUS, modulus of elasticity. The ratio of *stress* to *strain* in a given material. The strain may be a change in length (see *Young's modulus*); a twist or *shear* (see *rigidity modulus*), or a change in volume (see *bulk modulus*); the stress required to produce unit strain being in each case expressed in *dynes* per sq. cm.

ELASTICITY. The property of a body or material of resuming its original form and dimensions when *forces* acting upon it are removed.

ELASTIN. Elastic fibrous *protein* found in the connective tissues of vertebrates.

ELASTOMER. A material which after being stretched, will return to approximately its original length. Includes *natural rubber*, *synthetic rubbers*, and rubberlike *plastics*.

ELECTRET. *Dielectric* possessing a permanent electric *moment*.

ELECTRIC ARC. See *arc*.

ELECTRIC BELL. See *bell, electric*.

ELECTRIC BUZZER. See *buzzer, electric*.

ELECTRIC CHARGE. Science is unable to offer any explanation regarding the nature of an electric charge, but it is able to describe in some detail the properties of *matter* that is so charged. The *elementary particle* called an *electron* is said to be negatively charged with electricity, and the *proton* is said to be positively charged to an equal but opposite extent. These entities represent the basic units of electrically charged matter. Therefore, matter which contains an equal number of protons and electrons is electrically neutral, but matter which contains an excess of electrons possesses an overall negative charge; similarly matter which has a deficiency of electrons (i.e. an excess of protons) possesses an overall positive charge. These positive and negative conventions are purely arbitrary, but much of science is based upon them. It is an observed fact that a *force* of repulsion acts between like charges and a force of attraction acts between unlike charges: the region in which these forces act is called an *electric field*. Electric charges are also acted upon by forces when they move in a *magnetic field* which possesses a component at right angles to their direction of motion. The size of an electric charge is measured in *electrostatic units* or in *electromagnetic units*, the practical unit being the *coulomb*.

ELECTRIC CURRENT. An electric current is said to flow through a *conductor* when there is an overall movement of *electrons* through it. Current is measured in *amperes*.

ELECTRIC CURRENT, HEATING EFFECT OF. When an *electric current* flows through a *conductor* of finite *resistance*, *heat energy* is continuously generated at the expense of *electrical energy*. The quantity of heat produced is proportional to the resistance of the conductor, and is equal to $\dfrac{ei}{4 \cdot 2}$ or $\dfrac{i^2 r}{4 \cdot 2}$ *calories* per second, e being the *potential difference* in *volts*, i the current in *amperes*, and r the resistance in *ohms*.

ELECTRIC DISPLACEMENT. Consider a uniform *electric field* of strength E in free *space*; i.e. the electric *flux* through unit area perpendicular to the field is E. Now suppose a *dielectric* medium is introduced into the field. The electric flux at any point in the medium becomes modified owing to the interaction between E and the *atoms* of the dielectric, and assumes a new value D, called the electric displacement.

ELECTRIC FIELD of a charge. The region near an *electric charge*, in which a *force* is exerted on a charged particle; completely defined in magnitude and direction at any point by the force upon unit positive charge situated at that point. The field intensity, H, or *force* exerted upon a unit charge at a point r cm. from a charge q, is given by:

$$H = \frac{q}{Kr^2}$$

where K is the *dielectric constant* of the intervening medium, which may be taken as unity for air.

ELECTRIC INTENSITY. The strength of an *electric field*.

ELECTRIC LIGHT. Illumination produced by the use of *electricity*; may be produced by virtue of the heating effect of an *electric current* on a wire or *filament* (see *electric-light bulb*), by an electric arc (see *arc lamp*), or by the passage of electricity through a *vapour*, as in the *mercury vapour lamp* or fluorescent lamps.

ELECTRIC-LIGHT BULB. Glass bulb, often filled with nitrogen or some other chemically inactive *gas*, containing a wire or *filament*, usually made of wolfram. The passage of an *electric current* through the filament heats it to a white heat.

ELECTRIC MOTOR. Device for converting *electrical energy* into *mechanical energy*. Depends on the fact that when an *electric current* flows through a *conductor* placed in a *magnetic field* possessing a component at right angles to the conductor, a mechanical *force* acts upon the conductor. In its simplest form, consists of a coil or *armature* through which the current flows, placed between the poles of a powerful *electromagnet*, the *field magnet*; the mechanical force upon the conductor causes the armature to rotate.

ELECTRIC POLARIZATION. When an *electric field* is applied to an electrically neutral *atom*, a displacement of the *electrons* with respect to the positive *nucleus* occurs. (See *atom, structure of.*) This gives rise to a small electric *dipole* possessing an electric *moment* in the direction of the field. This effect occurs when a *dielectric* is placed in an electric field, the electric field acting upon each individual atom of the dielectric. The *resultant* total electric moment per unit volume is called the electric polarization.

ELECTRIC POTENTIAL at a point is the *work* necessary to bring unit positive *electric charge* from an infinite distance to that point. Analogous to a level; a positive electric charge would be driven from points of higher to lower potential. See *potential difference.*

ELECTRIC POWER, the rate of doing *work*. Measured in *watts*; a power of 1 watt does 1 *joule* of work per second. The power in watts is given by the product of the *potential difference* in *volts* and the *current* in *amperes*.

ELECTRIC SPARK. A discharge of *electricity*, accompanied by *light* and *sound*, through a *dielectric* or *insulator*.

ELECTRICAL CAPACITY. See *capacitance.*

ELECTRICAL CONDENSER. See *capacitor.*

ELECTRICAL ENERGY. *The energy* associated with *electric charges* and their movements. Measured in *watt*-hours or *kilowatt-hours*. One watt-hour equals 860 *calories*.

ELECTRICAL IMAGE. A set of point charges on one side of a conducting surface which would produce the same *electric field* on the other side of the surface (in its absence) as the actual electrification of that surface.

ELECTRICAL INDUCTION. See *induction.*

ELECTRICAL LINE OF FORCE. A line in an *electric field* whose direction is everywhere that of the field.

ELECTRICITY. General term used for all phenomena caused by *electric charge* whether static or in motion.

ELECTRICITY, FRICTIONAL, triboelectricity. A separation of *electric charge* which results from the rubbing together of different materials; e.g. on rubbing *celluloid* with rabbit's fur, the fur is found to possess a positive charge, and the celluloid receives an equal negative charge. The rubbing motion strips some of the *electrons* from the *atoms* or *molecules* of the fur, which collect on the surface of the celluloid.

ELECTRICITY, STATIC. *Electricity* at rest, in contradistinction to dynamic or current electricity. In the static case its effects are due purely to the *electrostatic field* produced by the charge, whereas in the case of current electricity other effects, in particular a *magnetic field,* are added.

ELECTROCARDIOGRAPH. ECG. An instrument for recording the *current* and *voltage* waveforms associated with the contraction of the heart muscle.

ELECTROCHEMICAL EQUIVALENT of an ion. The *weight* of the *ion* liberated or deposited by 1 *coulomb* of *electricity*. Expressed in grams, this is numerically equal to 1/96490 of the *chemical equivalent*, which is therefore liberated or deposited by 96490 coulombs, or one *faraday*. See *electrolysis*.

ELECTROCHEMICAL SERIES. See *electromotive series*.

ELECTROCHEMISTRY. The study of the processes involved in the interconversion of *electrical energy* and *chemical energy*.

ELECTRODE. *Conductor* by which an *electric current* enters or leaves an *electrolyte* in *electrolysis*, an electric *arc* or a vacuum tube (see *discharge in gases* and *thermionic valve*): the positive electrode is the *anode*, the negative one the *cathode*. In a *semiconductor* device, an element which emits or collects *electrons* or *holes*, or controls their movement by an *electric field*.

ELECTRODYNAMOMETER. An instrument for measuring *current, voltage*, or *power*, in both *direct current* and *alternating current* circuits. Depends upon the interaction of the *magnetic fields* of fixed and movable coils.

ELECTROENCEPHALOGRAPH. EEG. An instrument used for recording the rhythmical *electric currents* which pass through the brain. The pattern obtained can be correlated with certain human physiological states (e.g. sleep) and pathological states (e.g. epilepsy).

ELECTROFORMING. The production, or reproduction, of *metal* articles by the deposition of a metal upon an *electrode* during *electrolysis*.

ELECTROLYSIS. Chemical *decomposition* of certain substances (*electrolytes*) by an *electric current* passed through the substance in a dissolved or molten state. Such substances are ionized (see *ionic hypothesis*) into electrically charged *ions*, and when an electric current is passed through them by means of conducting *electrodes*, the ions move towards the oppositely charged electrodes, there give up their electric charges, become uncharged *atoms* or groups, and are either liberated or deposited at the electrode, or react chemically with the electrode, the *solvent*, or each other, according to their chemical nature.

ELECTROLYSIS, FARADAY'S LAWS OF. 1. The chemical action of a current of *electricity* is proportional to the quantity of electricity which passes. 2. The *weights* of substances liberated or deposited by the same quantity of electricity are proportional to their *chemical equivalents*. See *electrochemical equivalent*.

ELECTROLYTE. *Compound* which, in *solution* or in the molten state, conducts an *electric current* and is simultaneously decomposed by it.

The current is carried not by *electrons* as in *metals*, but by *ions* (see *electrolysis*). Electrolytes may be *acids*, *bases*, or *salts*.

ELECTROLYTIC CAPACITOR (CONDENSER). A fixed electrical *capacitor* in which one *electrode* is a *metal* (usually aluminium) foil coated with a thin layer of the metal *oxide*, and the other electrode is a non-corrosive *salt solution* or paste. The metal foil is maintained positive to prevent the removal of the oxide film by the hydrogen liberated. Tantalum sheets are also used as electrodes, immersed in an *electrolyte* of *sulphuric acid*. The advantage of electrolytic capacitors is that they provide a high *capacitance* in a limited space.

ELECTROLYTIC DISSOCIATION, THEORY OF. Explanation of the phenomena of *electrolysis* on the supposition that *molecules* of *electrolytes* are dissociated into electrically charged *ions* in solution. See *ionization*.

ELECTROLYTIC GAS, detonating gas. Mixture of hydrogen and oxygen, in a ratio of 2 to 1 by *volume*, formed by the *electrolysis* of *water*.

ELECTROLYTIC RECTIFIER. A *rectifier* consisting of two *electrodes* immersed in an *electrolyte*, which is used to convert an *alternating current* into a *direct current*. Depends on the properties of certain *metals* and *solutions* to allow current to flow in one direction only.

ELECTROMAGNET. Temporary *magnet* formed by winding a coil of wire round a piece of soft iron; when an *electric current* flows through the wire, the iron becomes a magnet.

ELECTROMAGNETIC PUMP. A device used for pumping *liquid metals*. A current is passed through the liquid metal which is contained in a flattened pipe placed between the poles of an *electromagnet*. The liquid metal is thus subjected to a *force* which acts along the axis of the pipe.

ELECTROMAGNETIC RADIATION. *Radiation* consisting of waves of *energy* associated with *electric* and *magnetic fields*, resulting from the acceleration of an *electric charge*. These electric and magnetic fields, which require no supporting medium and can be propagated through *space*, are at right angles to each other and to the direction of propagation. Electromagnetic waves travel through space with a uniform *velocity* of $2 \cdot 9979 \times 10^{10}$ cm. per second, or 186,282 miles per second. The nature of electromagnetic radiations depends upon their *frequency* (see *electromagnetic spectrum*). Electromagnetic radiation is emitted by *matter* in discontinuous units called *photons*.

ELECTROMAGNETIC SPECTRUM. The range of *frequencies* over which *electromagnetic radiations* are propagated. The lowest frequencies are *radio* waves, increases of frequency produce *infra-red radiation*, *light*, *ultra-violet radiation*, *X-rays*, *gamma-rays*, and finally the radiation associated with *cosmic rays*. See Table 6, page 336.

ELECTROMAGNETIC UNITS. E.M.U. System of electrical *units*, within the *C.G.S. system*, based on the unit *magnetic pole*, which repels a similar pole, placed 1 cm. away, with a *force* of 1 *dyne*. The E.M.U. of *electric current* is that current which, flowing in an arc of a *circle* of unit length and radius (i.e. 1 cm.), exerts a force of 1 dyne on a unit magnetic pole placed at the centre. The E.M.U. of *resistance* is that resistance in which *energy* is dissipated at the rate of 1 *erg* per second by the flow of 1 E.M.U. of current. The E.M.U. of *electromotive force* or *potential* is that potential which, applied across the ends of a *conductor* of 1 E.M.U. resistance, causes 1 E.M.U. of current to flow.

ELECTROMAGNETIC WAVES. See *electromagnetic radiation* and *electromagnetic spectrum*.

ELECTROMETER. Instrument for measuring *voltage* differences, which draws no current from the source. Essential for measuring *electrostatic* voltage differences.

ELECTROMOTIVE FORCE, E.M.F. The source of *electrical energy* required to produce an *electric current* in a circuit; a measure of its intensity. Defined as the rate at which electrical energy is drawn from the source and dissipated in a circuit when unit current is flowing in the circuit. Practical unit is the *volt*. See *potential difference*.

ELECTROMOTIVE SERIES. Electrochemical series. Potential series of the *metals*. A list of metals arranged in order of the magnitudes of their molar electrode potentials, i.e. the *potential difference* between the metal and a *normal solution* of one of its *salts*. Metals with high negative electrode potentials stand at the head of the electromotive series. The list represents the order in which the metals replace one another from their salts, a metal higher in the series replacing one lower down; similarly, metals placed above hydrogen will liberate it from *acids*. The chief metals in order are sodium, magnesium, aluminium, manganese, zinc, cadmium, iron, cobalt, nickel, tin, lead, hydrogen, copper, mercury, silver, platinum, gold.

ELECTRON. *Elementary particle* having a *rest mass* of $9 \cdot 1091 \times 10^{-28}$ gm., approximately 1/1836 that of a hydrogen *atom*, and bearing a negative *electric charge* of $4 \cdot 803 \times 10^{-10}$ electrostatic units. The electron is a constituent of all atoms (see *atom, structure of*). The positively charged *anti-particle* of the electron is the *positron*, and the word 'electron' is sometimes used to include both negative electrons (negatrons or negatons) and positive electrons (positrons or positons). A *free electron* is one which has been detached from its atomic *orbit*.

ELECTRON AFFINITY. In general, the tendency of an *atom* or *molecule* to accept an *electron* and form a negative *ion*. In particular, the *energy* liberated when one *gram-atom* of an *element* in the form of gaseous atoms is converted into negative ions. The *halogens* have high electron affinities.

ELECTRON CAPTURE. 1. The formation of a negative *ion* when a *free electron* is captured by an *atom* or *molecule* (also referred to as 'electron attachment'). 2. A *radioactive transformation* as a result of which a *nucleus* captures one of its *orbital electrons*.

ELECTRON DIFFRACTION. A *diffraction* effect resulting from the passage of *electrons* through *matter*, analogous to the *diffraction* of visible *light* or *X-rays*. The phenomenon of electron diffraction is the principle evidence for the existence of waves associated with electrons (see *de Broglie wave-length*). The diffraction of electrons when passed through *crystals* or thin *metal* foils, is used as a method of investigating crystal structure.

ELECTRON GUN. The source of *electrons* in a *cathode ray tube* or *electron microscope*. Consists of a *cathode* emitter of electrons, an *anode* with an aperture through which the beam of electrons can pass, and one or more focusing and control *electrodes*.

ELECTRON LENS. A system of *electric* or *magnetic fields* used to focus a beam of *electrons* in a manner analogous to an optical *lens*. Used in *electron microscopes*, etc.

ELECTRON MICROGRAPH. A photograph of an object obtained with an *electron microscope*.

ELECTRON MICROSCOPE. An instrument similar in purpose to the ordinary *light microscope*, but with a much greater *resolving power*. Instead of a beam of light to illuminate the object, a parallel beam of *electrons* from an *electron gun* is used. The object, which must be in the form of a very thin film of the material, allows the electron beam to pass through it; but, owing to differential *scattering* in the film, an image of the object is carried forward in the electron beam. The latter then passes through a magnetic or *electrostatic* focusing system (see *electron lens*) which is equivalent to the optical lens system in an ordinary microscope, i.e. it produces a much magnified image. This is received on a fluorescent screen and recorded by a camera.

ELECTRON MULTIPLIER. See *photomultiplier*.

ELECTRON PROBE MICROANALYSIS. A method of analysing a very small quantity of a substance by directing a finely focused *electron* beam on to it so that an *X-ray* emission is produced characteristic of the *elements* present in the sample. The diameter of the beam is usually about 1 *micron* and quantities as small as 10^{-13} gm. can be detected by this means. The method may be used quantitatively for elements whose *atomic numbers* exceed 11.

ELECTRON SPIN RESONANCE. A phenomenon exhibited by paramagnetic substances (see *paramagnetism*) due to their unpaired *electrons*. The *spin* of an unpaired electron is associated with a *magnetic moment* which may align itself in one of two ways with respect to an applied *magnetic field*, each possible alignment corresponding to a different *energy level*. By applying an alternating magnetic field at right angles to the first unvarying magnetic field transitions between these two energy levels can be made, falling in the *microwave* region of the *electromagnetic spectrum*, thus producing the phenomenon known as electron spin resonance. If, however, the paramagnetic *molecule* includes magnetic nuclei, these transitions will interact with the nuclear spin (see *nuclear magnetic resonance*) producing a series of lines rather than a single resonance. Electron spin resonance spectroscopy consists of analysing this *hyperfine structure* so that the electron can be located within the molecule, thus providing information about the molecule's structure.

ELECTRON-VOLT (*ev*). Unit of *energy* widely used in *nuclear physics*.

The increase in energy or the *work* done on an *electron* when passing through a *potential* rise of 1 *volt*. 1 electron-volt = $1 \cdot 6 \times 10^{-12}$ *ergs* approximately. 1 Mev is one million electron-volts.

ELECTRONEGATIVE elements and groups. *Radicals* which behave as negative *ions*; radicals taking up *electrons*, thus acquiring a negative *electric charge*, when united with other radicals by electrovalent bonds (see *valency, electronic theory of*). The *halogens*, oxygen, sulphur, and other non-metals are generally electronegative.

ELECTRONIC CHARGE. The negative *electric charge* of the *electron*, $1 \cdot 602 \times 10^{-19}$ *coulombs*, $4 \cdot 803 \times 10^{-10}$ *electrostatic units*.

ELECTRONICS. An applied physical science concerned with the development of electrical circuits using *thermionic valves, semiconductor* and other devices in which the motion of *electrons* is controlled.

ELECTROPHILIC REAGENTS. Cationoid reagents. *Reagents* which react at centres of high *electron* density. Essentially electron acceptors (e.g. *halogens*) which gain or share electrons from an outside *atom* or *ion*.

ELECTROPHORESIS, cataphoresis. The migration of the electrically charged *solute* particles present in a *colloidal solution* towards the oppositely charged *electrode*, when two electrodes are placed in the solution and connected externally to a source of *E.M.F.*

ELECTROPHORUS. Laboratory demonstration apparatus for showing electrostatic charging by *induction*.

ELECTROPLATING. Depositing a layer of *metal* by *electrolysis*, the object to be plated forming the *cathode* in an electrolytic tank or bath containing a *solution* of a *salt* of the metal which is to be deposited.

ELECTROPOSITIVE elements and groups. *Radicals* which behave as positive *ions*; radicals which give up *electrons*, thus acquiring a positive *electric charge*, when united with other radicals by electrovalent bonds (see *valency, electronic theory of*). The .netals and *acidic hydrogen* are generally electropositive.

ELECTROSCOPE. Instrument for detecting the presence of an *electric charge*. The gold-leaf electroscope consists of two rectangular leaves of gold foil attached to a conducting rod of *metal* held by an insulating plug; when the rod and leaves acquire an electric charge, the leaves diverge owing to the mutual repulsion of charges of like sign.

ELECTROSTATIC FIELD. A region in which a stationary electrically charged particle would be subjected to a *force* of attraction or repulsion as a result of the presence of another stationary *electric charge*.

ELECTROSTATIC GENERATOR. Machine designed for the continuous separation of *electric charge*. Examples include the *Wimshurst machine* and the *Van der Graaf generator*.

ELECTROSTATIC PRECIPITATION. A widely used method of controlling the pollution of air (or other *gases*). The gas, containing *solid* or *liquid* particles suspended in it, is subjected to a uni-directional *electrostatic field*, so that the particles are attracted to, and deposited upon, the positive *electrode*.

ELECTROSTATIC UNITS. ESU. A system of electrical *units* based upon the electrostatic unit of *electric charge*. The electrostatic unit of charge is that quantity of electricity which will repel an equal quantity, 1 cm. distant from it in a *vacuum*, with a *force* of 1 *dyne*.

ELECTROSTATICS. The study of static *electricity*.

ELECTROSTRICTION. The change in the dimensions of a *dielectric* when placed in an *electric field*.

ELECTROTYPING. Production of copies of plates of type, etc., by the electrolytic deposition of a layer of *metal* on a previously prepared mould. This is a cast of the object to be copied, made of *plastic* material and coated with a layer of *graphite* which acts as a *conductor* of electricity. It is then suspended to act as a *cathode* in an electrolytic bath (see *electroplating*) containing a *solution* of a *salt* of the metal required, usually copper. The passage of an *electric current* will deposit a layer of any required thickness of metal upon the cathode, the layer being a replica of the original type.

ELECTROVALENCY. See *valency, electronic theory of*.

ELECTROVALENT CRYSTAL. Ionic crystal. The type of *crystal* in which the component *ions* are held in their positions in the *lattice* by electrovalent bonds (see *valency, electronic theory of*). *Sodium chloride* is a typical example.

ELECTRUM. Natural *alloy* of gold (55%–85%) and silver.

ELEMENT (chem.). Substance consisting entirely of *atoms* of the same *atomic number*. The elements are listed in Table 1, pages 330–2.

ELEMENTARY PARTICLES. Particles which are thought to be the indivisible units of which all *matter* is composed. Over thirty such particles have been detected, only a few of which are stable (e.g. *proton, electron, neutrino*). The unstable particles (e.g. *neutrons, mesons, hyperons*) disintegrate spontaneously into two or more particles liberating *energy* in the process. In some contexts *photons* may also be considered as elementary particles. The conception of elementarity is still somewhat vague, recent work having suggested that protons and neutrons are not indivisible units, but composite entities consisting of a central core of unknown origin surrounded by a cloud of mesons.

ELEMENTS, MAGNETIC. See *magnetic elements*.

ELEVATION, ANGLE OF. If *C* is a point above the level of another point *A*, the angle of elevation of *C* from *A* is the *angle* which *C* makes with the horizontal plane *AX* through *A*. See Fig. 6, page 82.

ELEVATION OF BOILING POINT. Rise in the *boiling point* of a *solution* produced by a non-volatile substance dissolved in a *solvent*. For a *dilute* solution the elevation is proportional to the number of *molecules* or *ions* present, and the elevation produced by the same *molecular concentration* (or ionic concentration in the case of an *electrolyte*) is a constant for a particular solvent. This forms the principle of the boiling point method (ebullioscopic method) for the determination of *molecular weights*.

ELEVEN-YEAR PERIOD. A periodic change in occurrence of *sunspots*, the cycle being complete in approximately eleven years; associated with this is a cyclic variation in the magnitude of the *daily variation*.

ELINVAR*. Variety of *steel* containing 36% nickel and 12% chromium. The *elasticity* is almost unaffected by changes of *temperature*; used for hair-springs of watches.

ELLIPSE. Closed *plane* figure formed by cutting all elements of a right circular *cone* by a *plane*.

ELLIPSOID. Solid figure traced out by an *ellipse* rotating about one of its *axes*.

ELLIPTICALLY POLARIZED LIGHT. *Light* which can be resolved into two vibrations lying in *planes* at right angles, and of equal *frequency*. The electric *vector* at any point in the path of the wave describes an *ellipse* about the direction of propagation of the light. The form of this ellipse is determined by the *amplitudes* of these two vibrations and by the difference of *phase* between them. (See also *polarization of light*.)

ELUTRIATION. The washing, separation, or sizing of fine particles of different *weight* by suspending them in a current of air or *water*.

EMANATION, radium emanation. See *radon*.

EMERY. Mixture of *corundum* and iron oxide, usually *magnetite*, Fe_3O_4. Used as an *abrasive*.

EMETINE. $C_{29}H_{40}O_4N_2$. An *alkaloid* obtained from the roots of Brazilian ipecacuanha, m.p. 68° C. Used as an emetic and as a remedy for amoebic dysentery.

EMF. See *electromotive force*.

EMISSION OF RADIATION. The net rate at which a body emits *heat radiation* to its surroundings depends on the *temperature* of the body, the temperature of its surroundings and the nature of the surface of the body. Dull black surfaces have the greatest *emissive power* while brightly polished reflecting surfaces have least. See *Stefan's law*.

EMISSION SPECTRUM. *Spectrum* observed when *light* coming directly from a source is examined with a *spectroscope*.

EMISSIVE POWER, total. The total *energy* emitted from unit area of a surface of a body per second. The total emissive power depends upon the *temperature* of the body and the nature of its surface.

EMISSIVITY. The ratio of the total *emissive power* of a body to the total emissive power of a perfect black body at the same *temperature* (see *black body radiation*). The emissivity is a pure numeric, equal to the *absorptivity*.

EMITTER. One of the three *electrodes* in a *transistor*.

EMPIRICAL. Based upon the results of experiment and observation only.

EMULSIFYING AGENT. A substance, small quantities of which help to form or stabilize an *emulsion*.

EMULSION. A two-phase system in which the *disperse phase* consists of minute droplets of *liquid*.

EMULSION, PHOTOGRAPHIC. The light-sensitive coating on a *film* or plate (see *photography*). A 'nuclear emulsion' is a photographic emulsion specially prepared to record the tracks of *elementary particles* and nuclear fragments which pass through it.

EMULSOID SOL. See *colloidal solutions*.

ENAMEL. 1. Class of substances having similar composition to *glass* with the addition of tin dioxide, SnO_2, or other *infusible* substances to render the enamel *opaque*. 2. A finely ground oil *paint* containing a *resin*. 3. The external layer of teeth consisting mainly of calcium phosphate carbonate *salts*.

ENANTIOMORPHISM. Occurrence of substances in two crystalline forms, one being a mirror image of the other.

ENANTIOTROPIC substances. Substances which exist in two different physical forms, one being *stable* below a certain *temperature* (the *transition* temperature), the other above it. E.g. sulphur exists as alpha-sulphur at all temperatures below 96° C.; above this, the stable form is beta-sulphur.

ENDOCRINE GLANDS, ductless glands. Glands or organs producing *hormones* in the animal body.

ENDOENZYME. An *enzyme* which remains within a living *cell* and does not diffuse through the cell wall into the surrounding medium.

ENDOERGIC PROCESS. An *endothermic process* (often applied in the context of a *nuclear reaction*).

ENDOPLASM. Central part of the *cytoplasm* of living *cells*, usually distinct from the *ectoplasm* in that is is of greater fluidity and contains more granules.

ENDOPLASMIC RETICULUM. System of membranes within the *cytoplasm* of many types of living *cell*. Appears to be connected with *protein* synthesis as these membranes are often covered with *ribosomes* in cells which make large quantities of protein.

ENDOSMOSIS. Inward flow of *water* into a cell containing an *aqueous solution*, through a *semi-permeable membrane*, due to *osmosis*.

ENDOTHERMIC PROCESS. A process accompanied by the absorption of *heat*.

ENERGY. Capacity for doing *work*. Various forms of energy, interconvertible by suitable means, include *potential, kinetic, electrical, heat, chemical, nuclear,* and *radiant energy*. Interconversion between these forms of energy can only occur in the presence of *matter*. Energy can only exist in the absence of matter in the form of radiant energy.

ENERGY BANDS. *Orbital electrons* are associated with specific amounts of *energy*, the change from one *energy level* to another taking place in *quantized* steps. In a crystalline *solid* the energies of all the electrons and *atoms* fall into several 'possible' energy bands between which lie 'forbidden' bands. These bands may be depicted on an 'energy level diagram'. The range of energies corresponding to states in which the electrons can be made to flow, by an applied *electric field*, is called the *conduction band*. The range of energies corresponding to states which can be occupied by *valency electrons*, binding the *crystal* together, is called the *valence band*. The valence band in an ideal crystal is completely occupied at the *absolute zero* of temperature, but in real crystals above absolute zero some electrons are missing from the valence band, and it is these electrons which give rise to *holes*.

ENERGY LEVELS. An *atom* as a whole, or an individual *nucleus*, can exist only in certain definite states characterized by the *energy* of the state. Thus, for each different atom or nucleus, there exists a series of energy levels corresponding to these permissible states. The lowest stable energy level of an atom or nucleus is referred to as the *ground state*; atoms or nuclei at higher energy levels than the ground state are said to be excited. See *excitation*.

ENERGY-RICH BONDS. A term used in *biochemistry* to distinguish between chemical *bonds* which when broken yield a large amount of *free energy* and those which give only a small yield of free energy ('energy-poor bonds'). The energy referred to in this context is the free energy liberated on *hydrolysis*. Energy-rich bonds usually involve phosphate groups and in this respect *adenosine triphosphate (ATP)* is of particular significance.

ENERGY VALUE of a food. Measure of the *heat* energy available by the complete combustion of a stated *weight* of the food; often given in large *Calories* per lb. Takes no account of the value of the food from any other point of view, or sometimes even of the suitability of the food for use by the human *organism*.

ENGINE. A device for converting one form of *energy* into another, especially for converting other forms of energy into *mechanical* (i.e. *kinetic*) *energy*.

ENRICH. In general to increase the *abundance* of a particular *isotope* in a mixture of isotopes. In particular, to increase the abundance of the *fissile* isotope of a *nuclear fuel*.

ENTHALPY. Heat Content. H. A *thermodynamic* property of a substance given by, $H = U + pv$, where U is the internal *energy*, p the *pressure*, and v the *volume*.

ENTROPY. A quantity introduced in the first place to facilitate the calculations, and to give clear expression to the results of *thermodynamics*. Changes of entropy can be calculated only for a *reversible process*, and may then be defined as the ratio of the amount of *heat* taken up to the *absolute temperature* at which the heat is absorbed. Entropy changes for actual irreversible processes are calculated by postulating equivalent theoretical reversible changes. The entropy of a system is a measure of its degree of disorder. The total entropy of any isolated system can never decrease in any change; it must either increase (irreversible process) or remain constant (reversible process). The total entropy of the Universe therefore is increasing, tending towards a maximum, corresponding to complete disorder of the particles in it (assuming that it may be regarded as an isolated system). See *heat death of the Universe*.

ENZYME. A large group of *proteins* produced by living *cells*, which act as *catalysts* in the *chemical reactions* upon which life depends. The exact mechanism by which enzymes act is not fully understood; but it appears that certain parts of the enzyme *molecule* (called the 'active centres') combine with the *substrate* molecule in such a way that the substrate undergoes chemical changes very much more rapidly than it would in the absence of the enzyme, while the enzyme itself remains unchanged. As enzymes are not consumed in these reactions they are effective in only minute quantities. Nearly all enzymes are highly specific in their action and therefore enormous numbers of them are found in nature. Many enzymes require the assistance of certain accessory substances (e.g. *coenzymes*) for their proper functioning and some require precisely defined conditions of *temperature* and *pH* for their optimum performance.

Enzymes have an important bearing upon heredity; the characteristics which cells, and therefore *organisms*, possess is directly related to the enzymes which they contain: e.g. the person who inherits red hair has inherited a particular configuration of *nucleotides* in the *DNA* of his *chromosomes*, which is capable of producing a specific enzyme in the *cytoplasm* of his hair-producing cells, whose function it is to catalyse the synthesis of a red dye.

Enzymes are usually named by adding the suffix –ase to a word indicating the nature of the substrate (e.g. *amylase*) or the type of reaction involved (e.g. *dehydrogenase*). A few enzymes retain old names which relate to neither of these rules (e.g. *pepsin*, *trypsin*).

EPICENTRE. The point on the surface of the Earth which lies directly above the focus of an earthquake.

EPICYCLIC GEARS. A system of gears in which one or more wheels move around the outside, or the inside, of another wheel whose *axis* is fixed.

EPIDIASCOPE. An optical projector for throwing an enlarged image of either an *opaque* object or a transparency upon a screen. Used for illustrating lectures.

EPITHERMAL NEUTRONS. *Neutrons* which have *energies* in excess of the energy associated with thermal agitation. Neutrons which have speeds and energies intermediate between *fast* and *thermal neutrons* (i.e. between about 0.1 and 100 *electron-volts*).

EPOXY (EPOXIDE) RESINS. *Thermosetting resins* derived from epichlor-hydrin ($O.CH_2.CH.CH_2Cl$) and bis-phenol-A ($HO.C_6H_4.C(CH_3)_2$. C_6H_4OH). Used as structural *plastics*, in surface coatings and as *adhesives*.

EPSOM SALTS, magnesium sulphate. $MgSO_4.7H_2O$. White crystalline *soluble salt*.

EQUATION, CHEMICAL. Representation of a *chemical reaction*, using the *symbols* of the *elements* to represent the actual *atoms* and *molecules* taking part in the reaction; the re-arrangement of the various atoms of the substances taking part is thus shown. E.g. the chemical equation $H_2 + Cl_2 = 2HCl$ represents the reaction between hydrogen and chlorine to form *hydrogen chloride,* and states that a hydrogen molecule, consisting of two atoms of hydrogen (H_2), reacts with a similarly constituted chlorine molecule, to give two molecules of hydrogen chloride, each consisting of one hydrogen and one chlorine atom ($2HCl$). From a knowledge of the equation for any chemical reaction, and of the *atomic weights* of all the elements taking part, it is thus possible to calculate the proportions by *weight* in which the substances react, since the whole bulk of the reaction consists merely of the repetition, a vast number of times, of the process depicted by the equation.

EQUATION, MATHEMATICAL. A statement of equality between known and unknown quantities, true only for certain values of the unknown quantities. Thus the equation $3x = 15$ is true only when $x = 5$.

EQUATION OF STATE of a substance. Any equation connecting the *pressure p, volume v,* and *temperature t* of the substance. Some equations of state attempt to cover more than one *phase* of the substance, e.g. *van der Waals' equation of state,* and are approximate. Others are intended to be applied to one particular phase of the substance, e.g. the gaseous phase, and then only within certain limits of p, v, and t. With these limitations, these latter equations can represent the actual behaviour of the substance with greater accuracy.

EQUATION OF TIME. The difference between mean solar time, as given by a clock, and apparent solar time, i.e. sundial time. The time of rotation of the *Earth* upon its axis is not exactly equal to the time from noon to noon, the difference being caused by the motion of the Earth relative to the *Sun* to complete a circuit in one *year,* and also by the inclination of the *ecliptic* to the *Equator.*

EQUATOR, CELESTIAL. See *celestial equator.*

EQUATOR, MAGNETIC. See *magnetic equator.*

EQUATOR, TERRESTRIAL; the *Earth's* equator. *Great circle* of the Earth, lying in a *plane* perpendicular to the *axis* of the Earth, equidistant from the two Poles.

EQUILATERAL figure. Figure having all its sides equal in length. E.g. equilateral *triangle.*

EQUILIBRIUM. State of balance between opposing *forces* or effects.

EQUILIBRIUM, CHEMICAL. See *chemical equilibrium.*

EQUILIBRIUM CONSTANT. In any *chemical reaction* there is always a state of *chemical equilibrium,* at a given *temperature* and *pressure,* between the *concentration* of the reactants and the concentration of the products. The position of this equilibrium, under specific conditions, is expressed by the equilibrium constant, K, such that in the reaction $aA + bB = cC + dD$, K is given by:

$$\frac{(C_C)^c . (C_D)^d}{(C_A)^a . (C_B)^b}$$

where C_A is the concentration of the substance A, 'a' *molecules* of which take part in the reaction.

EQUIMOLECULAR MIXTURE. *Mixture* containing substances in equal molecular proportions; i.e. in the ratio of their *molecular weights*. E.g. *invert sugar*, formed by the *hydrolysis* of *cane-sugar*. Each *molecule* of the cane-sugar is split into a molecule of *glucose* and a molecule of *laevulose*, thus forming an equimolecular mixture of the two latter.

EQUINOX. The moment (or, astronomically, the point) at which the *Sun* apparently crosses the *celestial equator*; the point of intersection of the *ecliptic* and the celestial equator.

EQUIPARTITION OF ENERGY. In any physical system in thermal equilibrium the average *energy* per *degree of freedom* is the same, and equals $KT/2$, where $K = Boltzmann's constant$ and T = the *absolute temperature* of the system. This provides a means of calculating the total thermal energy of a system. Thus, in 1 *gram-atom* of a monatomic *gas*, each *atom* possesses three degrees of freedom (due to its *translatory motion*), and the total number of atoms is N (*Avogadro's number*). Hence the total energy per gram-atom of the gas is $3NKT/2$ or $= 3RT/2$, since $K = R/N$, where R is the *gas constant*.

EQUIPOTENTIAL LINES AND SURFACES. Lines and surfaces having the same *electric potential*.

EQUIVALENT, CHEMICAL. See *chemical equivalents*.

EQUIVALENT, ELECTROCHEMICAL. See *electrochemical equivalent*.

EQUIVALENT WEIGHT. See *chemical equivalents*.

EQUIVOCATION. A term used in *information theory* to indicate the rate of loss of information (per second or per symbol) at the receiving end of a *channel* of information due to *noise*.

ERBIUM. Er. Element. A.W. 167·26. At. No. 68. See *lanthanides*.

ERECTING PRISM. Right-angled optical *prism* used in optical instruments to render an inverted image upright.

ERG. Unit of *work* or *energy* in the *C.G.S. system* of units; the work done by a *force* of 1 *dyne* acting through a distance of 1 cm.

ERGONOMICS. The engineering aspects of the study of the relation between human workers and their working environment.

ERGOSTEROL. $C_{28}H_{43}OH$. White *solid*, m.p. 163° C. Member of the *sterol* group of *organic compounds*; occurs in small amounts in the *fats* of animals; converted into *vitamin* D_2 (*calciferol*) by the action of *ultraviolet radiation*.

ERINOID*. *Thermoplastic* material prepared from *casein* and *formaldehyde*.

ERYTHROCYTES. Red blood cells. The cells of the *blood* which contain *haemoglobin* and whose function it is to transport oxygen through the body. Erythrocytes have no means of propulsion, and in mammals the cells have no *nuclei*. Human blood contains approximately five million erythrocytes per cubic millimetre.

ESCAPE VELOCITY. Term used in space science; the *velocity* which a projectile or *space probe* would need to attain in order to escape from the Earth's *gravitational field*.

ESSENTIAL OILS. Natural *oils* obtained from plants, mostly *benzene derivatives* or *terpenes*. Used for their flavour or odour.

ESTER GUM. Rosin ester. A *compound* obtained by the *esterification* of *rosin* (colophony) or other natural gums, with a polyhydric *alcohol* (usually *glycerin*).

ESTERIFICATION. Formation of an *ester* by the *chemical reaction* of an *acid* with an *alcohol*; e.g. the action of *ethyl alcohol* on *acetic acid* to form *ethyl acetate* and *water*.

ESTERS. *Organic compounds* corresponding to *inorganic salts*, derived by replacing hydrogen of an *acid* by an organic *radical* or group. E.g. *ethyl acetate*, $CH_3COOC_2H_5$, is the ethyl ester of *acetic acid*, CH_3COOH. Many esters are pleasant-smelling *liquids* used for flavouring essences. Many vegetable and animal *fats* and *oils* also belong to this class.

ETALON. An *interferometer* used for studying fine *spectrum* lines. Depends upon the interference effects produced by multiple reflection between fixed, parallel, half-silvered *glass* or *quartz* plates.

ETHANE. C_2H_6. Second member of the *paraffin series* of *hydrocarbons*. Colourless odourless gas. B.p. $-88°$ C.

ETHANOL. See *ethyl alcohol*.

ETHANOLAMINES. *Organic compounds* derived from *ethanol* and *amino groups*: monoethanolamine, $NH_2CH_2CH_2OH$, has a m.p. of $10°$ C.; diethanolamine, $NH(CH_2CH_2OH)_2$ a m.p. of $28°$ C. and triethanolamine, $N(CH_2CH_2OH)_3$ a m.p. of $21°$ C. Used as *solvents* and in combination with *fatty acids* in the manufacture of *detergents* and cosmetics.

ETHENOID PLASTICS. A class of *thermoplastic resins* made from substances containing a *double bond*, e.g. *acrylic*, *styrene*, and *vinyl resins*.

ETHER (AETHER), THE. Hypothetical medium which was supposed to fill all *space*: postulated as a medium to support the propagation of *electromagnetic radiations*. Once the subject of controversy, now regarded as an unnecessary assumption.

ETHERS. A group of *organic compounds* with the general formula R-O-R′ formed by the *condensation* of two *alcohol molecules*. The compound commonly called 'ether' is diethyl ether, $C_2H_5.O.C_2H_5$, b.p. $34.6°$ C., made by dehydrating *ethyl alcohol* by means of concentrated *sulphuric acid*. Diethyl ether is used as an *anaesthetic* and as a *solvent*.

ETHYL ACETATE, 'acetic ether'. $CH_3COOC_2H_5$. Colourless *liquid* with a pleasant fruity smell, b.p. $77°$ C. Used as a *solvent* and in medicine.

ETHYL ALCOHOL, alcohol, ethanol, spirits of wine. Colourless inflammable *liquid* with a characteristic vinous odour and burning taste. B.p. $78.5°$ C. Prepared by the *fermentation* of sugars. Constituent of alcoholic beverages; used as a *fuel* and in the manufacture of other *organic compounds*. See *proof spirit* and *absolute alcohol*.

ETHYL FLUID. *Solution* of tetraethyl lead, $Pb(C_2H_5)_4$, and ethylene dibromide, $C_2H_4Br_2$, used as an anti-*knock* compound in motor *fuel*.

ETHYL GROUP. The *univalent alkyl radical* —C_2H_5

ETHYL NITRITE, nitrous ether, $C_2H_5NO_2$. *Volatile liquid* with a sweet smell, b.p. 17° C. Used in medicine.

ETHYLENE. C_2H_4. First member of the *olefine* series of *hydrocarbons*. Colourless inflammable *gas* with a sweetish smell. B.p. —103·9° C.

ETHYLENE DICHLORIDE, 'Dutch liquid'. $C_2H_4Cl_2$. Colourless oily *liquid*, b.p. 83·5° C. Used as a *solvent* and fumigant.

ETHYLENE GLYCOL, glycol. $(CH_2OH)_2$. Colourless viscous *liquid* with a sweet taste. B.p. 197° C. Used as an *anti-freeze* compound for radiators of petrol engines, and in the manufacture of certain *plasticizers*.

ETHYLENE-PROPYLENE RUBBER. EPR. A fully *saturated, stereo regular, synthetic rubber* prepared by the solution *polymerization* of approximately equal proportions of *ethylene* and *propylene*. Cannot be cured by sulphur vulcanization but satisfactory vulcanization can be achieved by using peroxide curing systems.

ETHYNE. See *acetylene*.

EUCHLORINE. Gaseous *mixture* of chlorine, Cl_2, and explosive chlorine peroxide, ClO_2.

EUDIOMETER. Glass tube for measuring volume changes in *chemical reactions* between *gases*.

EUGENICS. The study of the genetic control of human populations, with a view to improving their constitution, by selectivity encouraging breeding among those people considered by eugenicists to be the most desirable.

EUROPIUM. Eu. Element. A.W. 151·96. At. No. 63. See *lanthanides*.

EUTECTIC MIXTURE. A *solid solution* of two or more substances, having the lowest *freezing point* of all the possible mixtures of the components. This is taken advantage of in *alloys* of low *melting point*, which are generally eutectic mixtures.

EUTECTIC POINT. Two or more substances capable of forming *solid solutions* with each other have the property of lowering each other's *freezing point*; the minimum freezing point attainable, corresponding to the *eutectic mixture*, is termed the *eutectic point*.

EVAPORATION. Conversion of a *liquid* into *vapour*, without necessarily reaching the *boiling point*; used in concentrating *solutions* by evaporating off the *solvent*. As it is the fastest moving *molecules* that escape from the surface of a liquid during evaporation, the average *kinetic energy* of the remaining molecules is reduced, and therefore evaporation causes cooling.

EVEN-EVEN NUCLEUS. A *nucleus* which contains both an even number of *protons* and an even number of *neutrons*.

EVEN-ODD NUCLEUS. A *nucleus* which contains an even number of *protons* but an odd number of *neutrons*.

EXCESS (chem.). Greater quantity of one substance or *reagent* than is necessary to react exactly with a given quantity of another.

EXCESS ELECTRON. An *electron* is a *semiconductor* donated by an impurity, which is not required in the bonding system of the *crystal* and which is therefore available for *conduction* ('excess conduction').

EXCHANGE FORCE. 1. The type of *force* which holds *nucleons* together in the *nucleus* of an *atom*. Believed to result from the exchange of *mesons* between the nucleons. 2. Forces occurring in ferromagnetic materials. See *ferromagnetism*.

EXCHANGES, PREVOST'S THEORY OF. Bodies at all *temperatures* are constantly radiating *energy* to each other, those at constant temperature receiving in a given time as much energy as they emit.

EXCIMER. An excited *dimer*, formed by the association of excited and unexcited *molecules* (see *excitation*) which in the *ground state* would remain dissociated. Excimer *fluorescence* occurs in many polycyclic *hydrocarbons*.

EXCITATION. The addition of *energy* to a *nucleus*, an *atom* or a *molecule* transferring it from its *ground state* to a higher *energy level*. The 'excitation energy' is the difference in energy between the ground state and the excited state.

EXCITON. A non-conducting, non-localized, excited *electron* state in a *semiconductor*. It may be regarded as a bound *electron-hole* pair, or alternatively as an atomic *excitation* which is passed from *atom* to atom.

EXCLUSION PRINCIPLE. See *Pauli exclusion principle*.

EXOERGIC PROCESS. An *exothermic process* (often applied in the context of a *nuclear reaction*).

EXOSMOSIS. Outward osmotic flow. See *osmosis*.

EXOTHERMIC PROCESS. Process in which *energy* in the form of *heat* is released.

EXPANSION, COEFFICIENT OF. 1. Linear. The increase in length per unit length, caused by a rise in *temperature* of $1°$ C. 2. Area (superficial expansion). Increase in area per unit area caused by a rise in temperature of $1°$ C. 3. Volume. Increase in *volume* per unit volume caused by a rise in temperature of $1°$ C. For *isotropic* media, the area and volume coefficients are approximately double and treble the linear coefficient respectively, for the same substance.

EXPANSIONS OF GASES. A *perfect gas* expands by $1/273$ of its volume at $0°$ C. for each degree rise in *temperature*, the *pressure* being constant. Real gases obey this law only approximately at ordinary pressures, but the approximation becomes more and more valid as the pressure is reduced, i.e. as the gas tends towards a perfect gas.

EXPANSION OF LIQUIDS. The directly observed expansion is the *apparent expansion*, since the vessel containing the *liquid* also expands. The coefficient of true expansion is the sum of the coefficient of apparent expansion, and the coefficient of volume expansion of the containing vessel.

EXPANSION OF THE UNIVERSE. Widely accepted theory that the Universe is expanding, i.e. that clusters of *galaxies* are receding from each other. Based upon the evidence of the *red shift* (see also *Doppler effect*) and the theory of *relativity*. See *Hubble's Constant*.

EXPLICIT FUNCTION (math.). A variable quantity, x, is said to be an explicit function of y, when x is directly expressed in terms of y.

EXPLOSION. A violent and rapid increase of *pressure* in a confined space. May be caused by an external source of *energy* (e.g. *heat*) or by an internal *exothermic chemical reaction* in which relatively large *volumes* of *gases* are produced. Explosions may also occur as the result of the release of internal energy during an uncontrolled *nuclear reaction* (either *fission* or *fusion* or both).

EXPLOSIVES. Substances which undergo a rapid chemical change, with production of *gas*, on being heated or struck. The *volume* of gas produced being very great relative to the bulk of the *solid* explosive, great *pressures* are set up when the action takes place in a confined space.

EXPONENT (math.). The number indicating the *power* of a quantity. Thus the exponent of x in x^4 is 4.

EXPOSURE METER. (phot.). A *photo-electric cell* operating a suitable indicating meter, used in *photography* to assess the amount of *light* available, so that the correct shutter speed and *aperture* may be chosen for a given 'speed' of *film*.

EXTENDER. An *inorganic* powder added to *paints* to improve such properties as *film* formation, and to avoid settlement on storage. Also used in the *plastics* industry with reference to substances added to *glues* or synthetic *rubbers* which reduce their cost or to some extent modify their properties (e.g. *viscosity*).

EXTENSOMETER. Instrument for measuring the extension produced in a body under an applied *stress*.

EXTINCTION COEFFICIENT. A measure of the amount of *light* absorbed by a substance in *solution*. If light of intensity I_0 is passed through d cm. of a solution containing a *molecular concentration* c, of the dissolved substance, so that its intensity is reduced to I_T, then the extinction coefficient is given by:

$$\frac{1}{cd} . \log_{10} \frac{I_0}{I_T}$$

EXTRACTION. The process of separating a desired constituent from a *mixture*, by means of selective *solubility* in an appropriate *solvent*. Also used to describe any process by which a pure *metal* is obtained from ore.

EXTRAORDINARY RAY. See *ordinary ray*.

EXTRAPOLATION. Filling in values or terms of a series on either side the known values, thus extending the range of values.

EXTRINSIC SEMICONDUCTOR. A *semiconductor* in which the *carrier* density results mainly from the presence of impurities or other imperfections, as opposed to an intrinsic semiconductor in which the electrical properties are characteristic of the *ideal crystal*.

EYE-PIECE. In optical instruments, the *lens* or system of lenses nearest the observer's eye; generally used to view the image formed by the *objective*.

F

FACTOR (math.). A number or quantity is exactly divisible by its factors; thus the factors of 12 (i.e. the *integral* or whole-number factors) are 1, 2, 3, 4, 6, 12.

FACTOR, PRIME. Prime factors of a quantity are the *prime numbers* (i.e. numbers themselves possessing no *factors* other than themselves and unity) which, when multiplied together, give the quantity. Thus, the prime factors of 165 are 3, 5, and 11.

FACTORIAL NUMBER is the *product* of a number and all the consecutive positive whole numbers below it down to 1. Thus, factorial 5, written $\underline{|5}$ or $5! = 5 \times 4 \times 3 \times 2 \times 1 = 120$.

FACULAE. Large bright areas of the *photosphere* of the *Sun*, whose *temperatures* are higher than the average of the Sun's surface.

FAHRENHEIT DEGREE. $\frac{1}{180}$ of the difference between the *temperature* of melting *ice* and that of *water* boiling under standard atmospheric pressure (760 mm.).

FAHRENHEIT SCALE of temperature. *Temperature* scale in which the *melting point* of ice is taken as 32° F. and the *boiling point* of *water* under standard atmospheric pressure (760 mm.) as 212° F. 9 Fahrenheit degrees = 5 Centigrade degrees. To convert degrees F. to degrees C., subtract 32 from the F. value, multiply by 5 and divide by 9; to convert degrees C. to degrees F., multiply by 9, divide by 5, then add 32 to the result.

FAJANS' RULES. See *rules of Fajans*.

FALL-OUT. *Radioactive* substances deposited upon the surface of the Earth from the *atmosphere*. Three types of fall-out, subsequent to the *explosion* of a *nuclear weapon*, are recognized. 'Local fall-out' as a result of which large particles from the fire ball are deposited within a range of approximately 100 miles during the first few hours after the explosion. 'Tropospheric fall-out', during which fine particles are deposited around the globe, in the approximate *latitude* of the explosion, within a week or so. 'Stratospheric fall-out' consisting of the ultimate world-wide deposition, over a period of years, of the particles which were carried by the explosion into the *stratosphere*.

FARAD. Unit of *capacitance*. A capacitance of 1 farad requires an *electric charge* of 1 *coulomb* to raise its *potential* by 1 *volt*. Equal to 10^9 *electromagnetic units* and $8·99 \times 10^{11}$ *electrostatic units*. The usual practical unit of capacitance is the microfarad, which is 10^{-6} farads.

FARADAY, THE. Quantity of *electricity* required to liberate or deposit 1 *gram-equivalent* of an *ion*. 96,490 *coulombs*. See *electrochemical equivalent*.

FARADAY EFFECT. Faraday rotation. The rotation of the plane of vibration (see *polarization of light*) of polarized light on traversing an *isotropic* transparent medium placed in a *magnetic field* possessing a component in the direction of the light ray. Although originally restricted to light, the Faraday effect is now known to apply to other *electromagnetic radiations*. Thus, the plane of polarization of a *radar pulse* travelling through the *ionosphere* is rotated by the combined effects of the *ionization* and the Earth's magnetic field (see *magnetism, terrestrial*). By reflecting radar pulses from the *Moon*, or other Earth *satellites*, and measuring the total rotation, the extent of the ionization in the ionosphere can be calculated.

FAST FISSION. See fast *neutrons*.

FAST NEUTRONS. *Neutrons* resulting from *nuclear fission* that have lost little of their *energy* by collision and therefore travel at high speeds. It is usual to describe neutrons with energies in excess of $0 \cdot 1$ *Mev* as 'fast'. However, fission induced by fast neutrons is often described as 'fast fission' and in this context the neutrons are so described if they have energies in excess of the fission threshold of $^{238}_{92}U$, i.e. above $1 \cdot 5$ Mev.

FAST REACTOR. A *nuclear reactor* in which little or no *moderator* is used and in which, therefore, the *nuclear fissions* are caused by *fast neutrons*.

FATHOM. 6 feet; used as a unit of marine depth.

FATHOMETER. Depth-sounding instrument. The depth of water is measured by noting the time the *echo* of a *sound* takes to return from the sea bed.

FATIGUE OF METALS. Deterioration of *metals* owing to repeated *stresses* above a certain critical value; accompanied by changes in the crystalline structure of the metal.

FATS AND OILS. Simple *lipids* consisting of mixtures of various *glycerides* of *fatty acids*. Natural *organic compounds* which occur in plants and animals and serve as storage materials. The distinction between fats and oils (as distinct from *mineral oils*, which are *hydrocarbons*) is one of *melting point*; the term oil is usually applied to glycerides *liquid* at 20° C., the others being termed fats.

FATTY ACIDS. *Monobasic organic acids* having the general formula R.COOH, where R is hydrogen or a group of carbon and hydrogen atoms. The *saturated* fatty acids have the general formula $C_nH_{2n+1}COOH$. Many fatty acids occur in living things, usually in the form of *glycerides* in *fats and oils*.

FEBRIFUGE. See *antipyretic*.

FEEDBACK. In general, the coupling of the output of a process to the input. In 'negative feedback' a rise in the output *energy* is arranged to cause a decrease in the input energy (e.g. a *governor*). In 'positive feedback' a rise in the output energy is caused to reinforce the input energy. In particular, these terms are applied to electronic *amplifiers*, in which a portion of the output energy is used to reduce or increase the amplification, by reacting on an earlier stage according to the relative *phase* of the return.

FEHLING'S SOLUTION. Solution of *copper sulphate*, $CuSO_4$, *caustic soda*, NaOH, and *Rochelle salt*. Used for the detection and estimation of certain *sugars* and other *reducing agents*, which act upon the solution with the formation of a red precipitate of *cuprous oxide*, Cu_2O.

FELSPAR, feldspar. Name of a large group of rock-forming *minerals* consisting chiefly of alumino-silicates of potassium and sodium. Constituents of *granite* and other primary rocks.

FEMTO-. Prefix denoting one thousand million millionth (10^{-15}).

FERMAT'S PRINCIPLE OF LEAST TIME. The path taken by a ray of *light* or other *wave motion* in traversing the distance between any two points is such that the time taken is a minimum.

FERMENT. *Enzyme*; any substance which will produce *fermentation*.

FERMENTATION. Chemical change brought about in organic substances by living *organisms* (*yeast*, *bacteria*, etc.) by *enzyme* action. Usually applied to the alcoholic fermentation produced by the action of *zymase* on certain *sugars*, giving *alcohol* and *carbon dioxide* according to the equation $C_6H_{12}O_6 = 2C_2H_5OH + 2CO_2$.

FERMI. A unit of length, used in *nuclear physics*, equal to 10^{-13} cm.

FERMI-DIRAC STATISTICS. The branch of statistical mechanics used with systems of identical particles which have the property that their *wave function* changes sign if any two particles are interchanged. See *fermions*.

FERMIONS. Particles which conform to *Fermi-Dirac statistics*. The number of fermions are conserved throughout all nuclear interactions, but they are divided into two groups, *baryons* and *leptons*, which are distinguished from each other in that members of one group cannot transform into members of the other group.

FERMIUM. Fm. *Transuranic element*. At. No. 100. The most stable *isotope*, $^{252}_{100}$ Fm, has a *half-life* of only 30 hours.

FERRIC. Term denoting a *compound* of *tervalent* (trivalent) iron. Ferric *salts* are usually yellow or brown in colour.

FERRIC ALUM, iron alum. Crystalline ferric potassium sulphate, $Fe_2(SO_4)_3.K_2SO_4.24H_2O$. Violet *soluble crystals*.

FERRIC CHLORIDE. $FeCl_3.6H_2O$. Brown-yellow *deliquescent* crystalline *salt*.

FERRIC OXIDE. Fe_2O_3. Red insoluble *solid*, occurs naturally as *haematite*.

FERRIMAGNETISM. The type of *magnetism* occurring in materials in which the *magnetic moments* of adjacent *atoms* are anti-parallel, but of unequal strength, or in which the number of magnetic moments orientated in one direction outnumber those in the reverse direction. Ferrimagnetic materials therefore have a resultant magnetization similar to that of *ferromagnetism*. Typical ferrimagnetic materials are the *ferrites*.

FERRITE. 1. Name applied to several types of iron ore. 2. *Salt* of the hypothetical 'ferrous acid', derived from *ferric oxide*, Fe_2O_3.

FERRITES. A group of *ceramic* materials which exhibit the property of *ferrimagnetism*. Consists of iron oxide to which small quantities of *transition metal* oxides (e.g. cobalt and nickel oxides) have been added. The *spinel* ferrites have the formula $MO.Fe_2O_3$ where M is a *divalent* transition metal ion. More complex barium-containing ferrites have also been manufactured. By suitable combinations of metallic oxides, ferrites can be made which exhibit *ferromagnetism*, but as they are electrical *insulators* and therefore do not suffer from the effects of *eddy currents*, they can be used as cores in coils and *transformers* in *electronic* equipment at *frequencies* which would be impossible with ordinary ferromagnetic materials. Ferrites are also used in the construction of memory circuits in *computers* and, on account of their light weight, in the electrical equipment of aircraft.

FERRITIN. A *protein* found in the liver and spleen which contains iron. Acts as a reservoir of iron for the whole body.

FERRO-. Prefix denoting iron, especially in names of *alloys*; e.g. *ferromanganese*.

FERROCHROME. *Alloy* of chromium with 30%–40% iron, obtained by the reduction of *chromite* with carbon in an electric furnace.

FERROELECTRICS. *Dielectric* materials which have electrical properties analogous to certain magnetic properties such as *hysteresis*, e.g. *barium titanate* and *Rochelle salt*. Ferroelectric materials usually also have piezoelectric properties (see *piezo-electric effect*).

FERROMAGNETIC SUBSTANCES. See *ferromagnetism*.

FERROMAGNETISM. The *metals* iron, cobalt, nickel, and certain *alloys* are vastly more magnetic than any other known substance: these metals are said to be ferromagnetic. Ferromagnetism is due to unbalanced *electron spin* in the inner electron *orbits* of the *elements* concerned (see *atom, structure of*) which give the *atom* a resultant *magnetic moment*. The ionic spacing in ferromagnetic *crystals* is such that very large *forces*, called *exchange forces*, cause the alignment of all the individual magnetic moments of large groups of atoms to give highly *magnetic domains*. In an unmagnetized piece of iron, these domains are oriented at random, their magnetic axes pointing in all directions. The application of an external field serves to line up the domain axes, giving rise to the observed magnetism. Ferromagnetic substances have very large *magnetic permeabilities* which vary with the strength of the applied field. A given ferromagnetic substance loses its ferromagnetic properties at a certain critical temperature, the *Curie temperature* for that substance.

FERROMANGANESE. *Alloy* of manganese (70%–80%) and iron.

FERROSILICON. *Alloy* of silicon (15%) and iron, used in special *steels*.

FERROUS. Term denoting a compound of *bivalent* (divalent) iron; more loosely, pertaining to iron. Ferrous *salts* are generally pale green in colour.

FERROUS SULPHATE, green vitriol, copperas. $FeSO_4.7H_2O$. Pale green crystalline *soluble salt*. Made by dissolving scrap iron in dilute *sulphuric acid*. Used in *dyeing*, *tanning*, and *ink* manufacture.

FERTILE MATERIAL. *Isotopes* which can be transformed into *fissile material* by the absorption of *neutrons* (e.g. $^{238}_{92}U$, $^{232}_{90}Th$).

FERTILIZATION. The union of two sexually dissimilar *gametes* to form a *zygote*.

FERTILIZERS. Materials put into the *soil* to provide *compounds* of *elements* essential to plant life; more particularly nitrogen, phosphorus, and potassium. Nitrogen is provided in the form of *nitrates*, *ammonium salts*, *Nitrolime*, etc. (see *fixation of atmospheric nitrogen*); phosphorus is added in the form of *superphosphate*, *basic slag*, various *phosphates*, etc. Potassium is obtained from natural potassium salts. Products of organic *decomposition* and waste, manure, etc., contain these and other necessary elements and form valuable fertilizers.

FIBRIN. An *insoluble* substance precipitated in the *blood* of vertebrates in the form of a meshwork of fibres during the process of clotting. Fibrin is formed when *thrombin* acts upon *fibrogen*.

FIBROGEN. A *soluble protein* found in the *blood* of vertebrates which causes clotting of the blood by the action of the *enzyme thrombin* as a result of which *fibrin* is formed.

FIDELITY. A measure of the *frequency* response of a *sound*-producing system. 'High fidelity' systems are usually taken to be those which are capable of reproducing frequencies up to 12,000 cycles per second without distortion.

FIELD. The region in which an electrically charged body (see *electric field*), a magnetized body (see *magnetic field*), or a massive body (see *gravitational field*) exerts its influence. There may also be said to be a field between *nucleons* in extremely close proximity (less than 10^{-13} cm.) as a result of *exchange forces*. A field is thus a model for representing the way in which a *force* can exist between bodies not in contact.

FIELD COIL. A coil of wire used for magnetizing an *electromagnet*, e.g. in a *dynamo*.

FIELD EMISSION. The emission of *electrons* from an unheated surface as a result of a strong *electric field* existing at that surface.

FIELD LENS. The *lens* in the *eye-piece* system of optical instruments farthest from the eye.

FIELD MAGNET. *Magnet* which provides a *magnetic field* in the *dynamo*, *electric motor*, or other electrical machine.

FILAMENT. Thin thread. In incandescent *electric light bulbs* and *thermionic valves*, a wire of tungsten or other *metal* of high *melting point*, which is heated by the passage of an *electric current*.

FILLER. A *solid* substance added to synthetic *resins*, *paints*, and *rubbers*, either to modify their properties or to reduce their cost.

FILM. 1. (chem.). A thin layer of a substance formed on the surface of a *liquid* or at the interface between two immiscible liquids, usually only a few *molecules* thick. 2. (phot.). A flexible strip (usually *celluloid*) coated with a light-sensitive *emulsion*. See *photography*.

FILM BADGE. A badge containing a masked photographic *film* worn by workers in contact with *ionizing radiations* to indicate the extent of their exposure to these radiations.

FILTER. 1. (chem.). Device for separating *solids* or suspended particles from *liquids*. Consists of a porous material (e.g. filter-paper) through the pores of which only liquids and dissolved substances can penetrate. 2. (phys.). Material or device inserted in the path of an *electromagnetic radiation* to alter its *frequency* distribution.

FILTER PRESS. An apparatus used for carrying out *filtration*; consists of a series of frames (metal or wooden) the two sides of which are covered with filter cloth. The frames are clamped together and the *liquid* to be filtered is pumped into them so that the *solid* residue forms a cake between the cloths while the *filtrate* is drained off.

FILTRATE. Clear *liquid* after *filtration*; substance which has been filtered, containing no suspended matter.

FILTRATION. The process of separating *solids* from *liquids* by passing through a *filter*.

FINDER. Small low-powered *telescope* fixed parallel to the axis of a large telescope (usually astronomical) so that the object to be observed may be located and set in the field of vision of the large telescope.

FINENESS OF GOLD. Amount of gold in an *alloy* expressed as parts per thousand. Thus gold with a fineness of 900 is an alloy containing 90% gold. See also *carat*.

FIRE. Chemical action accompanied by evolution of *heat*, *light*, and *flame* (i.e. a glowing mass of *gas*). Generally applied to the chemical combination with oxygen of carbon and other *elements* constituting the substance which is being burnt. See *combustion*.

FIRECLAY. *Clay* consisting principally of *alumina*, Al_2O_3, and *silica*, SiO_2, which will only soften at high *temperatures* and which is therefore used as a *refractory* material. Fireclays often occur beneath *coal* seams.

FIRE-DAMP. Explosive mixture of *methane* (CH_4) and air, formed in coal mines.

FIRE EXTINGUISHERS. Devices for putting out *fires* by cutting off the supply of air necessary for combustion. Two main types are used. The *acid-carbonate* type contains *sodium carbonate*, Na_2CO_3, and *sulphuric acid*, H_2SO_4. On pressing the knob, the tube containing the acid is broken, and the acid acts upon the sodium carbonate giving a froth of liquid and *carbon dioxide*, which covers the burning material. The *pyrene** type contains *carbon tetrachloride*, CCl_4. These should not be used on burning metal.

FISCHER-TROPSCH PROCESS. A process for the manufacture of *hydrocarbon oils* from *coal*, *lignite*, or *natural gas*. The process essentially consists of the *hydrogenation* of *carbon monoxide*, CO, in the presence of *catalysts*; this results in the formation of hydrocarbons and *steam*.

FISSILE MATERIAL. *Isotopes* which are capable of undergoing *nuclear fission*. Sometimes the term is restricted to apply only to isotopes which are capable of undergoing fission upon impact with a slow *neutron* (e.g. $^{233}_{92}U$, $^{235}_{92}U$, $^{239}_{94}Pu$).

FISSION, NUCLEAR. See *nuclear fission*.

FISSION PRODUCTS. Both the stable and the unstable *isotopes* produced as the result of *nuclear fission*.

FISSION SPECTRUM. The *energy* distribution of the *neutrons* produced by the *nuclear fission* of a particular *fissile material*.

FITTIG'S SYNTHESIS. The preparation of *aromatic benzene derivatives* by the action of metallic sodium on a mixture of an *alkyl halide* and a brominated benzene *hydrocarbon*.

FITZGERALD-LORENTZ CONTRACTION. Explanation put forward independently by Fitzgerald (1893) and Lorentz (1895) to explain the result of the *Michelson-Morley experiment* on the supposition that a body moving with high *velocity* through the *ether* would experience a contraction in length in the direction of the motion. This contraction was later shown to be a direct consequence of the *relativity* theory.

FIXATION OF ATMOSPHERIC NITROGEN. Manufacture of *compounds* of nitrogen for use as *fertilizers*, from the free nitrogen in the air; made necessary by the increasing shortage of natural nitrogen compounds in the *nitrogen cycle*. This shortage is caused partly by increased cultivation of the *soil* due to increase of populations, and partly by the loss of nitrogen compounds from animal waste products by sewage disposal into the sea. The first practical process was the *Birkeland and Eyde process*; the *Haber* and *Serpek processes* are now the main ones used. In addition, certain *bacteria* in the soil fix atmospheric nitrogen.

FIXED AIR. Former name for *carbon dioxide*, CO_2.

FIXED ALKALI. Former name for *potassium* or *sodium carbonate*, to distinguish them from volatile alkali, ammonium carbonate.

FIXED POINT. Any accurately reproducible equilibrium *temperature*. Examples include the *ice point*, the *steam point*, and the *sulphur point*.

FIXED STARS. True *stars*; heavenly bodies termed fixed because they do not appear to alter their relative positions on the *celestial sphere*.

FIXING, PHOTOGRAPHIC. Rendering that portion of the sensitive *film*, plate, or paper which has not been affected by *light*, insensitive to exposure, after *developing*. Usually carried out by the action of *sodium thiosulphate*, $Na_2S_2O_3$ (*hypo*), which reacts with the unaffected *silver bromide* to give a *soluble* double *salt*, silver sodium thiosulphate, which is then washed away. See *photography*.

FLAME. Glowing mass of *gas* produced during *combustion*.

FLASH PHOTOLYSIS. See *photolysis*.

FLASH POINT. The lowest *temperature* at which a substance gives off sufficient inflammable *vapour* to produce a momentary flash when a small flame is applied.

FLAVOPROTEINS. Yellow conjugated *proteins* in which the *prosthetic group* is either flavine mononucleotide (FMN) or adenine dinucleotide (FAD). Flavoproteins are *enzymes* of the *dehydrogenase* type.

FLEMING'S RULES. Mnemonics for relating the direction of motion, *flux*, and *EMF* in electric machines. If the forefinger, second finger, and thumb of the right hand are extended at right angles to each other, the forefinger indicates the direction of the flux, the second finger the direction of the EMF, and the thumb the direction of motion in an electric *generator*. If the left hand is used the digits indicate the conditions obtaining in an *electric motor*.

FLINT. Natural variety of impure *silica*, SiO_2. 'Flints' of automatic lighters are composed of *pyrophoric alloys* of *metals* such as cerium and iron.

FLINT GLASS. Variety of *glass* containing lead silicate; used for optical purposes.

FLOCCULATION. The coagulation of finely divided particles into particles of greater mass.

FLOTATION, PRINCIPLE OF. The *weight* of *liquid* displaced by a floating body is equal to the weight of the body. A particular case of *Archimedes' principle*.

FLOTATION PROCESS. Separation of a *mixture*, e.g. of *zinc blende*, ZnS, and *galena*, PbS, making use of the *surface tension* of *water*. Zinc blende is not easily wetted by water and floats, supported by the surface film of water, while galena sinks. In modern practice, special materials are added to the water which cause one of the constituents to float in the froth produced by aerating and agitating the water. See *froth flotation*.

FLOWERS OF SULPHUR. Fine powder, consisting of very small *crystals* of *sulphur* obtained by the *condensation* of sulphur *vapour* during *distillation* of crude sulphur.

FLUE GAS. The gaseous products of *combustion* from a boiler furnace consisting predominantly of *carbon dioxide*, *carbon monoxide*, oxygen, nitrogen, and *steam*. Analysis of the flue gases is used to check the efficiency of the furnace. See *Orsat apparatus*.

FLUID. Substance taking the shape of the vessel containing it; *liquid* or *gas*.

FLUID DRACHM. See *drachm*.

FLUID MEASURE. See *apothecaries' fluid measure*.

FLUID OUNCE. British measure of *volume* of *liquids*. 28·41 c.c. See *apothecaries' fluid measure*.

FLUIDITY. The *reciprocal* of viscosity. The *C.G.S.* *unit* is the reciprocal of the *poise* known as the *rhe*.

FLUORENE, *ortho*-diphenylene methane. $C_{13}H_{10}$. *Aromatic hydrocarbon*; white crystalline *solid*, m.p. 116° C.

FLUORESCEIN. $C_{20}H_{12}O_5$. Dark red crystalline *organic compound*, m.p. $314°$ C. Dissolves in *alkaline solutions* to give a *liquid* of intense green *fluorescence*.

FLUORESCENCE. Property of many substances (e.g. quinine sulphate solutions, *paraffin oil*, *fluorescein* solutions) of absorbing *light* of one *wave-length* (i.e. *colour*, when in the visible region of the *spectrum*) and in its place emitting light of another wave-length or colour. Unlike *phosphorescence*, the phenomenon ceases immediately the source of light is cut off.

FLUORIDE. A *salt* of *hydrofluoric acid*. The presence of fluorides in minute proportions in drinking water is believed to increase the resistance of teeth to dental caries (decay).

FLUORINE. F. Element. A.W. $18·9984$ At. No. 9. Pale yellowish-green *gas*, resembling chlorine but more *reactive*. Occurs combined as *fluorspar* and as *cryolite*. Made by the *electrolysis* of a *solution* of potassium hydrogen fluoride in *anhydrous* hydrogen fluoride. The fluorine *organic compounds*, made by replacing hydrogen in organic compounds by fluorine, are assuming considerable industrial importance. See *fluorocarbons*.

FLUORITE. See *fluorspar*.

FLUOROCARBONS. A group of *synthetic organic compounds* (both *aliphatic* and *aromatic*) in which some or all of the hydrogen *atoms* have been substituted by fluorine atoms. Such compounds are usually non-inflammable, chemically resistant, and immiscible with *water* or *oil*. Poly*tetrafluoroethylene* (Teflon* and Fluon*) is a *polymer* used as a *plastic*, while the Freons* are *monomers* used as refrigerants and *solvents*.

FLUOROSCOPE. A fluorescent screen (see *fluorescence*) for the direct visual observation of *X-ray* images; used diagnostically in medicine.

FLUORSPAR. Natural calcium fluoride, CaF_2. Colourless *crystals*, often coloured by impurities. Used as a source of fluorine and its *compounds*.

FLUX (chem.). Substance added to assist fusion.

FLUX (phys.). The flux of any *vector* quantity (*electric intensity*, *magnetic intensity*, etc.) through an area is the product of the area and the component of the vector at right angles to the area. In *nuclear physics*, the *product* of the number of particles (including *photons*) per unit *volume* and their average *velocity*.

FLUX, LUMINOUS. The luminous flux through any area is the amount of *light* passing through that area per second. Measured in *lumens*.

FLUXMETER. Instrument for the measurement of *magnetic flux*. Essentially a moving coil *galvanometer* so designed that the coil experiences negligible restoring torque from its suspension system. A change in the magnetic flux through a flux coil connected to the galvanometer induces a current in the coil, thus causing a deflection of the galvanometer.

FOAM. A *colloidal* suspension of a *gas* in a *liquid*.

FOCAL LENGTH. Distance from the *optical centre* or pole to the principal *focus* of a *lens* or *spherical mirror*.

FOCUS. Point at which converging rays, usually of *light*, meet (real focus); or a point from which diverging rays are considered to be directed (virtual focus). For 'principal focus' see *lens* and *spherical mirrors*.

FOG. Effect caused by the *condensation* of *water vapour* upon particles of dust, soot, etc.

FOOD PRESERVATION. Prevention of chemical *decomposition* and of the development of harmful *bacteria* in foods. Generally effected by the sterilization of the food (i.e. by the destruction of bacteria in it) by heating in sealed vessels, i.e. canning; or by making the conditions unfavourable for the development of bacteria, by pickling, drying, smoking, etc.

FOOT. British unit of length; one-third of a *yard*; 30·48 cm.

FOOT-CANDLE. Unit of *illumination*. One *lumen* per square foot.

FOOT-LAMBERT. A unit of *luminance*. The luminance of a uniform diffuser emitting one *lumen* per sq. ft.

FOOT-POUND. Practical unit of *work*. Work done by a *force* of 1 pound weight acting through a distance of 1 foot.

FOOT-POUNDAL. Unit of *work* in the foot-pound-second system (see *F.P.S. system*); the work done by a *force* of 1 *poundal* acting through a distance of 1 foot.

FORBIDDEN BAND. See *energy band*.

FORCE. External agency capable of altering the state of rest or motion in a body; measured in *dynes* or *poundals*. The force, F., required to produce an *acceleration*, a, in a *mass*, m, is given by $F = ma$. If m is in grams, a in cm. per sec. per sec., F will be in *dynes*.

FORCES, PARALLELOGRAM OF. See *parallelogram of forces*.

FORCES, TRIANGLE OF. See *triangle of forces*.

FORMALDEHYDE. HCHO. *Gas* with an irritating smell, very *soluble* in *water*. 40% *solution* is known as *formalin*. Made by the *oxidation* of *methyl alcohol*. Used in the manufacture of *plastics* and *dyes*, in the textile industry, in medicine, and as a *disinfectant*.

FORMALIN. 40% *solution* of *formaldehyde*, used as a *disinfectant*.

FORMATE. A *salt* or *ester* of *formic acid*.

FORMIC ACID. HCOOH. Colourless, corrosive fuming *liquid* with a pungent smell. M.p. 8·4°, b.p. 100·5° C. Occurs in various plants and in ants. Made industrially from sodium formate, HCOONa, which is produced by the action of *carbon monoxide*, CO, on *sodium hydroxide*, NaOH. Used in dyeing, *tanning*, and *electroplating*.

FORMULA (chem.). The representation of a *molecule* or smallest portion of a *compound*, using *symbols* for the *atoms* of the *elements* which go to make up the molecule. E.g. the formula of *water*, H_2O, implies that the smallest portion of water that can exist independently consists of

2 hydrogen atoms chemically united with 1 oxygen atom. The structural formula represents the way in which the atoms in a molecule are actually believed to be joined by *valency bonds*. E.g. the structural formula of water is written H—O—H, indicating that 2 hydrogen atoms, having 1 valency each, are both attached to the *bivalent* oxygen atom. The empirical formula of a compound is its simplest formula, indicating only the numerical ratio of the atoms present in a molecule, but not necessarily their actual number. Thus the empirical formula of *hydrogen peroxide* is HO while its actual or *molecular formula* is H_2O_2.

FORMULA (math. and phys.). A statement of facts in a symbolical or general form, by substitution in which a result applicable to particular data may be obtained. Thus the time of swing of a *pendulum* is given by the formula $T = 2\pi\sqrt{\dfrac{l}{g}}$, showing the connexion between length and time of swing.

FORTIN BAROMETER. Mercury *barometer* which, used in conjunction with various correction tables, enables accurate measurements of atmospheric pressure to be made.

FOSSIL. Remains of an *organism* preserved in rocks in the *Earth's crust*. Usually only the hard parts (bones, shells, etc.) are so preserved, but occasionally remains of organisms having no hard parts have been recognized.

FOSSIL FUELS. Remains of *organisms* embedded in the surface of the Earth, with high carbon and/or hydrogen contents, which are used by man as *fuels* (e.g. *coal, oil, natural gas*). Most of the *energy* obtained from the *combustion* of fossil fuels derives from the *exothermic* conversion of carbon into *carbon dioxide* and of hydrogen into *water* (*steam*).

FOURIER ANALYSIS. The expansion of a mathematical *function* or of an experimentally obtained curve in the form of a trigonometric series. Used as a method of determining the harmonic components of a complex periodic wave.

FOURTH DIMENSION. Ordinary *space* has three dimensions, i.e. length, breadth, and thickness, each one at right angles to both the others. Mathematically it is possible to write down equations, similar to those governing relations between points in ordinary three-dimensional space, but connecting any number of imaginary dimensions. These are sometimes said to refer to a 'hyperspace' of many dimensions. In dealing with a material particle, it is necessary to state not only where it is, but when it is there. Thus time is somewhat analogous to a dimension of space. *Relativity* has shown in particular in what manner time may be regarded as a fourth dimension, so that all real events take place in a four dimensional *space-time continuum*.

FOWLER'S SOLUTION. A *solution* containing potassium arsenite; used in medicine.

F.P.S. SYSTEM, the foot-pound-second system of units. The British system of physical *units* derived from the three *fundamental units* of length, *mass*, and time, i.e. the foot, pound mass, and the *second*.

FRACTIONAL CRYSTALLIZATION. Separation of a *mixture* of dissolved substances by making use of their different *solubilities*. The *solution* containing the mixture is evaporated until the least *soluble* component crystallizes out.

FRACTIONAL DISTILLATION, fractionation. Separation of a *mixture* of several *liquids* which have different *boiling points*, by collecting separately 'fractions' boiling at different *temperatures*.

FRACTIONATING COLUMN. A long vertical column, containing rings, plates, or bubble caps, which is attached to a *still*. As a result of internal *reflux* a gradual separation takes place between high and low boiling 'fractions' of a liquid *mixture*.

FRACTIONATION. Separation of a *mixture*, usually of chemically related or otherwise similar components, into fractions of different properties. Term is usually applied to *fractional distillation*.

FRANCIUM. Fr. Element. At. No. 87. No known stable *isotope* and only one natural *radioactive* isotope, $^{223}_{87}$Fr (half-life 21 mins.). Belongs to *alkali metal* group of *elements*.

FRASCH PROCESS for the extraction of sulphur. Used to extract sulphur from deposits deep down under sand. A series of concentric pipes is sunk down to the level of the sulphur deposit, *superheated steam* is forced down to melt the sulphur, which is then forced to the surface by compressed air blown down the centre pipe.

FRAUNHOFER DIFFRACTION. The class of *diffraction* phenomena in which both the *light* source and the receiving screen are effectively at an infinite distance from the diffracting system. Compare *Fresnel diffraction*.

FRAUNHOFER LINES. Dark lines in the continuous *spectrum* of the *Sun*, caused by the absorption of certain *wave-lengths* of the *white light* from the hotter regions of the Sun, by chemical *elements* present in the cooler *chromosphere* surrounding the Sun.

FREE (chem.). Uncombined; applied to *elements* which occur as such.

FREE ELECTRON. An *electron* which is not attached to an *atom*, *molecule*, or *ion*, but is free to move under the influence of an *electric field*.

FREE ENERGY. F. A *thermodynamic* quantity representing the *energy* that would be liberated or absorbed during a *reversible process*. Defined, under conditions of constant *temperature* and *pressure*, by $F = H - TS$, where H is the heat content (*enthalpy*), T the *absolute temperature*, and S the *entropy*. Referred to chemical processes, the important quantity is not the absolute magnitude of F, but the change in free energy, ΔF (also called the chemical *affinity*), during a reaction, which is given by $\Delta F = \Delta H - T.\Delta S$. By convention, if a reaction gives out *heat* ΔH will be negative (as the system is losing heat to the surroundings). Therefore, if $T.\Delta S$ is not large compared to ΔH, ΔF will also be negative indicating that the reaction will proceed to *chemical equilibrium*. When equilibrium has been attained, $\Delta F = O$, and if ΔF is positive the reaction will only occur if energy is supplied in some way to force it away from equilibrium. As the entropy, S, is a measure of the molecular disorder of a system, and as a change of state involves a change of molecular orderliness, the term $T.\Delta S$ is dependant upon changes of state.

FREE RADICAL. A group of *atoms* (see *radical*), which usually exists in combination with other atoms, but which may exist independently for short periods (short-lived free radicals) during the course of a *chemical reaction*, or for longer periods (free radical of long life) under special conditions.

FREEZING. Change of state from *liquid* to *solid*; takes place at a constant *temperature* (*freezing point*) for any given substance under a given *pressure*. The freezing point normally quoted is that for standard atmospheric pressure.

FREEZING MIXTURES. Certain *salts* which, when dissolved in *water* or mixed with crushed *ice*, produce a considerable lowering of *temperature*. The action depends upon absorption of *heat of solution* by the dissolving salt; in the case of mixtures in contact with ice, the *melting point* of ice is lowered in the presence of a dissolved substance; *latent heat* of fusion of ice is absorbed, and the salt dissolves in the melting ice.

FREEZING POINT. The *temperature* of equilibrium between *solid* and *liquid* substance at a pressure of one standard atmosphere (760 mm. mercury).

FREEZING-POINT DEPRESSION. See *depression of freezing point*.

FRENCH CHALK. Powdered *talc*.

FRENKEL DEFECT. A *defect* in a *crystal lattice* caused by an *atom* or *ion* being removed from its normal position in the lattice (thus causing a *vacancy*) and taking up an *interstitial* position.

FREQUENCY of a vibratory motion (*wave motion*) is the number of vibrations per second. Numerically equal to the *velocity* divided by the *wave-length*.

FREQUENCY BAND. A range of *frequencies* of *electromagnetic radiations* falling within prescribed limits. See Table 6, page 336, for internationally agreed *radio frequency* bands.

FREQUENCY MODULATION. FM. The type of *radio* transmission system in which the *frequency* of a *carrier wave* is modulated rather than its *amplitude* (as in *amplitude modulation*). Provides a method of transmission free from 'static' interference.

FREQUENCY OF A VIBRATING STRING. The fundamental *frequency*, f, of a stretched string of length L, under tension T, is given by:

$$f = \frac{1}{2rL} \sqrt{\frac{T}{\pi d}}$$

where r is the radius of the string and d its *density*.

FRESNEL DIFFRACTION. Class of *diffraction* phenomena in which the *light* source or the receiving screen, or both, are at a finite distance from the diffracting system. Compare *Fraunhofer diffraction*.

FRIABLE. Easily crumbled.

FRICTION. Name given to *forces* offering resistance to relative motion between surfaces in contact.

FRICTION, COEFFICIENTS OF. If F_s = the frictional resistance when a body is on the point of sliding along a specified surface, F_k = the frictional resistance when steady sliding has been attained, and R = the perpendicular *force* between the surfaces in contact, the static coefficient of friction = F_s/R; the kinetic coefficient = F_k/R.

FRIEDEL-CRAFTS REACTION. Originally the *synthesis* of *aromatic hydrocarbons* by reacting *alkyl halides* with *benzene derivatives* in the presence of *anhydrous* aluminium chloride as a *catalyst*. Now extended to include the addition of *olefines* to, and the *condensation* of *alcohols* with, aromatic hydrocarbons in the presence of such catalysts as anhydrous ferric chloride, gallium chloride, boron trifluoride, and hydrogen fluoride.

FROTH FLOTATION. The separation of a *mixture* of finely divided minerals by agitating them in a froth of *water* and *oil*, so that some float and others sink. The process can be made selective by adjusting the nature of the froth with suitable *surface active agents*.

FRUCTOSE, fruit sugar, laevulose. $C_6H_{12}O_6$. Sweet *soluble* crystalline *monosaccharide sugar*, m.p. $102°-104°$ C. Occurs in sweet ripe fruits, in the nectar of flowers and in honey.

FRUSTUM. Any part of a solid figure cut off by a *plane* parallel to the base, or lying between two parallel planes.

FUEL. A substance which is used for producing *heat energy*, either by means of the release of its *chemical energy* by *combustion* (see *fossil fuels*) or its *nuclear energy* by *nuclear fission*.

FUEL CELL. A *cell* for producing *electricity* by *oxidation* of a *fuel*, thus converting *chemical energy* directly into *electrical energy*.

FUEL ELEMENT. An element of *nuclear fuel* for use in a *nuclear reactor*, usually uranium encased in a can.

FULLER'S EARTH. Name of a variety of *clay*-like materials which absorb *oil* and *grease*. Chemical composition varies; consists of *hydrated silicates* of magnesium, calcium, aluminium, and sometimes other *metals*. Used in scouring textiles and in refining *fats and oils*.

FULMINATE OF MERCURY, mercuric *iso*cyanate, $Hg(ONC)_2$. Substance which explodes violently on being struck; used for detonators to initiate *explosions*.

FUMIGATION. Destruction of *bacteria*, insects and other pests by exposure to poisonous *gas* or *smoke*.

FUNCTION (math.). One quantity y is said to be a function of another quantity x, written $y=f(x)$, if a change in one produces a change in the other. Thus, in the statement $y=3x^2+5x$ (i.e. $f(x) \equiv 3x^2+5x$), y is a function of x, and a change in the value of x produces a change in the value of y.

FUNDAMENTAL NOTE (phys.). See *quality of sound*.

FUNDAMENTAL UNITS. The *units* in which physical quantities (e.g. *viscosity*, *surface tension*, etc.) are measured, are not all independent; many of them are derived from a small number of fundamental units. In the *C.G.S. system*, the fundamental units chosen are the centimetre, gram mass, and second. See also *M.K.S. system*.

FUNGI. Simple plants which contain no *chlorophyll*. May consist of one cell or of many cellular filaments. Cause diseases of plants and of some animals, also cause decay of food, fabrics, and timber. Certain fungi are used in *brewing* and baking and for the production of *antibiotics*.

FUNGICIDE. Substance capable of destroying harmful *fungi*, such as moulds and mildews.

FUR IN KETTLES. *Insoluble* gritty deposit, consisting mainly of the *carbonates* of calcium, magnesium, and iron; formed by the *decomposition* of the *soluble bicarbonates* of these metals when *hard water* is boiled.

FURANE RESINS. A group of synthetic *resins* obtained by the partial *polymerization* of furfuryl alcohol ($C_4H_3O.CH_2OH$) or by the *condensation* of furfuryl alcohol with *furfural* or *formaldehyde*. Used as *adhesives*, metal coatings, etc.

FURFURAL. Furfuraldehyde. $C_4H_3.O.CHO$. *Liquid organic compound*, b.p. $161 \cdot 7°$ C.; used as *solvent* and in synthetic *resins*. See *furfural resins*, and *furane resins*.

FURFURAL RESINS. *Thermosetting* resins obtained by the condensation of *furfural* and *phenol* or its homologues. Used as *adhesive* and in the manufacture of moulding materials, varnishes, etc.

FUSE, ELECTRICAL. Device to prevent an unduly high *electric current* from passing through a *circuit*. Consists of a piece of wire made of *metal* of low *melting point*, e.g. tin, placed in series in the circuit. An excessive current will raise the *temperature* of the fuse wire sufficiently to melt it and thus break the circuit.

FUSED (chem.). In the molten state, usually applied to *solids* of relatively high *melting point*; or, having previously been melted and allowed to solidify.

FUSEL OIL. Mixture of *butyl* and *iso-amyl alcohols* (C_4H_9OH, $C_5H_{11}OH$) together with other organic substances; a *liquid* of unpleasant smell and taste; by-product of the *distillation* of alcohol produced by *fermentation*.

FUSIBLE ALLOYS. *Alloys* of low *melting point*; generally *eutectic mixtures* of metals of low melting point such as bismuth, lead, tin, and cadmium. *Wood's metal* and *Lipowitz alloy* both contain all four and melt below the *boiling point* of *water*. Fusible alloys having a melting point a little above the boiling point of water are used in the construction of automatic sprinklers, *heat* from a fire melting the metal and releasing a spray of water.

FUSION. Melting; melting together.

FUSION BOMB. See *nuclear weapons*.

FUSION, LATENT HEAT OF. See *latent heat*.

FUSION, NUCLEAR. See *nuclear fusion*.

FUSION MIXTURE. *Mixture* of *anhydrous* sodium and potassium carbonates, Na_2CO_3 and K_2CO_3.

G

g. Symbol for the value of the *acceleration due to gravity*.

GADOLINIUM. Gd. Element. A.W. 157·25. At. No. 64. See *lanthanides*.

GAIN. A term used in *electronics* with reference to an increase in signal power; usually expressed as the ratio of the output power (for example, of an *amplifier*) to the input power in *decibels*.

GALACTOSE. $CH_2OH.(CHOH)_4.CHO$. A *hexose sugar*, m.p. 166° C.; constituent of *lactose* and certain plant *polysaccharides*.

GALAXIES, extra-galactic nubulae. Gigantic *star*-clusters or 'island universes', separated by even vaster stretches of *space*. E.g. the *Galaxy*. See also *spiral galaxies*.

GALAXY, THE. *The Milky Way*. A cluster of some 10^{11} *stars*, one of which is the *Sun*. The Galaxy is a flat disc-shaped spiral structure, approximately 10^5 *light-years* across, with a slight bulge at the centre. The *solar system* is situated quite close to the central plane of this disc at a distance of about three-fifths of its radius from the centre.

GALENA. Natural lead sulphide, PbS. Heavy crystalline *mineral* of metallic appearance; principal ore of lead. Used as a *semiconductor* in *crystal rectifiers*.

GALLIUM. Ga. Element. A.W. 69·72. At. No. 31. Silvery-white *metal*, S.G. 5·9, m.p. 29·78° C. *Compounds* very rare; the metal is used in high-temperature *thermometers* and gallium arsenide is used as a *semiconductor*.

GALLON. Unit of volume or capacity. The British Imperial gallon is the *volume* occupied by ten pounds of *distilled water* under conditions precisely defined by the 1963 Weights and Measures Act. Equal to 4·54596 *litres*. The U.S. gallon is 0·8327 British gallons.

GALVANIZED IRON. Sheet iron coated with a layer of zinc to prevent *corrosion*, usually made by dipping into the molten metal.

GALVANOMETER. Instrument for detecting, comparing, or measuring small *electric currents*, but not usually calibrated in *amperes*; requires calibration when an actual current measurement is needed. Usually depends upon the magnetic effect produced by an electric current. See *ammeter*, and *ballistic galvanometer*.

GAMBOGE. Yellow substance obtained from the hardened gum-resin of the tree Garcinia Hanburii. Used as a *pigment* and for colouring varnishes.

GAMETE. Germ cell. A reproductive *cell*, usually *haploid* and sexually differentiated. The female gamete (or *ovum*) unites with the male gamete (or *spermatozoon*) during *fertilization* to produce a *zygote*, which develops into a new individual. Some animal and plant gametes are *diploid* and these cells are capable of developing into new individuals without fertilization, by the process of *parthenogenesis*.

GAMETOCYTE. A *cell* which undergoes *meiosis* to form *gametes*.

GAMMA-IRON. Allotropic form (see *allotropy*) of iron, stable at high *temperatures*. See *austenite*.

GAMMA RAYS. Gamma radiation. γ-rays. *Electromagnetic radiation* of the same nature, but shorter *wave-length* than *X-rays*. Emitted by the *nuclei* of *radioactive atoms* during *decay*. Gamma rays are emitted in *quantized* units called *photons*.

GARNET. Group of *minerals* of varying composition, mainly double *silicates* of calcium or aluminium with other *metals*. Several varieties are red in colour, and are used as gems.

GAS. A substance whose *physical state* (the gaseous state) is such that it always occupies the whole of the space in which it is contained. Consists of *atoms* or *molecules* which would move freely in a *perfect gas*, but which in a real gas are subject to small inter-molecular *forces* (*Van der Waals' forces*). See also *Kinetic theory of gases*.

GAS CARBON, retort carbon. Hard deposit consisting of fairly pure carbon, found on the walls of the *retorts* used for the *destructive distillation* of *coal* in the manufacture of *coal-gas*. Good *conductor* of *electricity*, used for making carbon *electrodes*.

GAS CHROMATOGRAPHY. Gas-liquid chromatography. A very sensitive method of analysing the components of a complex *mixture* of *volatile* substances. The apparatus consists of a long narrow tube, packed with an inert support material of uniform particle size (e.g. *diatomaceous earth*) that has been coated with a non-volatile *liquid* called the 'stationary phase', the whole tube and its contents being maintained in a thermostatically controlled oven. The sample to be analysed is carried through the tube by an *inert gas* (e.g. argon) so that the progress through the tube of various components of the mixture is selectively interfered with by the stationary phase, some components passing through the tube more rapidly than others. A detector measures the electrical *conductivity* of the gas leaving the column, differences being recorded on a strip chart which indicates peaks corresponding to the various components. The instrument is calibrated by analysing samples of known composition.

GAS CONSTANT, R. In the *gas equation*, $pv = RT$ the gas constant, R, equals $8\cdot314 \times 10^7$ *ergs* (or $1\cdot987$ *calories*) per degree Centigrade.

GAS EQUATION. An *equation* connecting the *pressure* and *volume* of a quantity of *gas* with the *absolute temperature*. For a *gram-molecule* of a *perfect gas*, $pv = RT$, where p = pressure, v = volume T = absolute temperature, and R = the *gas constant*.

GAS LAWS, THE. Statements as to the *volume* changes of *gases* under the effect of alterations of *pressure* and *temperature*. *Boyle's law* states that at constant temperature the volume of a given mass of gas is inversely proportional to the pressure; i.e. $pv =$ constant. Charles' law states that at constant pressure all gases expand by $1/273$ of their volume at $0°$ C. for a rise in temperature of $1°$ C.; i.e. the volume of a given mass of gas at constant pressure is directly proportional to the *absolute temperature*. The two laws may be combined in the expression $pv \propto T$, where T is the absolute temperature; or, for a *gram-molecule* of a gas, $pv = RT$ (see *gas equation*). This gives the behaviour of a gas when both temperature and pressure are altered. The gas laws are not perfectly obeyed by ordinary gases, being strictly true only for the *perfect gas*. See *gas laws, deviations from*.

GAS LAWS, DEVIATIONS FROM. *Gases* do not strictly obey the *gas laws*, but follow them more and more closely as the *pressure* of the gas is reduced. Various *equations* have been derived which attempt to give a better approximation to the behaviour of actual gases. The best known of these is *Van der Waals' equation*.

GAS MANTLE. Structure composed of the *oxides* of thorium (99%) and cerium (1%), made by impregnating a combustible fabric with a *solution* of the *nitrates* of the metals, and decomposing the nitrates by heat.

GAS MASER. A *maser* in which *microwave radiation* interacts with *gas molecules*.

GAS MASK, RESPIRATOR. Device for protecting the face and breathing organs against poisonous 'gases'. (These include poisonous *smokes*, etc., used in chemical warfare.) The air is drawn through a layer of *activated carbon* which adsorbs *vapours*, and also through a filter-pad which retains solid particles of smokes. Such an arrangement is effective against war 'gases' and smokes, but not against gases of low *molecular weight* such as *carbon monoxide* or *coal-gas*.

GAS OIL. Diesel oil. The *oil* left after *petrol* and *kerosene* have been distilled from crude *petroleum*. Used as a *fuel* for *diesel engines* and for carburetting *water gas*.

GAS THERMOMETER. Apparatus for measuring *temperature* by the alteration in *pressure* produced by temperature changes in a *gas* kept at constant *volume*, or by the alteration in volume of a gas kept at constant pressure. For practical purposes, other more convenient forms of thermometer are used whenever possible. However, the gas thermometer, operated at low pressure, gives the only direct means of determining *absolute thermodynamic temperatures*.

GAS TURBINE. An *engine* which converts the *chemical energy* of a *liquid fuel* into *mechanical energy* by internal *combustion*, the gaseous products of which are expanded through a *turbine*. Used as the power plant in aeroplanes (both turbo-propeller and turbo-jet driven), locomotives, and experimentally in motor-cars. Also used as an auxiliary power plant in electrical generating stations.

GASEOUS COMBINATION, law of. See *Gay-Lussac's law*.

GASEOUS PRESSURE, pressure of a *gas* exerted on the walls of the containing vessel; is caused by the bombardment of the *molecules* of the gas upon the walls of the vessel.

GASOLINE, gasolene, petrol. Mixture of *hydrocarbons* obtained from *petroleum*. See *petrol*.

GAUSS. Unit of *magnetic induction*. If a *magnetic field* of 1 *oersted* intensity exists in a medium of unit *magnetic permeability*, e.g. air, then the induction will be 1 gauss.

GAY-LUSSAC'S LAW OF GASEOUS COMBINATION. When *gases* combine, they do so in a simple ratio by *volume* to each other, and to the gaseous product, measured under the same conditions of *temperature* and *pressure*. Explained by *Avogadro's law*.

GEIGER COUNTER. Geiger-Muller Counter. Instrument for the detection of *ionizing radiations* (chiefly *alpha*, *beta*, and *gamma rays*), capable of registering individual particles or *photons*. Consists normally of a fine wire *anode* surrounded by a *coaxial* cylindrical *metal cathode*, mounted in a glass envelope containing *gas* at low *pressure*. A large *potential difference*, usually about 1000 *volts*, is maintained between the anode and the cathode. The *ions* produced in the counter by an incoming ionizing particle are accelerated by the applied potential difference towards their appropriate *electrodes*, causing a momentary drop in the potential between the latter. This voltage *pulse* is then passed on to various *electronic* circuits by means of which it can, if desired, be made to work a counter.

GEISSLER TUBE. Tube for showing the luminous effects of a *discharge* of *electricity* through various rarefied *gases*.

GEL. *Colloidal solution* which has set to a jelly, the *viscosity* being so great that the solution has the *elasticity* of a *solid*. Formation attributed to a mesh-like structure of the *disperse phase* or *colloid*, with the *dispersion medium* circulating through the meshwork.

GELATIN, gelatine. Complex *protein* formed by the *hydrolysis* of *collagen* in animal cartilages and bones, by boiling with *water*. *Soluble* in water; *solution* has the property of setting to a jelly. Used in foods, *photography*, as an *adhesive*, textile size, and in a variety of other arts and industries.

GELIGNITE. *Explosive* consisting of a *mixture* of *nitroglycerin*, *nitrocellulose*, saltpetre (*potassium nitrate*, KNO_3) and wood pulp.

GENE. A hypothetical unit, comprising part of a *chromosome*, which controls an individual inherited characteristic of an *organism* and which is capable of *mutation* as a unit. (See also *cistron*.) The gene is regarded as being a particular molecular configuration of the *nucleic acids* (which partially constitute a chromosome) at a particular point on the length of a chromosome. There is considerable evidence to support the belief that genes function by controlling the manufacture of *enzymes* in *cells*; each gene being responsible for the manufacture of one enzyme. See *genetic code*.

GENERATION TIME. The average lapse of time between the creation of a *neutron* by *nuclear fission* and a subsequent fission produced by that neutron.

GENERATOR. A machine for producing *electrical energy* from *mechanical energy*. See *dynamo*.

GENETIC CODE. The code by which inherited characteristics are handed from generation to generation. The code is expressed by the molecular configuration of the *chromosomes* of *cells*. Chromosomes consist of *deoxyribonucleic acid* (DNA) and *protein*, the code-bearing material being the DNA. Four different nitrogenous bases (*adenine, cytosine, guanine*, and *thymine*) occur in the *nucleotides* of DNA, and it appears that the sequence of three of these bases constitute a unit of the genetic code, in that each sequence of three bases codes for one of the twenty different *amino acids* that go to make up the *enzymes* which control the characteristics of a cell. Chromosomes, which almost always exist in the *nuclei* of cells, transfer their coded information to the *cytoplasm* of these cells (where the enzyme proteins are assembled in units called *ribosomes*) by way of a 'messenger' nucleic acid (*ribonucleic acid*).

GENETICS. The study of heredity, variation, development, and evolution.

GEODESIC. Shortest distance between two points on a spherical surface; arc of a *great circle*.

GEODESY. Surveying on a scale which involves making allowance for the curvature of the Earth.

GEOLOGICAL TIME SCALE. Geological periods. A scale of time which serves as a reference for correlating various events in the history of the Earth; it has been built up by studying the various strata of rocks which comprise the *Earth's crust* with special reference to the *fossils* found in them. The time scale is divided into three main 'eras', based upon the general character of the life which they contain, each era being subdivided into 'periods'. The Table on page 134 gives the names of these eras and periods, together with their approximate ages.

GEOLOGY. Scientific study of the *Earth's crust*.

GEOMETRICAL PROGRESSION. A series of quantities in which each term is obtained by multiplying the preceding term by some constant factor, termed the 'common ratio'. E.g. 1, 3, 9, 27, 81 . . ., each term being three times the preceding. For a series of n terms, having common ratio r and the first term a, the sum, $S = a(r^n - 1)/(r - 1)$; or, if r is less than 1, a more convenient expression is $S = a(1 - r^n)/(1 - r)$.

GEOMETRY. Mathematical study of the properties and relations of lines, surfaces, and solids in space.

GERMAN SILVER. *Alloy* of copper, zinc, and nickel in varying proportions, approximating to 5 parts Cu, 2 of Zn, and 2 of Ni.

GERMANIUM. Ge. Element. A.W. 72·59. At. No. 32. Brittle white *metal*. S.G. 5·35, m.p. 958·5° C. *Compounds* rare. Used in the *transistor*.

GERMICIDE. Substance capable of destroying *bacteria*.

GEOLOGICAL TIME SCALE

Era		Period	Time Scale millions of years
CENOZOIC	QUATERNARY	Holocene	·01
		Pleistocene (Glacial)	1
	TERTIARY	Pliocene	10
		Miocene	25
		Oligocene	40
		Eocene	60
		Paleocene	70
MESOZOIC (SECONDARY)		Cretacious	135
		Jurassic	180
		Triassic	225
PALAEOZOIC (PRIMARY)		Permian	270
		Carboniferous	350
		Devonian	400
		Silurian	440
		Ordovician	500
		Cambrian	600
PRE-CAMBRIAN			2,000

GETTER, vacuum getter. Substance used for removing the last traces of air or other *gases* in attaining a high *vacuum*. E.g. magnesium metal is used in *thermionic valves*; after exhausting and sealing the valve a small amount of magnesium which is left in the valve is vaporized by *heat* and combines chemically with any remaining oxygen and nitrogen.

GEV. Abbreviation for *giga electron-volt*, i.e. 10^9 electron-volts. In America this is usually written Bev where the 'B' represents the American billion.

GHOSTS (phys.). False lines appearing in a *line spectrum* due to imperfections in the ruling of the *diffraction grating* used.

GIANT STAR. *Star* possessing high *luminosity*.

GIGA-. Prefix denoting a thousand million (10^9).

GILBERT. The *C.G.S. unit* of *magnetomotive force* in *electromagnetic units*. Equal to $\dfrac{10}{4\pi}$ *ampere-turns*.

GILDING. Covering with a thin layer of metallic gold, often by *electrolysis* (see *electroplating*).

GILL. Unit of capacity equal to one quarter of a *pint*.

GILLION. 10^9, one thousand million.

GLACIAL ACETIC ACID. Pure *acetic acid*; *solid* crystalline acetic acid, below its *freezing point* ($16 \cdot 6°$ C.).

GLASS. Hard brittle *amorphous mixture*, usually *transparent* or *translucent*, of the *silicates* of calcium, sodium, or other *metals*. Ordinary soda glass is made by melting together sand (*silica*), *sodium carbonate*, and *lime*. Glass for special purposes may contain lead, potassium, barium, or other metals in place of the sodium, and boron oxide in place of the silica. See *crown glass, flint glass*.

GLASS FIBRE MATERIALS. Fine *glass* fibres, usually less than a thousandth of an inch in diameter, which are woven into a cloth and impregnated with various *resins*. Owing to their high *tensile strength* and *corrosion* resistance these materials are used in small boat-building and for some motor-car body parts.

GLASS WOOL. Material consisting of very fine *glass* threads, resembling cotton wool. Used for filtering and absorbing corrosive *liquids*.

GLAUBER'S SALT. Crystalline *sodium sulphate*, $Na_2SO_4.10H_2O$.

GLAZE. *Vitreous* covering for pottery. Chemically related to *glass*.

GLOBULAR CLUSTERS. Self-contained, approximately spherical clusters of about one hundred thousand *stars*; some hundred of these clusters are known to be distributed about the centre of the *Milky Way*, and although they appear to be outside the *Galaxy*, they are believed to be gravitationally associated with it.

GLOBULINS. Groups of *proteins soluble* in dilute *solutions* of mineral *salts*, such as *common salt*, NaCl; *Epsom salts*, $MgSO_4$, etc. Occur in many animal and vegetable tissues and fluids; e.g. lactoglobulin in milk, serum globulin in *blood*, vegetable globulins in seeds. Globulins are the main proteins of *antibodies*.

GLOVE BOX. A metal box which provides protection to workers who have to manipulate *radioactive* materials or which enables the manipulation of substances requiring a dust-free, *sterile*, or *inert* atmosphere. Manipulation is carried out by means of gloves fitted to ports in the walls of the box.

GLOW DISCHARGE. A silent discharge of electricity through a *gas* at low *pressure*, usually luminous. See *discharge in gases*.

GLUCINUM. See *beryllium*.

GLUCOSE, dextrose, grape-sugar. $C_6H_{12}O_6$. Colourless crystalline *soluble hexose sugar*. M.p. 146° C. Occurs in honey and sweet fruits. Other sugars and *carbohydrates* are converted into glucose in the human body before being utilized to provide *energy*. Glucose is an *optically active* substance, the naturally occurring sugar invariably being *dextrorotary*. Commercially prepared from *starch* and other carbohydrates by *hydrolysis*; used in brewing, jam-making, confectionery, etc.

GLUCOSIDES. Derivatives of *glucose* in which one hydrogen *atom* in the molecule is replaced by an organic *radical*. The term *glycoside* is applied generally to such *compounds* of all *sugars*.

GLUE. General name for *adhesives*, particularly those made by extracting hides, bones, cartilages, etc., of animals with *water*.

GLUTEN. *Protein* contained in wheat flour (8%–15%).

GLYCERIDES. *Esters* of glycerol (*glycerin*) with *organic acids*. Animal and vegetable *fats* are mainly composed of triglycerides of *fatty acids*, such as *stearic*, *palmitic*, and *oleic*, a *molecule* of such a triglyceride being derived by the combination of one molecule of glycerol with three fatty acid molecules.

GLYCERIN(E), glycerol. $CH_2OH.CHOH.CH_2OH$. Thick syrupy sweetish *liquid*, trihydric *alcohol*, *soluble* in *water*. B.p. 290° C. Occurs combined with *fatty acids* in *fats and oils*; obtained by the *saponification* of fats in the manufacture of *soap*. Used in the manufacture of *explosives* (see *nitroglycerin*), *plastics*, in pharmacy, and as an *anti-freeze*.

GLYCEROL. See *glycerin*.

GLYCOGEN, animal starch. Complex *carbohydrate* formed from *glucose* and *starch* in the liver and other organs of animals, serving as a *sugar* reserve.

GLYCOL. See *ethylene glycol*.

GLYCOLIPIDS. Compound *lipids* which consist of *compounds* of *fatty acids* with *carbohydrates*, and which contain nitrogen but no *phosphoric acid*. Found in brain tissues.

GLYCOLS, dihydric *alcohols*. *Organic compounds* derived from *aliphatic hydrocarbons* by the substitution of *hydroxyl groups* for two of the hydrogen *atoms* in the *molecule*. General *formula* $C_nH_{2n}OH_2$. See also *ethylene glycol*.

GLYCOLYSIS. The conversion of *glucose* into *lactic acid* by a series of *enzyme* catalysed reactions which occur in living *organisms*.

GLYCOSIDES. See *glucosides*.

GLYOXAL, diformyl. $(CHO)_2$. Yellow *crystals*, m.p. 15° C., b.p. 51° C. Used in the manufacture of *plastics*, and in textile finishing.

GLYPTAL RESINS, alkyd resins. Class of synthetic *resins* obtained by the reaction of *polyhydric alcohols* with *polybasic organic acids* or their *anhydrides*; e.g. *glycerol* and phthalic anhydride. See *phthalic acid*. Used chiefly for surface coatings.

GOLD. Au. Element. A.W. 196·967. At. No. 79. Bright yellow rather soft *metal*; m.p. 1063° C. S.G. 19·3. Extremely malleable and ductile. Not corroded by air or *water*; unattacked by most *acids*, but dissolves in *aqua regia*. Occurs mainly as the free metal; most *compounds* are unstable and easily reduced to gold. Extracted from ore and sand by the *amalgamation process* and the *cyanide process*. *Alloys* with copper or silver to give hardness are used for coinage, jewellery, and dentistry. Compounds are used in *photography* and medicine.

GOLD LEAF. Gold is the most malleable of *metals*, and can be beaten into leaves ·0001 mm. thick (i.e. 254,000 thicknesses to the inch). The leaf has the appearance of metallic gold, but transmits green *light*; i.e. appears green when held up to the light.

GOLD-LEAF ELECTROSCOPE. See *electroscope*.

GOLDSCHMIDT PROCESS. Preparation of *metals* from their *oxides* by the *thermit* method.

GONIOMETER. Instrument for the measurement of *angles* (of *crystals*).

GOOCH CRUCIBLE. A laboratory *filter* consisting of a shallow *porcelain* cup, the flat bottom of which is perforated with small holes over which a layer of *asbestos* fibres are placed.

GOVERNOR. A device for regulating the speed of an *engine* or machine, on the principle of negative *feedback*, so that its speed is kept constant under all conditions of loading. Often achieved by controlling the *fuel* consumption, so that a rise in speed is arranged to reduce the fuel intake and a fall in speed to increase it.

GRADIENT. Usually expressed as unit rise in height per number of units covered along the slope; i.e. the sine of the angle of rise (see *trigonometrical ratios*). Mathematically, the gradient is the ratio of the vertical distance to horizontal distance, i.e. the tangent of the angle. For small gradients the difference between the sine and the tangent is small.

GRADUATION. Marking the scale of an instrument, e.g. the stem of a *thermometer* is graduated in *degrees*.

GRAHAM'S LAW of gaseous diffusion. The velocity of *diffusion* of a *gas* is inversely proportional to the square root of its *density*.

GRAIN. British unit of *weight*. 1/7000 of a pound; 0·0648 gm.

GRAM, GRAMME. One of the *fundamental units* of measurement in the *C.G.S. system* of units. Unit of *mass*, 1/1000 of the mass of the International Prototype Kilogram, a platinum-iridium standard preserved in Paris.

GRAM WEIGHT. A unit of *force*, the pull of the Earth on the *gram* mass, varies slightly in different localities, depending on the value of g, the *acceleration due to gravity* at the given place. Force expressed in grams weight = force in *dynes* divided by the appropriate value of g at the place under consideration. A force of 1 gram weight = approx. 981 dynes. 1 gm. = 0·0353 oz.; 453·6 gms. = 1 lb.

GRAM-ATOM. The *atomic weight* of an *element* expressed in *grams*; e.g. 32 gms. of sulphur.

GRAM-EQUIVALENT. The equivalent weight in *grams*. See *chemical equivalents*.

GRAM-ION. The sum of the *atomic weights* of the *atoms* in an *ion* (see *electrolysis*) expressed in *grams*.

GRAM-MOLECULAR VOLUME. The *volume* occupied by one *grammolecule* of a *gas*. Approximately the same for all gases under the same conditions of *temperature* and *pressure*; at a pressure of 760 mm. and 0° C., equal to 22·415 *litres* for a *perfect gas*.

GRAM-MOLECULE, gram-molecular weight, mole, mol. The *molecular weight* of a *compound* expressed in *grams*. E.g. 18 gms. of *water*.

GRANITE. Heterogenous mixture of *felspar*, *quartz*, and *mica*.

GRAPE SUGAR. See *glucose*.

GRAPH. Diagram, generally plotted between axes at right angles to each other, showing the relation of one *variable* quantity to another. E.g. the variation of rainfall with time, or the variation in the value of a mathematical *function* as different values are assigned to one of the variables in the function.

-GRAPH. Suffix applied to instruments which automatically record or write down observations; e.g. *barograph*.

GRAPHITE, blacklead, plumbago. Natural *allotropic form* of carbon. Used for pencil leads, in electrical apparatus, and as a lubricant for heavy machinery. Also used as a *moderator* in *nuclear reactors*.

GRAPHITE-MODERATED REACTOR. See *nuclear reactor*.

GRATING. See *diffraction grating*.

GRAVIMETRIC ANALYSIS. Branch of *quantitative chemical analysis*. The amount of a substance present is determined by converting it, by a suitable *chemical reaction*, into some other substance of known chemical composition, which can be readily isolated, purified, and weighed.

GRAVITATION, Newton's law of. Every particle in the Universe attracts every other particle with a *force* which is directly proportional to the produce of the *masses* of the particles and inversely proportional to the square of the distance between them. Thus, the force of attraction between two masses M_1 and M_2, in *grams*, separated by a distance of d centimetres, is given by $F = \dfrac{G.M_1 M_2}{d^2}$ *dynes*, where G is the gravitational constant, 6.670×10^{-8} *C.G.S. units*.

GRAVITATIONAL FIELD. The region in which one massive body (i.e. a body which possesses the attribute of *mass*) exerts a *force* of attraction on another massive body.

GREASE. A semi-solid lubricant composed of emulsified *petroleum* oils and *soluble hydrocarbon soaps*.

GREAT CIRCLE. Circle obtained by cutting a *sphere* by a *plane* passing through the centre. E.g. regarding the Earth as a sphere, the *Equator* is a great circle, as are all the *meridians* of longitude. On the Earth's surface, an apparent straight line joining any two points is an arc of a great circle, i.e. a *geodesic*.

GREEK FIRE. Mixture of materials which caught fire when wetted; used by the ancient Greeks in naval warfare. Probably composed of sulphur, *naphtha*, and *quicklime* or similar materials.

GREEN VITRIOL, copperas. *Ferrous sulphate crystals*, $FeSO_4.7H_2O$.

GRID BIAS. A fixed *voltage* applied between the *cathode* and the *control grid* of a *thermionic valve* which determines its operating conditions.

GRIGNARD REAGENTS. *Alkyl* magnesium *halides*, prepared by the action of magnesium metal on alkyl halides in *ether* solution; e.g., C_2H_5MgI. Used in organic *synthesis*.

GROUND STATE. The most stable *energy* state of, a *nucleus*, *atom*, or *molecule*. The normal state of an atom when its circum-nuclear *electrons* move in *orbits* such that the energy of the atom is a minimum. See *atom, structure of*.

GROUND WAVES. Direct waves. *Electromagnetic radiations* of *radio frequencies* which travel more or less directly from transmitting *aerial* to receiving aerial, that is without reflection from the *ionosphere*. See *sky waves*.

GRÜNEISEN'S LAW. The ratio of the coefficient of *expansion* of a *metal* to its *specific heat* at constant pressure is a constant at all *temperatures*.

GUANIDINE. $HN:C(NH_2)_2$. Strongly *basic*, *water soluble*, crystalline *organic compound*.

GUANINE. 2-aminohypoxanthine. $C_5H_5N_5O$. One of the four nitrogenous bases occurring in the *nucleotides* of *nucleic acids* which plays a part in the formulation of the *genetic code*.

GUANO. Large deposits formed from the excrement and bodies of seabirds. Found on islands off the coast of Peru. Very rich in nitrogen and phosphorus *compounds*; valuable *fertilizer*.

GUIDED MISSILE. A missile (usually *rocket* propelled) whose flight path can be controlled during flight either by *radio* signals from an external source or by internal homing devices (pre-set or self-actuating).

GUM ARABIC. Gum Acacia. *Water soluble*, yellowish *gum* obtained from certain varieties of acacia. Used in food and pharmaceutical products and as an *adhesive*.

GUMS. General name applied to a large class of substances of vegetable origin, usually exuded from plants.

GUN-COTTON, *cellulose nitrate*, nitrocellulose. Powerful *explosive* formed by the action of *nitric acid* on *cellulose*.

GUN-METAL. Variety of *bronze* containing about 90% copper, 8%-10% tin, and up to 4% zinc.

GUNPOWDER. *Mixture* of *potassium nitrate*, KNO_3, powdered *charcoal*, and sulphur. When ignited, a number of *chemical reactions* take place, evolving *gases*, thus producing an *explosion* in a confined space.

GUTTA-PERCHA. Material very similar to *rubber*, obtained from the *latex* of certain Malayan trees; chemically, the *trans-form* of polyisoprene. A horny substance at ordinary temperatures; *thermoplastic*; at about 70° C. resembles unvulcanized rubber. Used for golf ball covers.

GYPSUM. Natural *hydrated* calcium sulphate, $CaSO_4.2H_2O$. Loses three-quarters of its *water of crystallization* when heated to 120° C., becoming *Plaster of Paris*.

GYRATION. Motion round a fixed *axis* or centre.

GYRO-COMPASS, gyroscopic compass. Compass which does not make use of *magnetism*, and is therefore not affected by magnetic storms, etc.; consists of a universally-mounted spinning wheel which has a rigidity of direction of axis and plane of rotation relative to space; the rotation being electrically maintained. See *gyroscope*.

GYROMAGNETIC RATIO. The ratio of the *magnetic moment* of an *atom* or *nucleus* to its *angular momentum*.

GYROSCOPE. Spinning wheel which is mounted in such a way that it is free to rotate about any axis; i.e. 'universally mounted'. Such a wheel has two properties upon which applications of the gyroscope depend – namely, 1. Rigidity in space (gyroscopic inertia); the support of the wheel may be turned in any direction without altering the direction of the wheel relative to space. 2. Precession. When a gyroscope is subjected to a *force* tending to alter the direction of its axis, the wheel will turn about an axis at right angles to the axis about which the force was applied.

H

HABER PROCESS. Industrial preparation of *ammonia*, for use in *fertilizers*, from atmospheric nitrogen. See *fixation of atmospheric nitrogen*. A heated mixture of nitrogen and hydrogen is passed over a *catalyst* under *pressure*; the *gases* combine to form ammonia gas according to the equation $N_2 + 3H_2 = 2NH_3$.

HAEMATITE. Natural *ferric oxide*, Fe_2O_3. Valuable ore of iron.

HAEMOGLOBIN. Red colouring matter (respiratory pigment) present in the red *blood cells*; consists of a *protein*, *globin*, combined with a *prosthetic group*, *haem*, the latter being a highly complex *organic compound* containing iron, nitrogen, carbon, hydrogen, and oxygen. Serves to carry oxygen, which is breathed in, round the body in the form of an easily decomposed compound, *oxy-haemoglobin*.

HAFNIUM, celtium. Hf. Element. A.W. 178·49. At. No. 72. Rare *metal*, S.G. 13·3, m.p. 1700° C. Used in the manufacture of tungsten *filaments*.

HAIR SALT. Natural aluminium sulphate, $Al_2(SO_4)_3.18H_2O$. White soluble crystalline *salt*.

HALF-LIFE. Half-value period. The time taken for the *activity* of a *radioactive isotope* to *decay* to half of its original value, that is for half of the *atoms* present to disintegrate. Half-lives vary from isotope to isotope, some being less than a millionth of a second and some more than a million years.

HALF-PERIOD ZONES. Division of a *wave front* into elements of area or zones such that secondary wavelets (see *Huygens' construction*) reaching a given point ahead of the wave from adjacent zones differ in *phase* by half a period, or π. This construction is used in theoretical investigations of *Fresnel diffraction* in simple cases.

HALF-THICKNESS. Half value layer. The thickness of a specified material which when introduced into the path of a given beam of *radiation*, reduces its intensity to one half of its original value.

HALF-WAVE PLATE. Plate of double refracting material (see *double refraction*) cut parallel to the *optic axis* and of such a thickness that a *phase* difference of π or 180° is introduced between the *ordinary ray* and the extraordinary ray for *light* of a particular *wave-length* (usually sodium light). The half-wave plate is chiefly used to alter the plane of vibration of plane-polarized light. See *polarization of light*.

HALIDE. *Binary compound* of one of the *halogen elements* (fluorine, chlorine, bromine or iodine); *salt* of the *hydride* of one of these.

HALL EFFECT. If an *electric current* flows in a wire placed in a strong transverse *magnetic field*, a *potential difference* is developed across the wire, at right angles to both the magnetic field and the wire.

HALL MOBILITY. Drift mobility. The mobility of *carriers* in a *semiconductor*; numerically the *velocity* of the carriers under the influence of an *electric field* of 1 *volt* per cm.

HALO. A luminous ring sometimes observed surrounding the *Sun* or the *Moon*. Caused by the *refraction of light* by *ice crystals* in the *atmosphere*.

HALOGENATION. The introduction of *halogen atoms* into a *compound* by addition or substitution.

HALOGENS. The four *elements* fluorine, chlorine, bromine, and iodine, having closely related and graded properties. (Astatine is also a member of the halogen group, but it has no stable *isotopes*.)

HAPLOID. Said of a biological *cell* which has a set of single (unpaired) *chromosomes*; e.g. *gametes*.

HARCOURT PENTANE LAMP. Lamp burning *pentane*, C_5H_{12}, under certain specified conditions. The lamp has been used as a standard source of *light*; the former unit of *luminous intensity*, the *international candle* was defined in terms of it.

HARD RADIATION. See *soft radiation*.

HARD WATER. *Water* which does not form an immediate lather with *soap*, owing to the presence of calcium, magnesium, and iron *compounds* dissolved in the water. The addition of soap produces an *insoluble* scum consisting of *salts* of these *metals* with the *fatty acids* of the soap, until no more is left in *solution*. Removal of these salts from solution renders the water soft. Hardness is divided into two types: 1. Temporary hardness, due to *bicarbonates* of the metals. These enter the water by the passage of the water, containing dissolved *carbon dioxide*, over *solid carbonates* (*chalk* or *limestone* deposits, etc.). Such hardness is removed by *boiling*, the soluble bicarbonates being decomposed into the insoluble carbonates (see *fur in kettles*), carbon dioxide and water. 2. Permanent hardness, due to *sulphates* of the metals. This is destroyed by the addition of washing-soda, *sodium carbonate*, which precipitates the insoluble carbonates. All hardness may be destroyed by the use of *zeolites*.

HARDENING OF FATS. Conversion of *liquid fats* (oils) consisting mainly of *triolein* into hard fats by the action of hydrogen in the presence of a *catalyst*. See *hydrogenation of oils*.

HARMONIC MOTION. See *simple harmonic motion*.

HARMONICS of a *wave motion*. Waves superimposed on a fundamental wave, having a *frequency* which is a whole multiple of the fundamental frequency. The second harmonic has a frequency twice that of the fundamental, the third harmonic three times, and so on.

HARTSHORN, SPIRITS OF. Solution of *ammonia* in *water*.

HEALTH PHYSICS. The branch of *physics* which deals with the effects of *ionizing radiation* on living *organisms*, with particular reference to the protection of humans from the ill-effects caused thereby.

HEAT. *Energy* possessed by a substance in the form of *kinetic energy* of atomic or molecular translation, rotation, or vibration. The heat contained by a body is the product of its *mass*, its *temperature*, and its specific heat (see *heat, specific*); usually measured in *calories*. Transmitted by *conduction, convection,* and *radiation*. The chief observable physical effects of a change in the heat content of a body may include rise in temperature; change of state from *solid* to *liquid* (melting), solid to *gas* (sublimation) and liquid to gas (*evaporation* and *boiling*); *expansion*; and electrical effects such as the *Peltier* and *Seebeck effects*.

HEAT CAPACITY. The quantity of *heat* required to raise the *temperature* of a body through 1° C. Numerically equal to the product of the *mass* of the body and its specific heat (see *heat, specific*).

HEAT DEATH OF THE UNIVERSE. The second law of thermodynamics (see *thermodynamics, laws of*) can be interpreted to mean that the *entropy* of a closed system tends towards a maximum and that its available *energy* tends towards a minimum. It has been held that the Universe constitutes a thermodynamically closed system, and if this were true it would mean that a time must finally come when the Universe 'unwinds' itself, no energy being available for use. This state is referred to as the 'heat death of the Universe'. It is by no means certain, however, that the Universe can be considered as a closed system in this sense.

HEAT, LATENT. Quantity of *heat* required to effect a change of state of 1 gm. of a substance from *solid* to *liquid* (latent heat of fusion) or from *liquid* to *vapour* (latent heat of vaporization) without change of *temperature*. At the *freezing* and *boiling points* of a substance, addition of heat produces no rise in temperature until the change of state is complete. *Energy* required to bring about the change of state is absorbed in the form of latent heat, and an equal amount of heat is liberated in reversing the process.

HEAT OF COMBUSTION. The amount of *heat* evolved by 1 *gram-molecule* of a substance when it is burned in oxygen.

HEAT OF FORMATION. The quantity of *heat* (usually expressed in *calories*) liberated or absorbed when 1 *gram-molecule* of a *compound* is formed from its *elements* in their normal state. The heat of formation of elements is, for the purpose of thermochemical calculations, taken as zero. See *Hess's law*.

HEAT OF NEUTRALIZATION. The quantity of *heat* evolved when 1 *gram-equivalent* of an *acid* or *base* is exactly neutralized. For all strong acids or bases, its value is approximately 13,700 *calories*.

HEAT OF REACTION. See *thermal value of a chemical reaction*.

HEAT OF SOLUTION. The quantity of *heat* evolved or absorbed when 1 *gram-molecule* of a substance is dissolved in a large volume of *water*.

HEAT PUMP. A machine for extracting *heat* from a *fluid* which is at a slightly higher *temperature* than its surroundings. For example, the rivers flowing through industrial towns are often slightly warmer than the ambient temperature as a result of the disposal of hot effluents in them. A heat pump can be used to raise the temperature of this 'low temperature heat', so that it can be usefully employed.

HEAT RADIATION. See *infra-red radiation*.

HEAT, SPECIFIC, of a substance. The quantity of *heat* required to raise the *temperature* of 1 gm. of the substance through 1° C.

HEAT, SPECIFIC, OF GASES. The two most important specific heats of a *gas* are (1) that measured at constant *pressure*, and (2) that measured at constant *volume*. The specific heat at constant pressure, C_p, is greater than that at constant volume, C_v; this is explained by the fact that a gas heated at constant pressure expands, and heat energy must be supplied equivalent to the *work* done in the expansion. The ratio C_p/C_v, denoted by γ (gamma), varies from 1·66 for *monatomic* gases to a little over 1 for gases with complex *molecules*. The value of gamma thus gives an indication of the number of *atoms* in the molecule of a gas.

HEAVISIDE-KENNELLY LAYER. A region of the *ionosphere*, between 55 and 85 miles above the surface of the *Earth* (for more recent designation of layers see *ionosphere*) which reflects *electromagnetic radiation* of *radio frequencies*. Inter-continental radio transmission, round the curved surface of the Earth, is possible because of the reflection of *sky-waves* by the Heaviside-Kennelly layer.

HEAVY HYDROGEN. See *deuterium*.

HEAVY SPAR. See *barytes*.

HEAVY WATER. Deuterium Oxide. D_2O. *Water* in which the hydrogen is replaced by *deuterium*. Present in natural water to the extent of about 1 part in 5000. Pure heavy water has S.G. 1·1, f.p. 3·82° C., b.p. 101·42° C. The term is also used when referring to water which contains appreciably more D_2O or HDO than natural water. Heavy water is used as a *moderator* in some *nuclear reactors*.

HECTARE. Metric unit of area; 10,000 square *metres*, 2·4711 acres.

HECTO-. Prefix denoting one hundred times.

HELIUM. He. Element. A.W. 4·0026. At. No. 2. *Inert gas* occurs in certain natural gases in the U.S.A.; occluded in *radioactive* ores (e.g. *monazite*, *pitch blende*) and in the *atmosphere* (1 part in 200,000). Non-inflammable, very light, valuable for filling airships and balloons.

HELIX. Spiral.

HEMICELLULOSES. Group of *carbohydrates* which on *hydrolysis* with dilute mineral *acids* yield *monosaccharides*. Found in *cell* walls of plants where they function as reserve food materials, especially in seeds.

HENRY, THE. Unit of self- and mutual inductance (see *self-induction*, *mutual induction*). An inductance such that a rate of change of current of 1 *ampere* per second produces an induced *E.M.F.* of 1 *volt*.

HENRY'S LAW. The *weight* of a *gas* dissolved by a definite *volume* of *liquid* at constant *temperature* is directly proportional to the *pressure*. From this it follows that the volume of a gas absorbed by a given volume of liquid at constant temperature is independent of the pressure. The law holds only for sparingly *soluble* gases at low pressures.

HEPARIN. A complex *organic acid* related to the *polysaccharides* but containing sulphur and nitrogen, which prevents the clotting of *blood* by interfering with the formation, and action, of *thrombin*. Used as an anti-coagulent.

HEPTA-. Prefix meaning seven.

HEPTANE. C_7H_{16}. Seventh member of the *paraffin series*. Exists in nine isomeric forms (see *isomerism*). Contained in light *petroleum*; normal-heptane has b.p. 98·4° C. and S.G. 0·68.

HERTZIAN WAVES, wireless waves, *radio* waves. *Electromagnetic radiation* covering a range of *frequency* from above 3×10^{10} cycles per second, corresponding to the shortest *radar* waves of 1 cm., to below $1·5 \times 10^5$ cycles (150 kilocycles) per second, corresponding to long radio waves of 2000 metres.

HERTZPRUNG-RUSSELL DIAGRAM. H-R diagram. A method of correlating data concerning *stars*. Consists of a *graph* in which the absolute *luminosity* of a star is plotted against its spectral type (obtained by examining the *spectra* of stars and arranging them in a sequence which reflects increasing *temperature*). This graph is thus essentially a plot of total *energy* output against surface temperature. The outstanding feature of this type of diagram is that most stars are concentrated in a narrow band running across the diagram: the stars at the upper end of the band are hot, bright, and bluish-white, while those at the lower end are cooler, dimmer, and reddish in colour. This band is called the 'main sequence' and stars which fall on it are called main sequence stars. It is mainly from H-R diagrams that the theory of *stellar evolution* has been derived.

HESS'S LAW. If a *chemical reaction* is carried out in stages, the algebraic sum of the amounts of *heat* evolved in the separate stages is equal to the total amount of heat evolved when the reaction occurs directly. consequence of the law of *conservation of energy* as applied to *thermochemistry*.

HETERO-. Prefix denoting other, different.

HETEROCYCLIC COMPOUNDS. *Organic compounds* containing a ring structure of *atoms* in the *molecule*, the ring including atoms of *elements* other than carbon. E.g. pyridine, C_5H_5N, having a *molecule* consisting of 5 carbon atoms and 1 nitrogen atom in a closed ring, with a hydrogen atom attached to each carbon atom.

HETERODYNE. A beat effect (see *beats*) produced by superimposing two waves of different *frequency*. Used extensively in *radio* receivers in which the received wave is combined with a wave (of slightly different frequency to the *carrier wave*) generated within the receiver. The two combining waves produce an *intermediate frequency* which is amplified and then *demodulated*. See *superheterodyne*.

HETEROGENEOUS. Not of a uniform composition; showing different properties in different portions.

HETERO-POLAR BOND. An electrovalent bond. See *valency, electronic theory of*.

HEURISTIC. Adjective describing the method of solving mathematical problems for which no *algorithm* exists: involves the narrowing down of the field of search for a solution by inductive reasoning from past experience of similar problems.

HEUSLER'S ALLOYS. *Alloys* containing neither iron, nickel, nor cobalt which exhibit strong *ferromagnetism*. Composed of copper, manganese, and aluminium.

HEXA-. Prefix denoting six; six times.

HEXAMETHYLENE TETRAMINE, hexamine, urotropine. $(CH_2)_6N_4$. White crystalline substance obtained by the *condensation* of *ammonia* with *formaldehyde*. Used in medicine and in the manufacture of *cyclonite*.

HEXAMINE*. Trade name for *hexamethylene tetramine*.

HEXANE. C_6H_{14}. Sixth member of the *paraffin series*. Exists in five isomeric forms (see *isomerism*). Contained in light *petroleum*; normal-hexane has b.p. 69° C. and S.G. 0·66.

HEXOGEN. See *cyclonite*.

HEXOSE. *Monosaccharide carbohydrate* whose *molecule* contains six carbon atoms, e.g. the *sugars glucose, fructose*, and *galactose*. Naturally occurring *polysaccharides* are usually made up of hexose units.

HIGH FIDELITY. See *fidelity*.

HIGH FREQUENCY. H.F. *Radio frequencies* between 3,000 and 30,000 *kilocycles* per second. See Table 6, page 336.

HIGH-FREQUENCY WELDING. Radio-frequency welding. A method of welding *thermoplastic* materials in which the *heat* required to fuse the surfaces together is generated by the application of *radio frequency electromagnetic radiation*.

HIGH-SPEED STEEL. Very hard *steel* containing 12%–22% tungsten, with chromium, vanadium, molybdenum, and small amounts of other *elements*; used for tools which remain hard even at red heat.

HIGH TENSION. High *voltage*.

HISTAMINE. $C_3H_3N_2.(CH_2)_2NH_2$. *Organic compound*, m.p. 83° C.; occurs in animal tissues when they are injured, causing dilation of blood vessels; also stimulates gastric secretion of *hydrochloric acid*.

HISTOGRAM. A type of graphical representation, used in *statistics*, in which frequency distributions are illustrated by rectangles.

HISTOLOGY. The study of the structure of the tissues and organs of living creatures.

HODOSCOPE. An apparatus for tracing the path of a charged particle (usually a *cosmic-ray* particle).

HOLE. The absence of an *electron* in the *valency* structure (see *energy bands*) of a crystalline *semiconductor*. The filling of these vacancies by electrons, which thereby create new holes, gives rise to 'hole conduction'. A hole may, therefore, be regarded as a mobile vacancy with a positive *electronic charge* and a positive *mass*, it is thus mathematically equivalent to a *positron*.

HOLMIUM. Ho. Element. A.W. 164·93. At. No. 67. See *lanthanides*.

HOLO-. Prefix denoting whole-; e.g. holohedral *crystal*, a crystal having the full number of faces for perfect symmetry.

HOMO-. Prefix denoting same-; e.g. *homogeneous*.

HOMOCYCLIC COMPOUNDS. *Organic compounds* the *molecules* of which contain a ring structure of *atoms* of the same kind (usually carbon). E.g. *benzene*, C_6H_6.

HOMOGENEOUS. Of uniform composition throughout.

HOMOLOGOUS PAIR. In *spectrographic analysis* an homologous pair consists of the particular spectral line (see *line spectrum*) utilized in the determination of the *concentration* of an *element* and an *internal standard line*, such that the ratio of the intensities of the *radiations* producing the lines remains unchanged with variations in the conditions of *excitation*.

HOMOLOGOUS SERIES. Series of chemical *compounds* of uniform chemical type, showing a regular gradation in physical properties, and capable of being represented by a general *molecular formula*, the *molecule* of each member of the series differing from the preceding one by a definite constant group of *atoms*. E.g. the *paraffin series*.

HOMOLOGUES. Members of the same *homologous series*; e.g. *methane*, CH_4, and *ethane*, C_2H_6.

HOMO-POLAR BOND. A covalent bond. See *valency, electronic theory of*.

HOOKE'S LAW. Within the *elastic limit*, a *strain* is proportional to the *stress* producing it. 'Ut tensio, sic vis.' See *elasticity, elastic modulus*.

HORIZONTAL INTENSITY of the Earth's magnetic field (see *magnetism, terrestrial*). The total *magnetic intensity* of the Earth's field may be resolved into two components, the horizontal and the vertical. If I=total intensity and ø the angle of dip (see *magnetic dip*) the horizontal intensity, $H = I \cos ø$.

HORMONES. Specific substances produced by the *endocrine glands* of higher animals, which are secreted into the *blood* and which are thus carried to all parts of the body where they regulate many metabolic functions of the *organism*. They are quick-acting and only a minute amount may have a profound effect on *metabolism*. Hormones are either *proteins* (e.g. *insulin*), *steroids* (e.g. *cortisone*), or relatively simple *organic compounds* (e.g. *adrenaline*).

HORN SILVER, cerargyrite, chlorargyrite. Natural silver chloride, AgCl. Important ore of silver.

HORNBLENDE. Rock-forming *mineral* consisting mainly of *silicates* of calcium, magnesium, and iron.

HORSE-POWER. H.P. British unit of *power*; *work* done at the rate of 550 *foot-pounds* per second. 1 H.P. = 746 *watts*.

HOT-WIRE INSTRUMENT. An electrical measuring instrument (*ammeter* or *voltmeter*) which depends upon the expansion, or change in *resistance*, of a wire which is heated by the passage of an *electric current*.

HUBBLE'S CONSTANT. The ratio of the distance between the *Local Group of galaxies* and a receding cluster of galaxies (see *expansion of the Universe*) to the rate at which the distant cluster recedes. The Hubble Constant therefore represents the hypothetical period of time since all the matter in the Universe was located in one 'super-dense' agglomeration, if it is assumed that its rate of expansion has been constant over this period. The value of Hubble's constant is variously estimated as being between 5 and 10 thousand million years.

HUMIDITY OF THE ATMOSPHERE. A measure of the *water vapour* present in the air. May be given in terms of *relative humidity*, or the 'absolute humidity' which is defined as the *mass* of *water* present in a cubic *metre* of the air.

HUMUS. Dark brown *colloidal* matter present in *soil* as the result of animal and vegetable *decomposition*. Important source of mineral nutrients for plants.

HUYGENS' CONSTRUCTION. Each point of a *wave front* may be regarded as a new source of secondary wavelets. Knowing the position of the wave front at any given time, the construction enables its position to be determined at any subsequent time.

HUYGENS' PRINCIPLE OF SUPERPOSITION. The resultant displacement at any point due to the superposition of any system of waves is equal to the sum of the displacements of the individual waves at that point. This principle forms the basis of the theory of *light interference*.

HYDRARGYRUM. See *mercury*.

HYDRATE. A *compound* containing combined *water*. Generally applied to *salts* containing *water of crystallization*.

HYDRATED. Opposite of *anhydrous*; containing chemically combined *water*; (*salt*) containing *water of crystallization*.

HYDRAULIC CEMENT. *Cement* which hardens in contact with *water*.

HYDRAULIC PRESS. Application of *Pascal's law*; a device whereby a *force* applied by a piston over a small area is transmitted through *water* to another piston having a large area; by this means very great forces may be obtained. See Fig. 9 on page 148.

HYDRAULICS. The practical application of *hydrodynamics* to engineering.

HYDRAZINE. $H_2N.NH_2$. A fuming strongly *basic liquid*, b.p. 113° C., powerful *reducing agent*.

HYDRIDE. *Binary compound* with hydrogen.

HYDRO-. Prefix denoting *water-*; e.g. *hydrogen*, water producer. In chemical nomenclature, often denotes a *compound* of hydrogen; e.g. *hydrochloric acid*.

HYDROCARBONS. *Organic compounds* which contain only carbon and hydrogen. Classified as either *aliphatic* or *aromatic compounds* (or a combination of both). Hydrocarbons may be either *saturated* or *unsaturated compounds*.

HYDROCHLORIC ACID, muriatic acid, spirits of salts. A *solution* of *hydrogen chloride*, HCl, in *water*. The concentrated *acid* contains 35%–40% HCl by weight, and is a colourless, fuming, corrosive *liquid*. Manufactured by the action of *sulphuric acid*, H_2SO_4, on *common salt*, or by the direct chemical combination of hydrogen and chlorine obtained by the *electrolysis* of brine. Used in chemical industry.

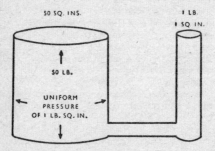

FIG. 9.

HYDROCYANIC ACID, prussic acid, hydrogen cyanide. HCN. Colourless, intensely poisonous *liquid* with a smell of bitter almonds. B.p. 26·5° C.

HYDRODYNAMICS. Mathematical study of the motion, *energy*, and *pressure* of *liquids* in motion.

HYDROELECTRIC POWER. *Electrical energy* obtained from water-power, the latter being used to drive a *dynamo*.

HYDROFLUORIC ACID. Solution of hydrogen fluoride, HF, in *water*. Term also applied to the compound HF itself, a colourless, corrosive fuming *liquid*, b.p. 19·5° C. Attacks *glass*; used for etching glass.

HYDROGEL. *Colloidal gel* in which *water* is the *solvent*.

HYDROGEN. H. Element. A.W. 1·00797 At. No. 1. Colourless, odourless, tasteless *gas*. Lightest substance known. Inflammable, combines with oxygen to form *water*. *Molecule* is *diatomic*; i.e. contains two *atoms*, written H_2. Occurs as water, H_2O; in *organic compounds*, and in all living things. Manufactured by the *Bosch process* and by *electrolysis*. Used in the *oxy-hydrogen burner*, as a *reducing agent*, in the manufacture of synthetic *ammonia* (see *fixation of atmospheric nitrogen*) and of synthetic *oil* (see

Fischer-Tropsch process) and for *hydrogenation of oils*. Three *isotopes* of hydrogen are known, the two 'heavy' isotopes, *deuterium* and *tritium*, are of importance in *nuclear physics*.

HYDROGEN ARSENIDE. See *arsine*.

HYDROGEN BOMB. See *nuclear weapons*.

HYDROGEN CHLORIDE. HCl. *Gas*, very *soluble* in *water*, giving a *solution* of *hydrochloric acid*.

HYDROGEN CYANIDE. See *hydrocyanic acid*.

HYDROGEN FLUORIDE. See *hydrofluoric acid*.

HYDROGEN ION. Positively charged hydrogen *atom*; *proton*. General properties of *acids* in *solution* are due to the presence of hydrogen ions.

HYDROGEN ION CONCENTRATION. Number of grams of *hydrogen ions* per *litre* of *solution*. Useful as a measure of the *acidity* of a solution and in this context is usually expressed in terms of $P_H = \log_{10} \dfrac{1}{[H^+]}$, where [H$^+$] is the hydrogen ion concentration. As pure *water* at ordinary *temperatures* dissociates slightly into *hydrogen ions* and *hydroxyl ions* ($H_2O \rightleftharpoons H^+ + OH^-$), the concentration of each type of ion being 10^{-7} *gram-molecules* per litre, the P_H of pure water will be $\log_{10} \dfrac{1}{10^{-7}}$ $= 7$: this figure is accordingly taken to represent neutrality on the P_H scale. If *acid* is added to water its hydrogen ion concentration will increase and its P_H will therefore decrease. Thus a P_H below 7 indicates acidity and similarly a P_H in excess of 7 indicates alkalinity.

HYDROGEN PEROXIDE, peroxide of hydrogen. H_2O_2. Thick, syrupy *liquid*, b.p. 150·2° C.; as usually sold, a *solution* of the pure compound in *water*. Gives off oxygen readily, used as a *disinfectant* and *bleaching agent*. Strength of solution usually given in terms of 'volume strength'; thus, 10 volume hydrogen peroxide will evolve 10 times its own volume of oxygen *gas*.

HYDROGEN PHOSPHIDE. See *phosphine*.

HYDROGEN SULPHIDE, sulphuretted hydrogen. H_2S. Colourless poisonous *gas* with a smell of bad eggs. Formed by the *decomposition* of organic matter containing sulphur; occurs naturally in some mineral waters. Prepared by the action of dilute *acids* on *sulphides* of *metals*; used in chemical analysis.

HYDROGENATION. Subjecting to the chemical action of, or causing to combine with, hydrogen.

HYDROGENATION OF COAL. The manufacture of artificial mineral *oil* from *coal* by the action of hydrogen; causing the carbon in coal to combine with hydrogen to form *hydrocarbons*. See *Bergius process*, *Fischer-Tropsch process*.

HYDROGENATION OF OILS. Artificial hardening of *liquid* animal and vegetable *oils* by the action of hydrogen. Liquid *fats and oils* contain a high percentage of liquid *triolein*, $C_{57}H_{104}O_6$, which may be converted into a solid *tristearin*, $C_{57}H_{110}O_6$, by the action of hydrogen in the presence of finely divided nickel which acts as a *catalyst*; the result being a hard fat of higher *melting point*.

HYDROLITH. Calcium hydride, CaH_2. Decomposed by *water*, used for the production of hydrogen, according to the equation $CaH_2 + 2H_2O = Ca(OH)_2 + 2H_2$.

HYDROLYSIS. Chemical *decomposition* of a substance by *water*, the water itself being also decomposed; reaction of the type $AB + H_2O = A(OH) + HB$. *Salts* of weak *acids*, weak *bases*, or both, are partially hydrolyzed in *solution*; *esters* may be hydrolyzed to form an *alcohol* and acid. See *saponification*.

HYDROMETER. Instrument for measuring the *density* or *specific gravity* of *liquids*. The common type consists of a weighted bulb with a graduated, slender stem; the apparatus floats vertically in the liquid being tested. In liquids of high density a greater length of stem is exposed than in liquids of low density.

HYDROPHILIC. Having an affinity for *water*. A hydrophilic *colloid* is one which readily forms a *stable solution* in *water*.

HYDROPHOBIC. Having no affinity for *water*; water-repellent. A hydrophobic *colloid* is one which will only form a *solution* in *water* with difficulty.

HYDROPONICS. Cultivation of plants without the use of *soil*, by the use of *solutions* of those mineral *salts* which a plant normally extracts from the soil.

HYDROSOL. *Colloidal solution*, as distinct from a *hydrogel*, water being the *solvent*.

HYDROSPHERE. Watery portion of the *Earth's crust*, comprising the oceans, seas, and all other waters. Composition by *weight* is given as oxygen $85 \cdot 8\%$, hydrogen $10 \cdot 7\%$, chlorine $2 \cdot 1\%$, sodium $1 \cdot 1\%$, magnesium $0 \cdot 14\%$, not more than $0 \cdot 05\%$ of any other *element* being present. The chief constituents are *water*, H_2O, *sodium chloride*, NaCl, and magnesium chloride, $MgCl_2$.

HYDROSTATICS. The mathematical study of *forces* and *pressures* in *liquids* or at rest.

HYDROXIDE. *Compound* derived from *water*, H_2O, by the replacement of one of the hydrogen *atoms* in the *molecule* by some other atom or group; compound containing the *hydroxyl group*. E.g. *sodium hydroxide*, NaOH.

HYDROXYL GROUP. The *univalent radical* or group consisting of one hydrogen and one oxygen *atom*, forming a part of a *molecule* of a *compound*. The —OH group. *Inorganic* compounds containing electro-valently bonded (see *valency, electronic theory of*) hydroxyl groups are *alkalis*; organic compounds containing covalently bonded hydroxyl groups are *alcohols*.

HYDROXYL ION. Negatively charged *ion*; free *hydroxyl group* bearing a negative *electric charge*. The presence of hydroxyl ions is the cause of the characteristic properties of *alkaline solutions*.

HYGRO-. Prefix denoting moisture, humidity. E.g. *hygrometer*.

HYGRODEIK. *Wet and dry bulb hygrometer* with a chart attached which enables the *relative humidity* to be obtained directly from the readings of the two *thermometers*.

HYGROMETER. Any instrument designed to measure the *relative humidity* of the *atmosphere*.

HYGROMETRIC STATE of the *atmosphere*. See *relative humidity*.

HYGROSCOPE. Instrument for showing variations of *relative humidity* of the air.

HYGROSCOPIC. Having a tendency to absorb moisture.

HYPER-. Prefix denoting over, above, beyond.

HYPERBOLA. Curve traced out by a point which moves so that its distance from a fixed point, the focus, always bears a constant ratio greater than unity to its distance from a fixed straight line, the directrix.

HYPERBOLIC FUNCTIONS. Six mathematical functions analogous to the *trigonometrical ratios*. The hyperbolic functions are sinh, cosh, tanh, cosech, sech, and contanh. Sinh x is defined as $\frac{1}{2}$ ($e^x - e^{-x}$) and cosh x as $\frac{1}{2}$ ($e^x + e^{-x}$). The remaining functions are derived from sinh and cosh, on the same basis as the related trigonometrical ratios.

HYPERFINE STRUCTURE OF SPECTRUM LINES. Very fine structure of certain *spectrum* lines observed when they are examined under very high resolution. The lines are caused either (a) by the presence of different *isotopes* of the *element* emitting the spectrum, or (b) if the atomic *nuclei* of the element possess a *spin*, and therefore a resultant *magnetic moment*.

HYPERMETROPIA. Long sight. Defect of vision; the subject is unable to see near objects distinctly. Corrected by the use of *convex* spectacle *lenses*

TABLE OF HYPERONS

NAME	ELECTRON MASSES	CHARGE	MEAN LIFE SECS.	DECAY PRODUCTS
Λ°	2183	0	$2\cdot5 \times 10^{-10}$	*nucleon* + *pion*
$\Sigma+$	2328	$+1$	$0\cdot8 \times 10^{-10}$	*nucleon* + *pion*
Σ°	2332	0	$< 10^{-11}$	Λ° + *photon*
$\Sigma-$	2340	-1	$1\cdot6 \times 10^{-10}$	*nucleon* + *pion*
Ξ°	2566	0	$1\cdot5 \times 10^{-10}$	Λ° + *pion*
$\Xi-$	2580	-1	$1\cdot3 \times 10^{-10}$	Λ° + *pion*

HYPEROL*. Trade name of a crystalline *compound* of *urea* and *hydrogen peroxide*; $CO(NH_2)_2.H_2O_2$. Evolves *hydrogen peroxide* by the action of *water*.

HYPERONS. A group of *elementary particles*, belonging to the class called *baryons*, which have greater *mass* than the *neutron* but very short lives. The Table on page 151 gives the known hyperons, each of which has a corresponding *anti-particle*. As all hyperons decay into nucleons, they may be regarded as excited nucleons.

HYPERSONIC. Adjective used to describe a speed in excess of Mach 5. See *Mach Number*.

HYPERTONIC. A *solution* is said to be hypertonic with respect to another if it has a greater *osmotic pressure*.

HYPNOTIC (chem.). Substance producing sleep.

HYPO-. Prefix denoting under, below.

HYPO (phot.). *Sodium thiosulphate*, $Na_2S_2O_3.5H_2O$. Formerly incorrectly called 'sodium hyposulphite'. Used in *photography*. See *fixing*.

HYPOCHLORITE. *Salt* of hypochlorous acid, HClO. Hypochlorites of sodium, potassium, and calcium are used as *disinfectants* and for *bleaching*, by virtue of their oxidizing properties.

HYPOTENUSE. The side opposite the right angle (i.e. the longest side) in a right-angled *triangle*.

HYPOTHESIS. Supposition put forward in explanation of observed facts.

HYPOTONIC. A *solution* is said to be hypotonic with respect to another if it has a smaller *osmotic pressure*.

HYPSOMETER. 'Height-measurer.' Apparatus for the determination of the *boiling point* of a *liquid*. Since the boiling points of liquids depend upon the *pressure*, and the atmospheric pressure varies with the altitude, the apparatus may be used for the determination of altitude above sea-level.

HYSTERESIS. A physical phenomenon chiefly met in the elastic and magnetic behaviour of materials. When a body is stressed, the *strain* produced is a function of the *stress*. On releasing the stress, the strain lags behind; i.e. the strain for a given value of stress is greater when the stress is decreasing than when it is increasing. On removing the stress completely, a residual strain remains. This lagging of effect behind cause is called *hysteresis*. It also occurs in induced *magnetism*. See *hysteresis cycle*.

HYSTERESIS CYCLE. Cycle of magnetizing field variations to which an initially demagnetized *ferromagnetic* substance is subjected. The magnetizing field is periodically reversed in direction until a steady state is reached in which the *magnetic induction* in the specimen at any instant is a *function* only of the magnitude of the magnetizing field and the sign of its rate of change at that instant. When this condition has been reached, a plot of induction against magnetizing field gives a 'hysteresis loop' or curve. Important magnetic properties of the substance, e.g. *coercive force*, *remanence*, the *energy* dissipated as *heat* during one cycle, etc, can be obtained from this curve.

HYSTERESIS LOOP. See *hysteresis cycle*.

I

IATROCHEMISTRY. Medieval medical *chemistry*; early attempts at the application of drugs to medicine.

ICE. *Water*, H_2O, in the *solid* state. Formed at the *freezing point* of water, $0°$ C. Less dense than water; thus water expands on freezing, and ice floats on water.

ICE POINT. The *temperature* of equilibrium between *ice* and *water* under normal atmospheric pressure (see *atmosphere, standard*); i.e. the *melting point* of ice. The ice point is assigned the value of $0°$ C. in the *Centigrade scale*.

ICONOSCOPE. A form of camera tube (see *camera, television*) in which an *electron* beam scans a *mosaic*, thus converting an optical image into an electrical signal.

-IDE. Chemical suffix denoting a *binary compound* of the two named *elements* or *radicals*; e.g. *hydrogen sulphide*, a compound of hydrogen and sulphur only.

IDEAL CRYSTAL. A *crystal* whose *lattice* is perfectly regular and which contains no foreign *atoms* or *ions* or other *defects* or imperfections.

IDEAL GAS. See *perfect gas*.

IDENTITY (math.). A statement of equality between known or unknown quantities, which holds true for all values of the unknown quantities. E.g. $3x = 2x + x$ irrespective of what value is assigned to x.

IGNIS FATUUS. Will-o'-the-wisp. Pale *flame* sometimes seen over marshy ground, probably caused by the *spontaneous combustion* of *methane*, CH_4, or other inflammable *gases*.

IGNITION. The action of setting fire to something. Initiating *combustion* by raising the *temperature* of the reactants to the *ignition temperature*; particularly the process or means of firing the explosive mixture in an *internal-combustion engine* by an *electric spark*.

IGNITION TEMPERATURE OR POINT of a substance is the *temperature* to which it must be heated before *combustion* can take place.

ILLUMINATION of a surface. The amount of *light* falling on unit area of the surface per second. Measured in *lumens* per unit area.

ILMENITE. Natural ferrous titanate, $FeTiO_3$. Ore of *titanium*.

IMAGE, REAL (phys.). An image formed by a *mirror* or *lens* at a point through which the *rays* of *light* entering the observer's eye actually pass. Such an image can be obtained on a screen.

IMAGE, VIRTUAL (phys.). An image seen at a point from which the *rays* of *light* appear to come to the observer, but do not actually do so; e.g. the image seen in a plane *mirror*. Such an image cannot be obtained on a screen placed at its apparent position, since the rays of light do not pass through that point.

IMAGINARY NUMBERS. Numbers with negative *squares*; thus $\sqrt{-1}$ is an imaginary number, denoted by i; $i^2 = -1$.

IMINO COMPOUNDS. Secondary *amines* of the form R.R′.NH where R and R′ are *alkyl radicals*.

IMMERSION OBJECTIVE, oil-immersion lens. Type of *objective* used in high-power *microscopes*, the lowest *lens* of the objective lens system being immersed in a drop of cedar-wood oil placed upon the slide to be examined. Such an arrangement causes more *light* to enter the system than if the oil were absent.

IMMISCIBLE. Incapable of being mixed to form a *homogeneous* substance; usually applied to *liquids*; e.g. *oil* and *water* are immiscible.

IMPACT. Collision of bodies. See *conservation of momentum*.

IMPEDANCE of an *alternating-current* circuit. The quantity which determines the *amplitude* of the current for a given *voltage*. For a circuit containing *resistance R*, *self-inductance L*, and *capacitance C* connected in series, the impedance of the circuit is given by the expression

$$Z = \left[R^2 + \left(L\omega - \frac{1}{C\omega} \right)^2 \right]^{\frac{1}{2}},$$ where ω is a constant, the *angular velocity*,

equal to $2\pi n$, n being the *frequency* of the alternating current.

IMPERMEABLE. Not permitting the passage of *fluids*.

IMPFING. 'Seeding' a *liquid* with a small *crystal* in order to induce crystallization.

IMPLICIT FUNCTION. A variable quantity, x, is said to be an implicit function of y, when x and y are connected by a relation which is not explicit. See *explicit function*.

IMPLOSION. The inward collapse of an evacuated vessel.

IMPULSE (phys.). Concept of a *force* acting during a very short time; given (for a constant force) by the product of the magnitude of the force and the time during which the force acts; equal to the total change of *momentum* produced by it.

IN VITRO. Said of experiments involving biological or biochemical processes which are carried out in 'glass' (i.e. after the *cells* or *tissues* in which the processes occur have been removed from the *organism* to which they belong) rather than in the living organism, when they are said to take place 'in vivo'.

IN VIVO. See *in vitro*.

INCANDESCENCE. State of glowing at high *temperatures*; white or bright-red heat.

INCIDENCE, ANGLE OF. The angle between a *ray* of *light* meeting a surface, and the *normal* to the surface at that point.

INCLINATION. See *magnetic dip*.

INCUBATOR. Box designed to maintain a constant internal *temperature* by the use of a *thermostat*; used for rearing chickens and prematurely-born infants, and in *bacteriology*.

INDETERMINANCY PRINCIPLE. See *uncertainty principle*.

INDEX (math.). The *exponent* of a quantity raised to a *power*; number indicating the power to which the quantity is raised. E.g. the index of a in $4a^5$ is 5.

INDIAN INK, Chinese ink. Black *ink* containing a *suspension* of carbon.

INDICATOR (chem.). Substance which, by a sharp *colour* change, indicates the completion of a *chemical reaction*. Frequently used in *volumetric analysis*. Indicators for *titrations* of *acids* and *alkalis* are usually weak *organic acids* or *bases*, yielding *ions* of a different colour from the un-ionized *molecules*. (See *ionization*.) E.g. *litmus* is red with acids and blue with alkalis, a change in colour indicating that *neutralization* is complete.

INDIGO. $C_{16}H_{10}N_2O_2$. Important blue *vat dye*, formerly extracted from plants of the genus Indigofera, in which it occurs as indican, a *glucoside*. Now manufactured artificially on a large scale.

INDIUM. In. Element. A.W. 114·82. At. No. 49. Soft silvery-white *metal*, S.G. 7·31, m.p. 156·4° C. *Compounds* rare. Used in electroplating and in dental *alloys*.

INDUCED CURRENT. See *induction*.

INDUCED RADIOACTIVITY. Artificial radioactivity. *Radioactivity* induced in naturally stable *elements* by bombarding them with *neutrons* or other high *energy* particles (or *photons*).

INDUCTANCE. See *self-induction*; *mutual induction*.

INDUCTION, CHARGING BY. A process of electrically charging an insulated *conductor*, using the *force* due to another nearby charge to separate the positive and negative charges existing on the conductor.

INDUCTION COIL. Instrument for producing a high *electromotive force* from a supply of low E.M.F. Essentially consists of a cylindrical soft-iron core, usually laminated to prevent losses due to *eddy currents*, round which are wound two coils, the primary and the secondary. The primary coil consists of a few hundred turns; rapid variation of an *electric current* in this coil, produced by a repeated interruption or break in the circuit by a mechanism similar to that in the electric *bell* produces an induced E.M.F. (see *induction, electromagnetic*) in the secondary coil, which contains a very large number of turns of thin wire.

INDUCTION, ELECTROMAGNETIC. When the *magnetic flux* through a circuit changes, an *electromotive force* is induced in the circuit. This phenomenon is called electromagnetic induction. The induced E.M.F. is equal to the rate of decrease of magnetic flux through the circuit (*Faraday's Law*). If the circuit is closed, this E.M.F. gives rise to an induced current, and the phenomenon forms the basis of the *dynamo*, *transformer*, etc. The induced current is in such a direction that its *magnetic field* tends to neutralize the change in magnetic flux producing it (*Lenz's Law*).

INDUCTION HEATING. A form of heating in which electrically conducting material is heated as a result of the *electric currents* induced in it by an alternating *magnetic field*.

INDUCTION, MAGNETIC. See *magnetic induction*.

INDUCTION MOTOR. A type of *electric motor* in which an *alternating current* supply fed to the primary winding sets up a flux causing *electrical currents* to be induced in the secondary winding of the *rotor*. The interaction between these currents and the flux causes the rotor to rotate.

INDUCTOMETER. A calibrated variable *inductance*.

INELASTIC COLLISION. A collision between bodies in which there is a loss of total *kinetic energy*. Referred to *nuclear physics*, an inelastic collision is one in which an incoming particle causes *excitation* or breaking up of the struck *nucleus*.

INELASTIC CROSS-SECTION. See *cross-section*.

INERT. Not easily changed by *chemical reaction*.

INERT GASES, noble gases, rare gases. The *elements* helium, neon, argon, krypton, xenon, radon. Chemically inactive, although some *compounds* have been reported. Argon occurs in appreciable amounts (0·8%) in the air; the others, with the exception of radon, occur in the air in very minute amounts.

INERTIA (phys.). Tendency of a body to preserve its state of rest or uniform motion in a straight line.

INERTIAL CONTROL. A method of automatic control used in *guided missiles* which depends upon the *forces* of *inertia*.

INFINITESIMAL. A quantity smaller than any assignable quantity; the concept is obtained by imagining a quantity decreasing indefinitely without actually becoming zero.

INFINITY. ∞. That quantity which is greater than any assignable quantity.

INFORMATION THEORY. A branch of *cybernetics* which attempts to define the amount of information required to control a process of given complexity. See *bit, noise, redundancy, equivocation, channel capacity*.

INFRA-RED RADIATION, invisible heat radiation, radiant heat. *Electromagnetic radiation* possessing *wave-lengths* between those of visible *light* and those of *radio* waves, i.e. from approximately 7500 *Ångström units* to 1 mm. Infra-red radiation has the power of penetrating *fog* or haze which would scatter ordinary visible light; thus photographs taken on a plate made sensitive to infra-red radiation may often disclose detail invisible on an ordinary plate or to the naked eye.

INFUSIBLE. Difficult to melt; having a very high *melting point*.

INFUSORIAL EARTH. See *kieselguhr*.

INJECTION MOULDING. A process by which *thermoplastic* articles are moulded. The thermoplastic material is softened in a heated chamber and then injected under pressure through an orifice into a cool closed mould.

INKS. Deeply coloured *liquids* of varied composition; many black and blue-black inks owe their colour to *organic compounds* of iron.

INORGANIC (chem.). Of *mineral* origin; not belonging to the large class of carbon *compounds* which are termed *organic*.

INORGANIC CHEMISTRY. The study of the *elements* and their *compounds*. Inorganic chemistry usually includes the study of elemental carbon, its *oxides*, *metal carbonates*, and *sulphides*, while all other carbon compounds belong to the study of *organic chemistry*.

INSECTICIDE. Substance used for killing insect pests.

INSOLATION. Exposure to the *rays* of the *Sun*.

INSOLUBLE. Not capable of forming a *solution* (in *water*, unless some other *solvent* is specified). Relative term, since most substances have been shown to dissolve in water to some extent.

INSTANTANEOUS FREQUENCY. The rate of change of *phase* of an oscillation, expressed in *radians* per second divided by 2π.

INSULATION. Prevention of the passage of *electricity*, or *heat*, by *conduction*.

INSULATOR. Non-conductor of *electricity* or *heat*.

INSULIN. *Hormone* produced in the pancreas; controls the *sugar metabolism* in the body. When injected, lowers the *blood* sugar content and so relieves the symptoms of diabetes mellitus. Insulin is one of the few *proteins* the detailed structure of which is known.

INTEGER. Whole number.

INTEGRAL. 1. Consisting of whole numbers or *integers*. 2. Mathematical *function* obtained by the process of *integration*. See Table 4, page 334.

INTEGRAL CALCULUS. Branch of the *calculus* making use of the processes of *integration*.

INTEGRATION. Mathematical process used in the *calculus*; the inverse process of *differentiation*. Gives a method of finding the areas enclosed by curves, and of finding solutions to other problems involving the summation of *infinitesimals*. See Table 4, page 334.

INTENSIFIER (phot.). A substance used to increase the density or contrast of an image on a photographic *film* or plate. Usually a *compound* from which a *metal* (e.g. silver, lead, uranium, etc.) can be deposited.

INTENSITY, ELECTRICAL. See *electric intensity*.

INTENSITY, MAGNETIC. See *magnetic intensity*.

INTENSITY OF ILLUMINATION. See *illumination*.

INTER-. Prefix denoting between, among.

INTERFACE. The surface which separates two chemical *phases*.

INTERFERENCE OF WAVE MOTIONS (phys.). The addition or combination of waves; if the crest of one wave meets the trough of another of equal *amplitude*, the wave is destroyed at that point; conversely, the super-position of one crest upon another leads to an increased effect (see also *Huygens' principle of superposition*). The *colour* effects of thin films are due to interference of *light* waves; *beats* produced by two notes of similar *frequency* are the result of the interference of *sound* waves.

INTERFEROMETER. Any instrument which divides a *beam* of *light* into a number of beams and re-unites them to produce *interference*. Uses include the accurate determination of *wave-lengths* of light, the testing of *prisms* and *lenses*, the examination of the *hyperfine structure of spectrum lines*, measurement of the diameters of *stars* and the determination of the number of light waves of a certain wave-length in the standard *metre*. See also *radio interferometer*.

INTERFERON. A *protein* which is produced in many animal *cells* as the result of the presence of *viruses* (either active or inactive) in the cell, and which appears to act as a form of protection against these viruses.

INTERGALACTIC SPACE. The *space* between *galaxies*, in which intergalactic *matter* may occur.

INTERMEDIATE FREQUENCY. In *superheterodyne radio* receivers, the carrier wave frequency of the incoming radio wave is changed to a fixed intermediate frequency by *heterodyne* action, for ease of amplification before detection.

INTERMEDIATE NEUTRONS. *Neutrons* with *kinetic energies* between those of *epithermal* and *fast neutrons*, i.e. between 100 *electron-volts* and 0·1 *Mev*.

INTERNAL-COMBUSTION ENGINE. An *engine* in which *energy* supplied by a burning *fuel* is directly transformed into *mechanical energy* by the controlled *combustion* of the fuel in an enclosed cylinder behind a piston. Usually applied to the petrol-burning or oil-burning (*Diesel*) engine.

INTERNAL STANDARD LINE. In *spectrographic analysis* an internal standard line is a line within the *line spectrum* of the material being analysed, due to a known amount of an *element* present in, or added to, the material. See also *homologous pair*.

INTERNATIONAL CANDLE. Former unit of *luminous intensity*. A point source emitting *light* uniformly in all directions at one-tenth of the rate of the *Harcourt pentane lamp* burning under specified conditions. Now replaced by the *candela*.

INTERNATIONAL TEMPERATURE SCALE. See *temperature scale, international*.

INTERPLANETARY SPACE. The *space* between the *planets* within the *solar system*.

INTERPOLATION. Filling in intermediate values or terms of a series between known values or terms.

INTERRUPTED CONTINUOUS WAVES. ICW. A *continuous wave electromagnetic radiation* which is switched on and off at an *audiofrequency*.

INTERSTELLAR MATTER. Clouds of hydrogen *atoms* or *molecules*, mixed with a small proportion of dust, which exist between *stars*. The *density* of these clouds is very low, ranging between some 10 and 1000 atoms per c.c. (compared to about 10^{19} molecules per c.c. for a *perfect gas* at *N.T.P.*).

INTERSTELLAR SPACE. The *space* between *stars* within a *galaxy*, in which *interstellar matter* may occur.

INTERSTITIAL. An additional *atom* or *ion* situated between the normal sites in a *crystal lattice*, causing a *defect*.

INTERSTITIAL COMPOUND. See *compound, interstitial*.

INTRA-. Prefix denoting within; e.g. intra-molecular *forces* are forces within the *molecule*, while inter-molecular forces are forces between molecules.

INTRINSIC ENERGY. It is assumed in calculations in *thermochemistry* that every substance possesses a definite quantity of intrinsic *energy*, i.e. energy which is inherent in the substance, and which may be in part released in the form of *heat* if the substance takes part in a *chemical reaction*. In a chemical action, no energy is gained or lost, and the sum of the intrinsic energies of the reacting substances is equal to the sum of the intrinsic energies of the final products plus or minus the energy given out or absorbed as heat during the reaction. See *Hess's law*. In *thermodynamics* the intrinsic energy of a material system is its total store of energy of all kinds. The absolute magnitude is not usually important, but changes in the intrinsic energy of a system, which depend only upon its initial and final conditions (and are therefore independent of the path of change), are used in thermodynamic calculations.

INTRINSIC SEMICONDUCTOR. See *extrinsic semiconductor*.

INULIN. A *soluble polysaccharide* consisting of *fructose* units; occurs in many plants as a stored food.

INVAR*. *Alloy* containing $63 \cdot 8\%$ iron, 36% nickel, $0 \cdot 2\%$ carbon. Has a very low coefficient of *expansion*. Used for balance wheels of watches and in other accurate instruments which would otherwise be affected by *temperature* changes.

INVERSE SQUARE LAW. A law which states that the intensity of an effect at a point B due to a source at A varies inversely as the *square* of the distance AB. Examples include the *illumination* of a surface, *gravitational field*, field due to an *electric charge*, etc. Thus, the illumination of a surface 1 foot away from a source will be 9 times as great as that of a surface 3 feet away.

INVERSE TRIGONOMETRICAL FUNCTIONS. If $y = \sin x$ (see *trigonometrical ratios*), then the inverse trigonometrical function of x is $\sin^{-1}y$ (or arc sin y), where $\sin^{-1}y$ is the *angle* whose sine is y. Similar inverse functions exist for the other trigonometrical ratios.

INVERSE VARIATION. One quantity is said to vary inversely as another, or to be inversely proportional to another, if the *product* of the two is a constant.

INVERSION OF CANE-SUGAR. The conversion of *cane-sugar* (*sucrose*, $C_{12}H_{22}O_{11}$) into a mixture of equal amounts of *glucose* and *laevulose*, two isomeric sugars (see *isomerism*) having the formula $C_6H_{12}O_6$. The action is one of *hydrolysis* and may be carried out by the action of the *enzyme invertase*, or by boiling with dilute *acids*. The resulting mixture is *laevorotatory*, while a solution of cane-sugar is *dextrorotatory*, inversion of the *optical rotation* being thus obtained.

INVERSION TEMPERATURE. See *Joule-Thomson effect.*

INVERT SUGAR. Mixture of *glucose* and *laevulose* in equal proportions, obtained by the *inversion of cane-sugar.*

INVERTASE, sucrase. *Enzyme* contained in *yeast*; converts *cane-sugar* into *glucose* and *laevulose.* See *inversion of cane-sugar.*

INVERTER. A device for converting *direct current* into *alternating current.*

IODIDE. *Binary compound* with iodine; *salt* of hydriodic acid, HI.

IODINE. I. Element. A.W. 126·90. At. No. 53. Blackish-grey, crystalline *solid.* S.G. 4·95. M.p. 114° C. B.p. 184° C. Very *volatile,* gives rise to a violet *vapour.* Very slightly *soluble* in *water,* readily soluble in *alcohol* (giving 'tincture of iodine') and in potassium iodide solution, KI. *Compounds* occur in seaweed; sodium iodate, $NaIO_3$, occurs in crude *Chile saltpetre.* Essential to the functioning of the thyroid gland; lack of iodine in the diet is a cause of goitre. Used in medicine, chemical *analysis,* and *photography.*

IODINE VALUE. A measure of the amount of *unsaturated fatty acid* present in a sample of *fat, oil, resin,* or other natural product. The *weight* of iodine absorbed by 100 *gm.* of the substance.

IODOFORM. CHI_3. Yellow, crystalline *solid* with a peculiar odour. M.p. 119° C. Used as an *antiseptic.*

ION. Electrically charged *atom* or group of atoms. Positively charged ions (*cations*) have fewer *electrons* than is necessary for the atom or group to be electrically neutral; negative ions (*anions*) have more. Thus, the *proton,* the hydrogen atom without its circum-nuclear electron, is a *hydrogen ion*; the *alpha-particle* is a helium ion. Gaseous ions can be produced in *gases* by *electric sparks,* the passage of energetic charged particles, *X-rays, gamma-rays, ultra-violet radiation,* etc. Ions in *solution* are due to the *ionization* of the dissolved substance (see *ionic hypothesis*).

ION EXCHANGE. Certain substances have the power of acting on *solutions* containing *ions,* such as solutions of *salts,* and replacing some of the ions by others; e.g. in a typical *cation* exchange ('base exchange') action, when *hard water* is passed through a suitable ion exchange resin or a *zeolite,* the calcium ions in the water are replaced by sodium ions. In *anion* exchange *acid radicals* or anions are exchanged similarly. Ion exchange has many important industrial uses in addition to water softening.

ION MOBILITY. The *velocity* of an *ion* in a unit *electric field.*

IONIC CRYSTAL. See *electrovalent crystal.*

IONIC HYPOTHESIS. Originally introduced to explain the phenomena of *electrolysis,* etc. Ionic *compounds* consist of oppositely charged *atoms* or groups of atoms termed *ions.* When an *electric current* is passed through such a compound in the dissolved or molten state, the ions are attracted to the oppositely charged *electrodes.*

IONIZATION. The formation of *ions.*

IONIZATION CHAMBER. A device for measuring the amount of *ionizing radiation.* Consists of a gas-filled chamber containing two *electrodes* (one of which may be the chamber wall) between which a *potential difference* is maintained. The radiation ionizes gas in the chamber and an instrument connected to one electrode measures the *ionization current* produced.

IONIZATION CURRENT. The *electric current* produced by the movement of *ions* or *electrons* in an *electric field* as a result of *ionizing radiation*.

IONIZATION POTENTIAL. The *work* which must be done, measured in *electron-volts*, to remove an *electron* from an *atom*. See *atom, structure of*.

IONIZING RADIATION. *Radiation* (either *electromagnetic* or corpuscular) which is capable of causing *ionization*, either directly or indirectly. *Electrons* and *alpha particles* are considerably more effective in this respect than *neutrons* or *gamma-rays*.

IONOSPHERE. The region of the Earth's *upper atmosphere* in which *free electrons* arising from *ionization* occur, mainly as a result of *ultra-violet radiation* and *X-rays* from the *Sun*. The ionosphere is useful in that it enables inter-continental *radio* transmission round the curved surface of the Earth to be achieved, as a result of its property of reflecting *electromagnetic radiations* of *radio frequencies* (see *sky wave*); but it is an obstacle to *radio astronomy* because it reflects a large proportion of the radiation that arrives from extra-terrestrial sources. The ionosphere is usually divided into three regions: the D-region between 50 and 90 kilometres above the Earth, the E-region (the *Heaviside-Kennelly layer*) between 90 and 150 kms., and the F-region (the Appleton layer) above 150 kms. At night the electron concentration in the E-region falls off due to recombination with *ions*, but the F-region remains substantially ionized owing to the lower *density* of ions and their consequent infrequency of collisions with electrons. With the advent of artificial Earth *satellites* it is now possible to study the electron density of the different regions of the ionosphere from the top side.

IONOSPHERIC WAVE. See *sky wave*.

IRIDIUM. Ir. Element. A.W. 192·2. At. No. 77. Rare *metal* resembling, and occurring together with, platinum. S.G. 22·42, m.p. 2454° C. Extremely hard and resistant to chemical action. *Alloys* of platinum and iridium are used for fountain-pen nib-tips, *crucibles* for fine analytical work, and numerous other purposes where extreme hardness and a high *melting point* are required.

IRIS. 1. The coloured part of the eye of vertebrates. 2. A diaphragm forming an adjustable opening over a *lens* in an optical instrument.

IRON. Fe. (Ferrum.) Element. A.W. 55·847. At. No. 26. White, magnetic *metal*, S.G. 7·86, m.p. 1535° C. Physical properties are greatly modified by the presence of small amounts of other metals and of carbon. Occurs as *magnetite*, Fe_3O_4; *haematite*, Fe_2O_3; *siderite*, $FeCO_3$; *limonite*, hydrated Fe_2O_3; and as *pyrites* in combination with sulphur. Extracted by the *blast furnace* process. According to the method and conditions of working and cooling, the carbon in iron and *steel* may be present in various forms, upon which the particular properties of the metal depend. *Compounds* of iron are essential to the higher forms of life. See *pig iron, cast iron, wrought iron*.

IRON ALUM. See *ferric alum*.

IRON, COMPOUNDS OF. See under the required *ferric* or *ferrous* compound.

IRRADIATION. Exposure to *radiation* of any kind. Artificial *radioactive isotopes* are made by irradiation of stable isotopes with *neutrons* in a *nuclear reactor*. Intense irradiation can alter the physical and chemical properties of *solids*, but even small doses may be used for sterilization of food owing to the sensitivity of biological *cells* to irradiation by *ionizing radiation*.

IRREVERSIBLE PROCESS. Term of considerable importance in *thermodynamics*. Any but a completely *reversible process*.

IRREVERSIBLE REACTION. A *chemical reaction* which proceeds to completion, and in which the resulting products do not react to form the original substances. See *chemical equilibrium*.

IRRITABILITY. The property of living *organisms* which enables them to respond to external stimuli.

ISENTROPIC. Of equal *entropy*.

ISINGLASS. Product containing about 90% *gelatin*. Made from the swimming bladders of fish. Used for clarifying alcoholic beverages.

ISLAND UNIVERSES. See *galaxies*.

ISO-. Prefix denoting equal.

ISOBAR. Line connecting points having equal (atmospheric) *pressure*.

ISOBARIC SURFACE. Surface of equal (atmospheric) *pressure*. An altimeter will record constant height when moving along such a surface. The intersection of an isobaric surface with the ground is along an *isobar*.

ISOBARS. *Isotopes* of different *elements*, which although having different *atomic numbers*, have identical *mass numbers*. E.g. the tin isotope, $^{115}_{50}Sn$, and the indium isotope, $^{115}_{49}In$, are isobars, 115 being the mass number and 50 and 49 the atomic numbers. Isobars have the same number of *nucleons*, but different numbers of *protons* in their *nuclei*.

ISOCHORE. A line which graphically represents the relationship between the *pressure* and the *temperature* of a *liquid* or *gas*, the *volume* of the system being kept constant.

ISOCHROMATIC FILM. See *orthochromatic film*.

ISOCLINAL. Line connecting points of equal angle of *magnetic dip*.

ISODIAPHERES. *Nuclides* in which the difference between the number of *neutrons* and *protons* is the same, e.g. a nuclide and its *decay* product after it has emitted an *alpha-particle* are isodiapheres.

ISODIMORPHISM. The phenomenon of a *dimorphous* substance being isomorphous (see *isomorphism*) with another dimorphous substance in both its forms.

ISODYNAMIC LINE. Line passing through points of equal *horizontal intensity* of the Earth's magnetic field (see *magnetism, terrestrial*).

ISOELECTRIC POINT. The *pH value* at which a substance or system (e.g. a *protein solution*) is electrically *neutral*; at this value *electrophoresis* does not occur when a direct *electric current* is applied.

ISOGONAL LINE. Line passing through points of equal *magnetic declination*.

ISOGONISM (chem.). Type of *isomorphism* where two substances having little or no chemical resemblance have the same crystalline form.

ISOMERISM. 1. Existence of two or more chemical *compounds* with the same *molecular formula* but having different properties owing to a different arrangement of *atoms* within the *molecule*. E.g. ammonium cyanate, NH_4CNO, and *urea* $CO(NH_2)_2$ are isomers. 2. In *nuclear physics nuclei* having the same *atomic number* and the same *mass number*, but which exist in different *energy* states are said to be isomeric. E.g. a nucleus in its *ground state* and a nucleus in a *metastable* excited state are isomers.

ISOMERS. See *isomerism*.

ISOMORPHISM. Similarity or identity of crystalline form, usually indicating similar or analogous chemical composition; e.g. the *alums* are isomorphous.

ISOPRENE. $CH_2:CH.C(CH_3):CH_2$. Colourless *liquid*, b.p. $34°$ C. Natural *rubber* consists mainly of a polymer of isoprene. See *polymerization*.

ISOSCELES TRIANGLE. *Triangle* having two of its sides equal.

ISOSTERISM. Phenomenon of substances having *molecules* with the same number of *atoms* and the same total number of *electrons*; this leads to similarity in physical properties. E.g. *carbon dioxide*, CO_2, and *nitrous oxide*, N_2O.

ISOTHERM, isothermal line. Line connecting points at an equal *temperature*.

ISOTHERMAL CHANGE. Change taking place at constant *temperature*. E.g. the isothermal *expansion of a gas*. See *adiabatic*.

ISOTONES. *Atoms* whose *nuclei* contain the same number of *neutrons*, but which are of different *atomic number*.

ISOTONIC SOLUTIONS. *Solutions* having the same *osmotic pressure*, being of the same *molecular concentration*.

ISOTOPES. *Atoms* of the same *element* (i.e. having the same *atomic number*) which differ in *mass number* are called isotopes of that element. The isotopes of an element are identical in chemical properties, and in all physical properties except those determined by the *mass* of the atom. The different isotopes of an element contain different numbers of *neutrons* in their *nuclei*. Nearly all elements found in nature are mixtures of several isotopes. See *atom, structure of*.

ISOTOPES, SEPARATION OF. As the *isotopes* of an *element* have identical chemical properties but some slightly different physical properties, their separation depends upon physical operations. The following methods are used: *diffusion* (either *gaseous* or *thermal*); *distillation*; centrifuging of *gases* or *liquids*; *electrolysis* (depending upon different rates of discharge or *ionic mobility* of isotopic *ions*); electromagnetic or electrostatic methods (depending upon different mass-to-charge ratios between isotopic ions and their consequent separation in a steady *magnetic field* or an *electric field* varied at *radio frequencies*).

ISOTOPIC NUMBER. Neutron excess. The difference between the number of *neutrons* in an *isotope* and the number of *protons*.

ISOTOPIC SPIN. Isobaric spin. A *quantum number*, T, used to work out the properties of groups of *elementary particles* when the members of the group are identical in all respects except that of *electric charge*. E.g. the *nucleon* has isotopic spin, $T = \frac{1}{2}$, and its two states, the *proton* and the *neutron* are then described as different orientations of that spin in a fictitious 'isotopic space'. The word 'spin' is not intended to imply any conventional image of rotation in this context, it is used in analogy to *angular momentum* to which the concept of isotopic spin bears a close formal resemblance. Isotopic spin is conserved in all *strong nuclear interactions*.

ISOTOPIC WEIGHT. The *atomic weight* of an individual *isotope*. Isotopic weights are very nearly *integral* (whole numbers), the *integer* being called the *mass number* of the isotope concerned.

ISOTROPIC. Substances exhibiting uniform properties throughout, in all directions.

-ITE. Suffix denoting, in chemical nomenclature, a *salt* of the corresponding -ous *acid*; e.g. *sulphite* from sulphurous acid.

IVORY BLACK. Form of carbon obtained from *animal charcoal*, by dissolving out *inorganic compounds*, such as calcium phosphate, by means of *hydrochloric acid*.

J

JASPER. Coloured impure form of natural *silica*, SiO_2.

JAVELLE WATER, eau de Javelle. *Solution* containing potassium hypochlorite, KOCl; made by the action of chlorine on a cold solution of *potassium hydroxide*, KOH. Used for *bleaching* and as a *disinfectant*.

JET. Very hard, lustrous form of natural carbon, allied to *coal*.

JOULE, THE. Unit of *work*. 1 joule = 10^7 ergs. The work done in 1 second by a current of 1 *ampere* flowing through a *resistance* of 1 *ohm*.

JOULE'S EQUIVALENT. See *mechanical equivalent of heat*.

JOULE'S LAWS. 1. The *intrinsic energy* of a *gas* at constant *temperature* is independent of its *volume*. Joule's law is obeyed strictly only by a *perfect gas*, real gases show deviations from it. 2. The *heat* produced by an *electric current* I, passing through a *conductor* of *resistance* R, for a time t, is proportional to I^2Rt.

JOULE-THOMSON EFFECT, Joule-Kelvin effect. When a *gas* expands through a porous plug, a change of *temperature* occurs, proportional to the *pressure* difference across the plug. The temperature change is due partly to a departure of the gas from *Joule's law*, the gas performing internal work in overcoming the mutual attractions of its *molecules* and thus cooling itself; and partly to deviation of the gas from *Boyle's law*. The latter effect can give rise either to cooling or heating, depending upon the initial temperature and pressure difference used. For a given mean pressure, the temperature at which the two effects balance, resulting in no alteration of temperature, is called the 'inversion temperature'. Gases expanding through a porous plug below their inversion temperature are cooled, otherwise they are heated.

JUNCTION RECTIFIER. A *rectifier* based upon a *semiconductor junction*.

JUNCTION TRANSISTOR. A *transistor* having a *base electrode* and two or more electrodes connected to *semiconductor junctions*.

JUPITER (astr.). *Planet*, having twelve small *satellites*, with its *orbit* between those of *Mars* and *Saturn*. Largest of the planets, diameter 88,730 miles. Mean distance from the *Sun* = 483·64 million miles. *Sidereal period* ('year') = 11·86 years. *Mass* approximately 317·89 times that of the *Earth*. Surface temperature probably about − 150° C.

K

KAINITE. Double *salt* of magnesium sulphate and potassium chloride, $MgSO_4.KCl.3H_2O$. Occurs naturally in Poland and in the *Stassfurt Deposits*. Valuable source of potassium salts.

KALIUM. See *potassium*.

KAOLIN. See *China clay*.

KATABOLISM. See *catabolism*.

KATHODE. Negative *electrode*. See *cathode*.

KATION. See *cation*.

KEEPERS OF MAGNETS. Short bars of soft iron used to prevent permanent *magnets* from losing their *magnetism*.

KELP. Sea-weed or its *ash*, used as a source of iodine.

KELVIN EFFECT. See *Thomson effect*.

KELVIN SCALE OF TEMPERATURE. The same as the *absolute thermodynamic temperature*. The Kelvin scale was redefined in 1954, being based upon the *triple point* of *water* as the fundamental fixed point, attributing to it the temperature of 273·16° K. exactly.

KEPLER'S LAWS. 1. The *planets* move about the *Sun* in *ellipses,* at one focus of which the Sun is situated. 2. The *radius vector* joining each planet with the Sun describes equal areas in equal times. 3. The ratio of the *square* of the planet's year to the cube of the planet's mean distance from the Sun is the same for all planets.

KERATIN. *Protein* forming the principal constituent of wool, hair, horns, and hoofs.

KEROSENE, kerosine. See *paraffin oil*

KERR EFFECT. When *plane-polarized light* is reflected from a highly polished *pole* of an *electromagnet* the light becomes *elliptically polarized*. Similarly, if a *beam* of light is passed through certain transparent *liquids* or *solids* to which a *potential difference* is applied, the plane of polarization of the light is rotated through an angle which depends upon the magnitude of the applied potential difference. This effect is made use of in the 'Kerr cell'.

KETEN(E). $CH_2:CO$. Colourless *gas*, first member of the ketene series of the general formula $CR_2:CO$.

KETO-ENOL TAUTOMERISM. The type of *tautomerism* which occurs in *ketones* as the result of the migration of a hydrogen *atom* from an *alkyl group* to the *carbonyl group*. Thus, *acetone* contains in addition to ketone *molecules* ($CH_3.CO.CH_3$, the keto-form) a small proportion of molecules having the structure of an *unsaturated alcohol* ($CH_2:COH.CH_3$, the enol-form).

KETONES, THE. Series of *organic compounds* having the general formula $RR'\,C:O$, where R and R' are *univalent hydrocarbon radicals*. E.g. *acetone*, dimethyl ketone, $(CH_3)_2CO$.

KEV. Symbol for 1000 *electron-volts*.

KICKSORTER. See *pulse height analyser*.

KIESELGUHR, diatomaceous earth, infusorial earth. Mass of *hydrated silica* (SiO_2) formed from skeletons of minute plants known as diatoms. Very porous and absorbent. Used for filtering and absorbing various *liquids*, in the manufacture of *dynamite* and in other industries.

KILLED SPIRITS OF SALTS. *Solution* of zinc chloride, $ZnCl_2$, made by acting with zinc on *hydrochloric acid*. Used in soldering.

KILO-. Prefix denoting a thousand, thousandfold, in the *metric system*.

KILOCYCLE. Measure of *frequency*. 1000 *cycles*.

KILOGRAM, kilogramme. 1000 *grams*. Practical continental unit of *mass* and *weight* represented by the international prototype preserved in Paris. 2·2046 lb.

KILOMETRE. 1000 *metres*. Practical continental unit of distance. 1094 yards, 0·6214 mile.

KILOTON BOMB. A *nuclear weapon* with an explosive power equivalent to one thousand tons of *T.N.T.* (approximately 10^{12} *calories*).

KILOWATT. Unit of *power*. 1000 *watts*.

KILOWATT-HOUR, Board of Trade unit. Practical unit of *work*. Work done when a rate of work of 1000 *watts* is maintained for 1 hour.

KINEMATICS. The branch of *mechanics* which is concerned with the phenomena of motion without reference to *mass* or *force*. Kinematics deals with motion from the standpoint of measurement and precise description, while *dynamics* is concerned with the causes or laws of motion.

KINETIC ENERGY. The *energy* which a body possesses by virtue of its motion. The kinetic energy of a *mass* m, moving with *velocity* v, is $\frac{1}{2}mv^2$. The energy will be in *ergs* if m is in grams and v is in cm. per second. The kinetic energy of rotation of a body whose *moment of inertia* about an *axis* is I, and whose *angular velocity* about this axis is ω, is $\frac{1}{2}I\omega^2$. Again the energy will be in ergs if I is in gm.cm^2 and ω is in *radians* per second.

KINETIC THEORY OF GASES. Mathematical explanation of the behaviour of *gases* on the assumption that gases consist of *molecules* which are in ceaseless motion in space, the *kinetic energy* of the molecules depending upon the *temperature* of the gas; the molecules are considered to be perfectly elastic particles which collide with each other and with the walls of the containing vessel. The *pressure* exerted by a gas on the walls of the vessel is due to the collisions of the molecules with it. The *gas laws* may be shown to be in full agreement with this theory.

KINK INSTABILITY. In a *thermonuclear reaction* experiment, an instability in the magnetically confined *plasma* resulting from a local deformation of the plasma. The kink tends to grow because the *magnetic lines of forces* of the self-induced confining field are crowded on the *concave* side of the kink.

KIPP'S APPARATUS. Device used in laboratories for the production of a supply of any *gas* which can be evolved by the action of a *liquid* on a *solid* without heating.

KIRCHHOFF'S LAWS.   I. In any network of wires the algebraic sum of the *electric currents* which meet at a point is zero.   2. The algebraic sum of the *electromotive forces* in any closed circuit or mesh is equal to the algebraic sum of the products of the *resistances* of each portion of the circuit and the currents flowing through them.

KISH. Variety of *graphite* occasionally formed in iron *smelting* furnaces.

KJELDAHL FLASK. A round-bottomed glass flask with a long wide neck, used in the estimation of nitrogen by the Kjeldahl method.

KLYSTRON. An *electron* tube used to generate or amplify *electromagnetic radiation* in the *microwave* region, by *velocity modulation*. Consists of two or more *resonant cavities* in which the electrons, from an *electron gun,* are concentrated into 'bunches'.

KNOCKING in the *internal-combustion* (petrol) *engine.* Violent *explosions* in the cylinder, often due to over-compression of the *mixture* of air and petrol vapour before sparking.

KNOCK-ON COLLISION (phys.). A process in which an *elementary particle* or *nucleus* is set in motion by being struck by another high *energy* particle (or *photon*). The term is also used in relation to collisions as a result of which an *electron* is knocked out of its atomic *orbit* by some other particle. The 'knock-on' particle is the particle set in motion as the result of the collision.

KNOT. Unit of speed; I *nautical mile* per hour.

KOLRAUSCH'S LAW. When *ionization* is complete, the *conductivity* of an *electrolyte* is equal to the sum of the conductivities of the *ions* into which the substance dissociates.

KOVAR*. An *alloy* of cobalt, iron, and nickel which has a coefficient of *expansion* similar to that of *glass*. Used for glass-to-metal seals, particularly in *thermionic valves* and *transistors*.

KREBS CYCLE. See *citric acid cycle*.

KRYPTOL*. Mixture of *graphite, carborundum*, and *clay*, used as an electrical *resistance* in electric furnaces.

KRYPTON. Kr. Element. A.W. 83·80. At. No. 36. *Inert gas*, occurs in the *atmosphere* (1 part in 670,000).

KUPFER-NICKEL. Natural nickel arsenide, NiAs. Important ore of nickel.

L

LABELLED COMPOUND. A *compound* in which a stable *atom* is replaced by a *radioactive isotope* of that atom. The path taken through a mechanical or biological system by such a labelled compound can be traced by the *radiation* emitted by the 'labelled atom'. See also *radioactive tracing* and *tritiated compound*.

LABILE. Prone to undergo change or displacement; unstable.

LACHRYMATOR. See *tear-gas*.

LACTASE. *Enzyme* which catalyses the conversion of *lactose* into *glucose*. Present in the digestive juices of mammals.

LACTIC ACID. $CH_3CH(OH)COOH$. *Organic acid*, occurring in three stereoisomeric forms (see *stereoisomerism*). Colourless crystalline *solid*, m.p. 18° C. *dl*-lactic acid, a mixture of equal amounts of (*dextrorotatory*) *d*-acid and (*laevorotatory*) *l*-acid, is formed by the action of certain *bacteria* on the *lactose* of milk during souring. The *d*-form, sarcolactic acid, occurs in muscle tissue. The optically inactive *dl*-form is used in dyeing and *tanning*.

LACTOSE, milk sugar. $C_{12}H_{22}O_{11}$. Hard, gritty, crystalline, *soluble*, *disaccharide sugar*, m.p. 203° C., less sweet than *cane-sugar*. Occurs in the milk of all mammals. *Hydrolysis* gives a mixture of *glucose* and *galactose*. In the action of certain *bacteria* on milk ('lactic acid fermentation') lactose is converted into *lactic acid*.

LAEVOROTATORY. Rotating or deviating the plane of vibration of *polarized light* to the left (observer looking against the oncoming light). See *optical activity*.

LAEVULOSE, fructose, fruit sugar. $C_6H_{12}O_6$. See *fructose*.

LAKE. In dyeing, a coloured *insoluble* substance formed by the chemical combination of a *soluble dye* with a *mordant*.

LAMBERT. A unit of *luminance*. The luminance of a uniform diffuser of *light* which emits one *lumen* per sq. cm.

LAMBERT'S LAW OF ILLUMINATION. The *illumination* of a surface upon which the *light* falls normally from a *point source*, is inversely proportional to the *square* of the distance between the surface and the source. If the *normal* to the surface makes an angle θ with the direction of the *rays*, then the illumination is proportional to cos θ.

LAMINA. A thin sheet.

LAMINAR FLOW. The flow of a *fluid* which closely follows the shape of a streamlined surface without turbulence.

LAMINATED IRON. Thin sheets of iron (or, more frequently *stalloy**) used for cores of *transformers* instead of solid iron cores, in order to reduce losses due to *eddy currents*.

LAMP-BLACK. Soot; *allotropic* form of *carbon*.

LANOLINE. *Wax*-like material obtained from wool-grease. Contains *cholesterol*, $C_{27}H_{45}OH$, and other complex *organic* substances. Readily absorbed by the skin; used in ointments and cosmetics.

LANTHANIDES. Lanthanons. Rare earths. Group of rare metallic *elements* with *atomic numbers* from 57 to 71 inclusive. The properties of these *metals* are all very similar and resemble those of aluminium. The elements occur in *monazite* and other rare minerals. See Table 5, page 335.

LANTHANUM. La. Element. A.W. 138·91. At. No. 57. See *lanthanides*.

LAPIS LAZULI. Sodium aluminium silicate containing sulphur. Rare mineral of beautiful blue colour.

LARGE CALORIE, kilogram-calorie, Calorie. 1000 *calories*.

LARMOR PRECESSION. The orbital motion of the *electrons* about the *nucleus* of an *atom* is usually such as to give the atom a *resultant angular momentum* and a *magnetic moment*. These two properties cause the atom to precess (see *precessional motion*) about the direction of any applied *magnetic field*. This is Larmor precession, and its *frequency* is the Larmor frequency.

LASER. Light Amplification by Stimulated Emission of Radiation. An optical *maser*. The laser produces a powerful, highly directional, *monochromatic*, and *coherent* beam of *light*. It works on essentially the same principle as the maser, except that the 'active medium' consists of, or is contained in, an optically transparent cylinder with a reflecting surface at one end and a partially reflecting surface at the other. The stimulated waves make repeated passages up and down the cylinder, some of them emerging as light through the partially reflecting end. In the *ruby* laser, the chromium *atoms* of a cylindrical shaped ruby *crystal* are 'pumped' to an excited state (see *excitation*) by a flash lamp, and it can then be made to emit *pulses* of highly coherent light. Lasers have also been constructed using a mixture of *inert gases* (helium and neon) to produce a continuous beam. Another type of laser consists of a cube of specially treated gallium arsenide, which is capable of emitting *infra-red radiation* when a current is passed through it.

LATENT HEAT. See *heat, latent*.

LATERAL. In a sideways direction.

LATERAL INVERSION. The inversion produced by a plane *mirror*. Seen when the image of a printed page is observed in a mirror.

LATEX. Milky fluid produced by certain plants, contains *proteins, carbohydrates, lipids, alkaloids, gums*, etc. The most important is the latex from *rubber* trees which yields natural rubber on coagulation.

LATITUDE of a point of the Earth's surface is its *angular distance* from the *equator* measured upon the curved surface of the Earth.

LATITUDE, LINES OF; parallels of latitude. Circles parallel to the *equator*, joining points of equal *latitude*; the equator itself is latitude 0°, while the poles are latitude 90°.

LATTICE. 1. The regular network of fixed points about which *molecules*, *atoms*, or *ions* vibrate in a *crystal*. 2. In a *nuclear reactor*, a structure consisting of discrete bodies of *fissile* and non-fissile material (especially *moderator*), arranged in a regular geometrical pattern, is called a lattice.

LATTICE ENERGY. The *energy* required to separate the *ions* of a *crystal* to an infinite distance from each other.

LAUDANUM. Alcoholic *tincture* of *opium*.

LAUGHING GAS, nitrous oxide. N_2O. Colourless gas with a sweetish taste, used as a mild *anaesthetic* in dentistry, etc.

LAURYL ALCOHOL. $C_{12}H_{25}OH$. Crystalline *solid*, m.p. 24° C., used in the manufacture of *detergents*.

LAWRENCIUM. Lw. *Transuranic element*, At. No. 103. The last element to be produced, the only known *isotope*, $^{257}_{103}Lw$, has *half-life* of only 8 Secs.

LD50. See *median lethal dose*.

LEACHING. Washing out a *soluble* constituent.

LEAD. Pb. (Plumbum.) Element. A.W. 207·19. At. No. 82. Soft, bluish-white *metal*, S.G. 11·34, m.p. 327·4° C. Occurs chiefly as *galena*, PbS. Extracted by roasting the ore in a *reverberatory furnace*. *Compounds* are poisonous. Metal is used in the lead *accumulator*, in *alloys* and in plumbing; compounds are used in *paint* manufacture.

LEAD ACCUMULATOR. See *accumulator*.

LEAD ACETATE, sugar of lead. $(CH_3COO)_2Pb.3H_2O$. White crystalline *soluble salt*, m.p. 280° C., with a sweet taste.

LEAD-CHAMBER PROCESS. Manufacture of *sulphuric acid* by the action of *nitrogen dioxide*, NO_2, on *sulphur dioxide*, SO_2, to give *nitric oxide*, NO, and *sulphur trioxide*, SO_3. The former reacts with oxygen from the *air* to give NO_2 again; the SO_3 combines with *water* to give sulphuric acid, the process being carried out in large lead chambers.

LEAD DIOXIDE, lead peroxide. PbO_2. *Amorphous*, dark brown powder.

LEAD MONOXIDE. See *litharge*.

LEAD PEROXIDE. See *lead dioxide*.

LEAD, RED. See *red lead*.

LEAD, WHITE. See *white lead*.

LEBLANC PROCESS, salt-cake process. Almost obsolete process for the manufacture of *sodium carbonate*, Na_2CO_3. *Common salt* is converted into *sodium sulphate*, Na_2SO_4 ('salt-cake') by heating with *sulphuric acid*. This is heated with *coal* and *limestone*; the sodium sulphate is reduced by the carbon to sodium sulphide, which then reacts with the limestone to give sodium carbonate and calcium sulphide.

LE CHATELIER PRINCIPLE. If a system in *equilibrium* is subjected to a *stress*, the system tends to react in such a way as to oppose the effect of the stress.

LECITHINS. Class of *organic compounds* occurring in living *organisms*.

Chemically very similar to *fats*, but the *molecule* contains the *elements* nitrogen and phosphorus in addition to carbon, hydrogen, and oxygen.

LECLANCHÉ CELL. *Primary cell* with a positive *electrode* or pole of carbon surrounded by a mixture of *manganese dioxide* and powdered carbon in a porous pot. This stands in a *solution* of *ammonium chloride*, the *electrolyte*, in a jar which also contains the negative electrode of zinc. When the external circuit is completed, a current flows, chlorine *ions* in the electrolyte moving towards the zinc and ammonium ions towards the carbon electrode. The chlorine ions react with the zinc to form zinc chloride, and the ammonium ions decompose at the positive electrode to give *ammonia* and hydrogen. The hydrogen liberated tends to cause *polarization* of the cell. This tendency is partly counteracted by the manganese dioxide, which oxidizes the hydrogen. The *E.M.F.* is approximately 1·5 *volts*. Leclanché cells are widely used for many purposes which require an intermittent current. The common *dry cell* is a special form of Leclanché cell.

LENGTH, BRITISH UNITS OF.

12 lines	= 1 inch	= 2·5400 cm.
12 ins	= 1 foot.	
3 ft	= 1 yard	= 0·9144 metre.
22 yds	= 1 chain.	
10 chains	= 1 furlong	= 201·17 metres.
8 fur.	= 1 mile	= 1609·3 metres.

LENGTH, METRIC UNITS OF.

10 millimetres	= 1 centimetre	= 0·3937 inch.
100 cm.	= 1 metre	= 1·0936 yard.
1000 m.	= 1 kilometre	= 0·62137 mile.

LENS. Any device which causes a *beam* of *rays* to converge or diverge on passing through it. The optical lens is a portion of a *transparent* refracting medium (see *refraction of light*), usually *glass*, bounded by two surfaces, generally curved. Such lenses are classified according to the nature of the surfaces into bi-*concave*, bi-*convex*, plano-convex, etc. The centres of the *spheres* of which the lens surfaces are considered to form a part, are termed the *centres of curvature*; the line joining these is the *optical axis*, the *optical centre* is a point on the axis within the lens; all rays passing through this point emerge without deviation. A parallel beam of *light* incident on a lens is made to converge (convex lens) or diverge (concave lens). The point of divergence or convergence is called a principal focus. Regarding all distances as being measured from the optical centre, and taking all distances as positive when measured in a direction opposite to that of the incident light, the distances of the object and image from the lens are given by the formula $1/v - 1/u = 1/f$, where u and v are the distances from the lens of object and image respectively, and f is the *focal length*, i.e. the distance of the focus from the lens. Electrostatic and electromagnetic lenses, for converging beams of *electrons* and other elementary charged particles, are also of importance, e.g. in the *electron microscope*. See *electron lens*.

LENZ'S LAW. When a circuit and a *magnetic field* move relatively to each other, the *electric current* induced in the circuit will have a magnetic field opposing the motion. See *induction, electromagnetic*.

LEPTON. A collective name for *electrons*, *muons*, and *neutrinos*. The number of leptons minus the number of corresponding anti-leptons taking part in a process is called the 'lepton number'; a quantity which appears to be conserved in all processes. See *fermions*.

LEUCOCYTES. White *blood cells*. The cells of the *blood* which contain no *haemoglobin*. There are several types of leucocytes, the main function of which is the combating of infection. Human blood contains between 5000 and 10,000 leucocytes per cubic millimetre.

LEVER. Rigid bar which may be turned freely about a fixed point of support, the fulcrum. The *mechanical advantage* of a lever is given by the ratio of the perpendicular distance of the line of action of the effort from the fulcrum, to the perpendicular distance of the line of action of the resistance from the fulcrum.

LEWISITE, chlorovinyl dichlorarsine. $ClCH:CHAsCl_2$. Oily liquid; war 'gas' with lethal *vesicant* properties. Destroyed by *oxidizing agents*, e.g. *bleaching powder*.

LEYDEN JAR. Form of electrostatic *capacitor* of historical interest.

LIBRATION. An oscillation of the *Moon's* face from side to side. Due to libration about 58% of the Moon's surface can be seen from the Earth.

LIEBIG CONDENSER. See *condenser* (chem.).

LIGHT. Name given to the agency by means of which a viewed object influences the observer's eye. Consists of *electromagnetic radiation* within the *wave-length* range 4×10^{-5} cm. to 7×10^{-5} cm. approximately; variations in the wave-length produce different sensations in the eye, corresponding to different *colours*. See *colour vision*.

LIGHT QUANTUM. See *photon*.

LIGHT, VELOCITY OF. Mean value is $2 \cdot 9979 \times 10^{10}$ cm./sec.= 186,281 miles/sec. The special significance of the velocity of light in the Universe was revealed by the special theory of *relativity*. According to this now accepted theory, the velocity of light is absolute (i.e. independent of the velocity of the observer) and represents a limiting velocity in that the velocity of no body can exceed it. The special significance of the velocity of light is apparent from its presence in the *mass-energy equation* which follows from the special theory of relativity. In this equation the velocity of light appears as the 'connecting link' between *mass* and *energy*.

LIGHT-YEAR. Astronomical measure of distance; the distance travelled by *light* (see *light, velocity of*) in one year. Approximately 6×10^{12} miles (6 million million miles).

LIGHTNING. Electric discharge in the form of a spark or flash between two charged clouds, or between a cloud and the *Earth*.

LIGHTNING CONDUCTOR. A *conductor* of *electricity* connected to earth and ending in one or more sharp points attached to a high part of a building. The effect of a passing *electric charge*, such as an electrically charged cloud, is to produce a discharge of electricity of opposite charge from the conductor; since the density of charge is greatest at the more pointed parts of the conductor, the strength of the *electric field* in the air near the sharp points will become so great as to make the air a conductor of electricity. Thus a stream of electricity of opposite charge to that of the cloud will proceed from the sharp points, causing a quiet neutralization of charges instead of an accumulation which may become great enough to break down the insulation of the air and thus cause a lightning discharge.

LIGNIN. Complex *organic* material which occurs in the woody tissues of plants, often combined with *cellulose*. The preparation of pure cellulose by removing the lignin is an important step in the manufacture of pulp for the *paper* and *rayon* industries.

LIGNITE, brown coal. Brownish-black, natural deposit resembling *coal*. Contains a higher percentage of *hydrocarbons* than ordinary coal; probably of more recent origin.

LIGROIN. *Mixture* of *hydrocarbons* of the *paraffin series*; generally applied to a mixture having b.p. 70°–120° C.

LIME. *Quicklime*, calcium oxide, CaO. White *solid* made by heating *limestone* in lime-kilns. *Slaked lime*, calcium hydroxide, $Ca(OH)_2$, is a white solid formed by the action of *water* ('slaking') on quicklime. Term sometimes loosely applied to calcium *salts* in general.

LIMESTONE. Natural *calcium carbonate*, $CaCO_3$.

LIME-WATER. Solution of *calcium hydroxide*, $Ca(OH)_2$, in *water*. Turns milky by the action of *carbon dioxide*, CO_2, owing to the formation of *insoluble calcium carbonate*, $CaCO_3$.

LIMIT, limiting value (math.). Mathematical concept. A *function* of a variable quantity x, written $f(x)$, approaches a limiting value k as x approaches a value a, if the difference $k - f(a + \delta)$ may be made smaller than any assignable value by making δ sufficiently small.

LIMIT OF SPECTRAL SERIES. The lines appearing in the *line spectrum* of any *element* can be grouped into definite series. The shortest *wavelength* of any such series is called the limit of the series. At this series limit, the lines crowd closer and closer together from the long wavelength side.

LIMONITE. Natural *hydrated* form of *ferric oxide*, Fe_2O_3. Ore of iron.

LINE OF SIGHT VELOCITY. Radial velocity. The *velocity* at which a heavenly body approaches, or recedes from, the Earth. Measured spectroscopically by observing the shift of the spectral lines (see *spectrum*) of *elements* within the body, relative to those of the same elements on Earth. See *Doppler effect*.

LINE PAIR. In *spectrographic analysis* a line pair consists of the particular spectral line (see *line spectrum*) utilized in the determination of the *concentration* of an *element* and the *internal standard line* with which it is compared.

LINE SPECTRUM. *Spectrum* (*emission* or *absorption*) consisting of definite single lines, each corresponding to a particular *wave-length*; characteristic of an *element* in the atomic state.

LINEAR ACCELERATOR. Linac. Apparatus for accelerating *ions* to high *energies*. Consists of a row of cylindrical *electrodes* separated by small gaps and having a common axis. Alternate electrodes are connected to each other and a *high-frequency potential* is applied between the two sets of electrodes. The frequency, and the lengths of the different electrodes, are such that the ions are accelerated each time they cross a gap between two electrodes.

LINEAR MOTOR. A form of *induction motor*, in which the *stator* and *rotor* are linear instead of cylindrical and parallel instead of *coaxial*.

LINEAR RELATIONSHIP. A relationship existing between two *variable* quantities which are directly proportional to each other. A *graph* representing the manner in which such quantities vary with each other will be a straight line.

LINES OF FORCE. See *electrical lines of force*; *magnetic lines of force*.

LINKAGE between *atoms*. See *valency*.

LINNAEAN SYSTEM. See *binomial nomenclature*.

LINOLEIC ACID. $C_{18}H_{32}O_2$. Yellow, oily liquid, *unsaturated fatty acid* which occurs in various vegetable oils, particularly *linseed oil* Once known as *vitamin* F, but its function in this capacity is now discredited.

LINSEED OIL. A vegetable *oil* extracted from the seeds of flax plants. Contains *glycerides* of *oleic acid* and other *unsaturated fatty acids*. Being easily oxidized and polymerized it is widely used in the *paint* and varnish industries and for manufacturing linoleum.

LIPASE. *Enzyme* with the power of hydrolyzing (see *hydrolysis*) *fats*.

LIPIDS. Lipoids. Group of *organic compounds* which are *esters* of *fatty acids* and which are characterized by being *insoluble* in *water* but *soluble* in many organic *solvents*. Usually divided into three groups: (1) 'Simple lipids' which include *fats and oils* as well as *waxes*; (2) 'Compound lipids' which include *phospholipids* and *glycolipids*; (3) 'Derived lipids' of which the most important are the *steroids*.

LIPOCLASTIC, lipolytic. Fat-splitting; applied to *enzymes* having the power of hydrolyzing (see *hydrolysis*) *fats* into the *fatty acid* and glycerin; e.g. *lipase*.

LIPOWITZ' ALLOY. Fusible *alloy*, m.p. 65°–70° C.; consists of 50% bismuth, 27% lead, 13% tin, 10% cadmium.

LIQUATION. Separation of a *solid mixture* by heating till one of the constituents melts and can be drained away.

LIQUEFACTION OF GASES. A *gas* possessing a *critical temperature* above room temperature may be liquefied merely by increasing the *pressure* on it. Otherwise, the gas must first be cooled to below its critical temperature and then compressed; or, if desired, cooled directly to its *boiling point* under normal pressure. The methods of cooling are (1) by *evaporation* under reduced pressure, as in the *cascade liquefier*; (2) by using the principle of the *Joule-Thomson effect* (the Linde process); (3) by causing the gas to expand against an external pressure; in so doing the gas does *work*, thereby cooling itself. This principle is used in the Claude process.

LIQUID. A state of *matter* intermediate between a *solid* and a *gas*, in which the *molecules* are relatively free to move with respect to each other but are restricted by cohesive *forces* to the extent that the liquid maintains a fixed *volume*. Liquids assume the shape of the vessel containing them, but are only slightly compressible.

LIQUID AIR. Pale blue *liquid*, containing mainly liquid oxygen, b.p. $-182 \cdot 9°$ C., and liquid nitrogen, b.p. $-195 \cdot 7°$ C.

LIQUID DROP MODEL OF THE NUCLEUS. A hypothetical model of the atomic *nucleus* in which its properties are compared to those of a drop of *liquid*.

LISSAJOUS FIGURE. The *locus* of the *resultant* displacement of a point on which two or more simple periodic motions are impressed. In the common case, two periodic motions are at right angles and are of the same *frequency*. The Lissajous figures then become, in general, a series of *ellipses* corresponding to the possible differences of *phase* between the two motions.

LITHARGE, lead monoxide. PbO. Reddish-yellow crystalline *solid*, m.p. 888° C. Used in the manufacture of *glass*, *paints*, varnishes, and *glazes*.

LITHIUM. Li. Element. A.W. 6·939. At. No. 3. Light, silvery-white *alkali metal*, m.p. 186° C. S.G. 0·534; lightest *solid* known. Chemically resembles sodium, but is less active. Used in *alloys*.

LITHOPONE. Mixture of zinc sulphide, ZnS, and barium sulphate, BaSO$_4$. Used in *paints* as a non-poisonous substitute for *white lead*.

LITHOSPHERE. See *Earth's crust*.

LITMUS. *Soluble*, purple substance of vegetable origin; turned red by *acids* and blue by *alkalis*. Used as an *indicator*.

LITRE. Unit of *volume* in the *metric system*. The volume of 1 *kilogram* of pure air-free *water* at 4° C. and 760 mm. pressure. Often taken to be equal in volume to 1000 c.c.; actually = 1000·028 c.c. Subdivided into 1000 millilitres, ml., used synonymously with c.c.

LIVER OF SULPHUR. Mixture of *sulphides* and other sulphur *compounds* of potassium, obtained by fusing *potassium carbonate*, K$_2$CO$_3$, with sulphur. Used as an *insecticide* and *fungicide* in gardening.

LIXIVIATION. Extraction of *soluble* material from a *mixture* by washing with *water*.

LOADED CONCRETE. Normal *concrete* to which has been added some material containing *elements* of high *atomic number* (e.g. iron or lead shot). Used in the shielding of *nuclear reactors*.

LOCAL GROUP OF GALAXIES. The cluster of *galaxies* to which the *Galaxy* belongs. Distant clusters of galaxies are receding from the Local Group. See *expansion of the Universe*.

LOCAL OSCILLATOR. The *oscillator* in a *heterodyne* or *superheterodyne radio* receiver which produces the *radio frequency* oscillation with which the received wave is combined.

LOCUS (math.). The locus of a point is the line which can be drawn through adjacent positions of the point, thus tracing out the path of the point in space.

LODESTONE. Magnetic variety of natural iron oxide, Fe_3O_4, *magnetite*.

LOGARITHMIC SCALE. A scale of measurement in which an increase of one unit represents a tenfold increase in the quantity measured (for common *logarithms*).

LOGARITHMS. If a number, a, is expressed as a *power* of another number, b, i.e. if $a=b^n$, then n is said to be the logarithm of a to base b, written $\log_b a$. Common logarithms are to base 10. Multiplication, division, and other computations are shortened by the use of common logarithms; the addition of logarithms of numbers gives the logarithm of the *product* of the numbers; similarly *division* can be performed by subtraction of the logarithms. Logarithms corresponding to ordinary numbers have been tabulated, and calculations are carried out by the use of such tables. Natural or Napierian logarithms are to the base 'e' (which has the value 2.71828). $\log_e a = 2.303 \log_{10} a$. See also *characteristic* and *mantissa*.

LOGIC. In an automatic data processing system, the systematic scheme which defines the interactions of the physical entities representing data.

LONE PAIR OF ELECTRONS. A pair of unshared *valency electrons* which are responsible for the formation of co-ordinate bonds. See *valency, electronic theory of*.

LONG SIGHT. See *hypermetropia, presbyopia*.

LONGITUDE. The angle which the terrestrial *meridian* through the geographical poles and a point on the Earth's surface makes with a standard meridian (usually through Greenwich) is the longitude of the point.

LONGITUDE, LINES OF. Imaginary *meridians* on the Earth's surface, referred to a standard meridian; *great circles* of the Earth intersecting at the poles.

LONGITUDINAL. Lengthwise; in a line with the length of the object under consideration.

LONGITUDINAL WAVES. Waves in which the vibration or displacement takes place in the direction of propagation of the waves; e.g. *sound* waves. See also *transverse waves*.

LOSCHMIDT'S NUMBER. The number of *molecules* per c.c. of a *perfect gas* at *N.T.P.*; equal to 2.687×10^{19}.

LOUDNESS OF SOUND. The magnitude of the physiological response of the ear to *sound*. As the ear responds differently to different *frequencies*, the loudness of a sound will depend to a certain extent on its frequency. However, loudness can be roughly correlated with the *cube root* of the intensity of sound, and different levels can be conveniently compared by the units *decibel* and *phon*.

LOVIBOND TINTOMETER*. A *colorimeter* in which the *colour* of a liquid, surface, powder, or light source is compared with a series of glass slides of standardized colours.

LUMEN. Unit of luminous flux (see *flux, luminous*). The amount of *light* emitted per second in unit *solid angle* by a uniform *point source* of one *candela* intensity; i.e. the amount of light falling per second on unit area placed at unit distance from such a source.

LUMINANCE. The *luminous intensity* of any surface in a given direction per unit of orthogonally projected area of that surface, on a plane perpendicular to the given direction.

LUMINESCENCE. Emission of *light* from a body from any cause other than high *temperature*. *Fluorescence* and *phosphorescence* are particular cases of luminescence.

LUMINOSITY. 1. The property of emitting *light*. 2. The amount of light emitted by a *star*, irrespective of its distance from the *Earth*.

LUMINOUS INTENSITY. The amount of *light* emitted per second in unit *solid angle* by a *point source*, in a given direction. The unit of luminous intensity is the *candela*. The term is restricted to point sources.

LUMINOUS PAINT. *Paint* prepared from phosphorescent *compounds* such as calcium sulphide, etc., which glows after exposure to *light*. See *phosphorescence*.

LUNAR CAUSTIC. *Silver nitrate* $AgNO_3$, usually fused and cast into sticks.

LUTETIUM, cassiopeium. Lu. Element. A.W. 174·97. At. No. 71. See *lanthanides*.

LUX, metre candle. Unit of *illumination*; one *lumen* per square metre.

LYDDITE. *Explosive* consisting of *picric acid* (trinitrophenol, $C_6H_2OH\text{-}(NO_2)_3$, mixed with 10% *nitrobenzene* and 3% *Vaseline*.

LYMAN SERIES. A series of lines which occurs in the *ultra-violet* region of the *spectrum* of hydrogen.

LYOPHILIC COLLOID. 'Solvent-loving colloid.' See *colloidal solutions*.

LYOPHOBIC COLLOID. 'Solvent-hating colloid.' See *colloidal solutions*.

LYSOL*. A mixture of the *cresols* with a *solution* of *soft soap*. Used as a *disinfectant*.

M

MACH NUMBER. The ratio of the speed of a *fluid* or body, to the local speed of *sound*. The speed of a fluid or body is therefore said to be *supersonic* if its Mach number is greater than unity.

MACHINE. Defined mathematically as a device for overcoming resistance at one point by the application of a *force*, usually at some other point. Generally understood to be any arrangement for the purpose of taking in some definite form of *energy*, modifying it and delivering it in a form more suitable for the desired purpose.

MACRO-. Prefix denoting large, in contrast to *micro-*, small.

MACROMOLECULE. Very large *molecule*, generally of a *polymer*. See *polymerization*.

MAGELLANIC CLOUDS. Two small patches of *light* which appear, from the southern hemisphere, to be detached from the main bright band of *stars* which constitute the *Milky Way*. These objects are separate *galaxies* being two of the smaller members of the *Local Group* to which our *Galaxy* belongs.

MAGENTA, fuchsine. $C_{20}H_{22}N_3OCl$. Red dye, prepared from *aniline* and *toluidine*.

MAGIC NUMBERS. The numbers 2, 8, 20, 28, 50, 82, and 126. Atomic *nuclei* containing these numbers of *neutrons* or *protons* have exceptional stability.

MAGNADUR*. A *ferrite* used for making permanent *magnets*.

MAGNALIUM*. Light *alloy*, S.G. 2 to 2·5; aluminium with from 5% to 30% magnesium.

MAGNESIA. Magnesium oxide, MgO; 'magnesia alba' of pharmacy is *basic* magnesium carbonate; 'fluid magnesia' is a *solution* of magnesium bicarbonate.

MAGNESIUM. Mg. Element. A.W. 24·312. At. No. 12. Light, silvery-white *metal*, S.G. 1·74, m.p. 651° C., tarnishes easily in air. Burns with an intense white *flame* to form magnesium oxide, MgO. Occurs as magnesite, $MgCO_3$; *dolomite*, $MgCO_3.CaCO_3$; *carnallite*, $KCl.MgCl_2.6H_2O$, and in many other *compounds*. Essential to life as it occurs in *chlorophyll*. Prepared by *electrolysis* of fused carnallite. Used in lightweight *alloys*, and in *photography*, signalling, and incendiary bombs. Compounds used in medicine.

MAGNESIUM SULPHATE. See *Epsom salts*.

MAGNET, permanent. *Ferromagnetic substance* which has a permanent *magnetic field* and *magnetic moment* associated with it. See also *magnetic domains*.

MAGNETIC AMPLIFIER. A device for the amplification of small *direct currents* and of low *frequency alternating currents*. Depends upon the fact that the output from the secondary coil of a *transformer* due to an alternating current in the *primary coil* is also a function of a direct current (the signal to be amplified) in a third winding on the transformer core.

MAGNETIC BOTTLE. Term used to describe any configuration of *magnetic fields* used in the *containment* of a *plasma* during controlled *thermonuclear reaction* experiments.

MAGNETIC DECLINATION, magnetic variation, variation of the compass. The *angle* between the *planes* of the geographic and *magnetic meridian*. See *magnetism terrestrial*.

MAGNETIC DIP, angle of dip. Inclination. The *angle* between the direction of the Earth's magnetic field (see *magnetism, terrestrial*) and the horizontal; i.e. the angle through which a magnetic needle will 'dip' from the horizontal when suspended free to swing in a vertical plane in the *magnetic meridian*. See *dip circle*.

MAGNETIC DOMAINS. The fact that *ferromagnetic* substances are not necessarily always magnetized, led to the theory that they consist of separate domains, each of which is spontaneously magnetized, but the *magnetic moments* of which may not be aligned. If an external *magnetic field* is applied to the substance the magnetic moments of the domains (not the domains themselves) are rotated so that they lie parallel to the field; the substance then acts as a permanent *magnet*.

MAGNETIC DRUM. A cylinder coated with magnetic material for storing information in a *computer*. The information is stored in the magnetic coating in the form of magnetic *dipoles*, the orientation or polarity of which can be used to indicate one of the digits in a *binary notation*.

MAGNETIC ELEMENTS. The three quantities, *magnetic declination*, angle of dip (see *magnetic dip*), and the *horizontal intensity*, which define completely the Earth's magnetic field (see *magnetism, terrestrial*) at any point.

MAGNETIC EQUATOR. Line of zero *magnetic dip* lying fairly near the geographical *equator*, but passing North of it in Africa and the Indian Ocean, and South of it in America and the Eastern Pacific.

MAGNETIC FIELD. A *field* of *force* which is said to exist at any point if a small coil of wire carrying an *electric current* experiences a *couple* when placed at that point. A magnetic field may exist at a point as a result of the presence of either a permanent *magnet* or of a circuit carrying an *electric current*, in the neighbourhood of the point.

MAGNETIC FIELD OF ELECTRIC CURRENT. A wire or coil carrying an *electric current* is surrounded by a *magnetic field*. The direction of the field relative to the current may be determined by the following corkscrew rule: If a corkscrew, held in the right hand, is turned along the conductor in the direction of the current, the movement of the thumb indicates the direction of the magnetic field produced. The intensity of the magnetic field at the centre of a circular coil of wire of radius r cm., consisting of n turns, in which a current of I *amperes* is flowing, is $\dfrac{2\pi nI}{10r}$ *oersteds*.

MAGNETIC FIELD, STRENGTH OF. See *magnetic intensity*.

MAGNETIC FLUX through any area is the product of the area and of the component of the *magnetic intensity* at right angles to that area. The unit of magnetic flux is the *maxwell*.

MAGNETIC INDUCTION. Consider a uniform *magnetic field* of strength H in free space; i.e. the *magnetic flux* through unit area perpendicular to the field is H. Now suppose a material medium to be introduced into the field. The magnetic flux at any point in the medium becomes modified owing to the interaction between H and the *atoms* of the medium, and assumes a new value B, which is called the magnetic induction of the medium. See *gauss*.

MAGNETIC INTENSITY, strength of *magnetic field* at a point. The *force* which would be exerted on unit north *magnetic pole* situated at that point. Measured in *oersteds*.

MAGNETIC IRON ORE. See *magnetite*.

MAGNETIC LINE OF FORCE, line of magnetic force. A line whose direction at each point is that of the *magnetic field* at that point; the path along which a free *magnetic pole* would travel.

MAGNETIC MERIDIAN. See *magnetism, terrestrial*.

MAGNETIC MIRRORS. The regions of high field strength at the end of an externally generated *magnetic field* used in the *containment* of a *plasma* in controlled *thermonuclear reaction* experiments. *Ions* which enter these regions of high field strength reverse their direction of motion (are reflected) and return to the central region of the plasma in which they become trapped.

MAGNETIC MOMENT, moment of a magnet. The *couple* required to hold a *magnet* at right angles to a field of unit *magnetic intensity*; the product of the *magnetic pole strength* and the length of the magnet.

MAGNETIC PERMEABILITY, μ. The ratio of the *magnetic induction* to the external *magnetic field* (H) causing the induction. For most substances μ has a constant small value. When μ is less than 1, the material is said to be *diamagnetic*; if μ is greater than 1, it is *paramagnetic*. A few substances, notably iron, have very large values of μ, which tend to fall as H increases so that the magnetic induction tends to a limiting value called the *saturation value*. Such substances are said to be *ferromagnetic*.

MAGNETIC POLE. A *magnet* appears to have its *magnetism* concentrated at two points termed the poles. If a bar magnet is suspended to swing freely, one of these, the North-seeking, North, or positive pole, will point North, and the other South. Unlike poles attract, and like poles repel each other. The *force* of attraction or repulsion between two poles varies inversely as the *square* of the distance between them (see *inverse square law*). The force between two poles of strength m_1 and m_2 (see *magnetic pole strength*) situated d centimetres apart in vacuum is $m_1 m_2/d^2$ *dynes*.

MAGNETIC POLE STRENGTH. The strength of a *magnetic pole* measured in terms of the unit magnetic pole; see *magnetic pole, unit*.

MAGNETIC POLE, UNIT. Unit *magnetic pole* is one of such a strength that when situated 1 centimetre from an equal pole in *vacuum*, the *force* between the poles will be 1 *dyne*.

MAGNETIC POTENTIAL. Magnetomotive force. Concept analogous to *electric potential*; the difference of magnetic potential between two points is measured by the *work* done in carrying *unit magnetic pole* from one point to the other.

MAGNETIC STORM. Sudden disturbance in the Earth's magnetic field (see *magnetism, terrestrial*) associated with *sunspot* activity. Affects *compasses* and *radio* transmission.

MAGNETIC SUSCEPTIBILITY. Ratio of the intensity of *magnetization* produced in a substance to the intensity of the *magnetic field* to which it is subjected.

MAGNETIC TAPE. *Plastic* tape coated with a *ferromagnetic* powder, used in tape recorders. The tape is passed over the gap in a magnetic circuit which is modulated in accordance with information to be recorded. The tape retains a record of the modulation which can be 'played back' through a suitable circuit.

MAGNETIC VARIATION. See *magnetic declination.*

MAGNETISM. The branch of physics concerned with *magnets* and *magnetic fields*. See *diamagnetism, paramagnetism, ferromagnetism,* and *ferrimagnetism.*

MAGNETISM, TERRESTRIAL, the Earth's magnetism. The Earth possesses a *magnetic field*, the intensity of which varies with time and locality. The field is similar to that which would be produced by a powerful *magnet* situated at the centre of the Earth and pointing approximately North and South. A magnetized needle suspended to swing freely in all planes will set itself pointing to the Earth's magnetic North and South poles, at an angle to the horizontal (see *magnetic dip*). The vertical plane through the *axis* of such a needle is termed the *magnetic meridian*, defined as the vertical plane which contains the direction of the Earth's magnetic field. The cause of the Earth's magnetism is not definitely known. The variations of the Earth's magnetic field with time are of two types, the 'secular' and the 'diurnal'. The secular variations are slow changes in the same sense, but at different rates, as a result of which the Earth's magnetic field has decreased by some 5% over the last hundred years. The cause of these variations is unknown. The diurnal variations are much smaller and more rapid variations which have been shown to be associated with changes in the *ionosphere* related to *sunspot* activity.

MAGNETITE, magnetic iron ore. Natural black *oxide* of iron, Fe_3O_4.

MAGNETIZATION, INTENSITY OF. The *magnetic moment* per unit volume of a magnetized body.

MAGNETO. Small *dynamo* provided with a *spark-coil*, for *ignition* of petrol vapour in petrol *internal-combustion engines.*

MAGNETOHYDRODYNAMICS. MHD. A method of generating *electricity* by subjecting the *free electrons* in a high velocity *flame* or *plasma* to a strong *magnetic field*. The free electron concentration in the flame is increased by the thermal *ionization* of added substances of low *ionization potential* (e.g. containing sodium or potassium). These electrons constitute a current when they flow between *electrodes* within the flame, under the influence of the external magnetic field. It is hoped to use

MHD to increase the overall *efficiency* of conventional power stations, by extracting a certain amount of *energy* in this way from the flame that is used to raise *steam* for the *turbo-generators*.

MAGNETOMETER. Instrument for comparing strengths of *magnetic fields*, and *magnetic moments*. Consists of a short *magnet* with a long, non-magnetic pointer at right angles across it, pivoted at the junction. The pointer swings along a circular scale, thus enabling deflections of the short magnet to be measured.

MAGNETOMOTIVE FORCE. MMF. See *magnetic potential* and *gilbert*.

MAGNETON. A *unit* for measuring the *magnetic moments* of atomic particles. The 'Bohr magneton', β, is equal to $\dfrac{eh}{4\pi mc} = 9\cdot27 \times 10^{-21}$ *ergs* per *gauss*, where e and m are the charge and mass of the *electron*, h is *Planck's constant*, and c is the *velocity of light*. The 'nuclear magneton' is equal to $\beta \cdot \dfrac{m}{M} = 5\cdot05 \times 10^{-24}$ ergs per gauss, where M is the mass of the *proton*.

MAGNETOSTRICTION. A change in the dimensions of *ferromagnetic substances* on magnetization.

MAGNETRON. A *thermionic valve* capable of producing high power oscillations in the *microwave* region. Consists of a heater, a central *cathode*, and an *anode* with a number of radial segments, all enclosed in an evacuated container which is situated in the gap of an external *magnet*. The movement of the *electrons* is controlled by a combination of crossed *electric* and *magnetic fields*. Used extensively in *radar*.

MAGNIFICATION produced by *microscope* (or other optical instrument). The ratio of the linear dimensions of the final image to the linear dimensions of the object.

MAGNIFYING GLASS. A *convex lens*. See *microscope, simple*.

MAGNIFYING POWER OF A COMPOUND MICROSCOPE. The ratio of the *angle* subtended at the eye by the final image to the angle subtended by the object placed at the least distance of distinct vision (i.e. the shortest distance from the eye at which the object can be seen distinctly).

MAGNIFYING POWER OF A LENS. Ratio of the *angle* subtended at the eye by the *virtual image* to the angle subtended by the object when placed at the least distance of distinct vision; this latter is generally taken to be 25 cm.

MAGNITUDE OF STARS. The apparent magnitude is a measure of the relative apparent *brightness* of *stars*. A star of any one magnitude is approximately $2\cdot51$ times brighter than a star of the next magnitude. E.g. a star of the first magnitude is $(2\cdot51)^3$ times as bright as a star of the fourth magnitude. The absolute magnitude is defined as the apparent magnitude a given star would have at the standard distance of 10 *parsecs*.

MAGNOX. A magnesium *alloy* used for sheathing uranium *fuel elements* in certain types of *nuclear reactor*.

MAIN SEQUENCE STARS. See *Hertzprung-Russell diagram*.

MAJORITY CARRIERS. In a *semiconductor*, the type of *carrier* which constitutes more than half the total number of carriers.

MALACHITE. Natural *basic* copper carbonate, $CuCO_3.Cu(OH)_2$. Bright green *mineral*.

MALIC ACID, hydroxysuccinic acid. $COOH.CH_2.CH(OH).COOH$. White crystalline *organic acid*, m.p. 98°–99° C. Occurs in unripe apples and other fruits.

MALLEABILITY. Capacity of being hammered out into thin sheets.

MALONYL UREA. See *barbiturates*.

MALT. Grain (usually barley) which has been allowed to germinate and then heated and dried. See *brewing*.

MALT SUGAR. See *maltose*.

MALTASE. *Enzyme* occurring in *yeast* and other *organisms*. Hydrolyzes (see *hydrolysis*) *maltose*, malt sugar, into *glucose*.

MALTOBIOSE. See *maltose*.

MALTOSE, malt sugar, maltobiose. $C_{12}H_{22}O_{11}$. Hard crystalline *soluble disaccharide sugar*, less sweet than *cane-sugar*. Formed in *malt* by the action of the *enzyme diastase* on *starch*.

MANGANESE. Mn. Element. A.W. 54·938. At. No. 25. Reddish-white, hard brittle *metal*. S.G. 7·20, m.p. 1260° C. Occurs as *pyrolusite*, MnO_2, from which it is extracted by *reduction* with carbon or aluminium. Used in numerous *alloys*.

MANGANESE BRONZE, manganese brass. A copper-zinc *alloy* containing up to 4% manganese.

MANGANESE DIOXIDE, manganese peroxide, MnO_2. Heavy, black powder; occurs naturally as *pyrolusite*. Used as a source of manganese metal, as an *oxidizing agent*, in *glass* manufacture, in *Leclanché cells*, as a *catalyst* in the laboratory preparation of oxygen, etc.

MANGANESE STEEL. Very hard variety of *steel* containing up to 13% manganese.

MANGANIN. *Alloy* containing 83% copper, 13% manganese, 4% nickel. Electrical *resistance* affected only slightly by change in *temperature*; used for resistance coils.

MANOMETER. Any instrument used for measuring gaseous *pressure*.

MANTISSA. The decimal, always positive, portion of a common *logarithm*.

MARBLE. Form of natural *calcium carbonate*, $CaCO_3$.

MARGARINE. Butter substitute prepared from purified vegetable and animal *fats and oils*. Milk is added to a suitable blend of fats; bacterial action in the milk produces a butter-like flavour; vitamins A and D (see *vitamins*) and suitable colouring materials are added.

MARKOWNIKOFF'S RULE. When addition occurs between a hydrogen *halide* and an unsymmetrical *olefine*, the *halogen atom* becomes attached to the carbon *atom* with the least number of hydrogen atoms.

MARS (astr.). *Planet*, with two small *satellites*, having its *orbit* between those of the *Earth* and *Jupiter*. Mean distance from the *Sun* = 141·63 million miles. *Sidereal period* ('year') = 686·98 days. Mass 0·107 that of the Earth, diameter 4,220 miles. Probably possesses an atmosphere containing oxygen. Surface temperature about 0° C. No evidence of life on the planet is available.

MARSH GAS. See *methane*, CH_4.

MARSH'S TEST. Sensitive test for arsenic. Depends upon the formation of *arsine* when arsenic or its *compounds* are present in a *solution* evolving hydrogen. When the arsine is passed through a narrow, heated tube, it is decomposed and leaves a deposit of metallic arsenic.

MASER. Microwave Amplification by Stimulated Emission of Radiation. A class of *amplifiers* and *oscillators* which makes use of the internal *energy* of *atoms* and *molecules* to obtain low noise-level amplification and *microwave* oscillations of precisely determined *frequencies*. Stimulated emission, which is the basic principle on which these devices work, is the emission by an *atom* in an excited *quantum* state (see *excitation*) of a *photon*, as the result of the impact of a photon from outside of exactly equal energy. Thus the stimulating photon, or wave, is augmented by the one emitted by the excited atom. A maser consists of an 'active medium' (either in the gaseous or *solid state*), in which most of the atoms can be 'pumped' to an excited state by subjecting the system to *electromagnetic radiation* of frequencies which differ from that of the stimulating frequency. The active medium is enclosed in a *resonant cavity* so that a wave is built up with only one mode of oscillation, which is equivalent to a single output frequency. Masers can also be made to operate at optical frequencies, when they are referred to as optical masers or *lasers*.

MASS. It is a matter of observation that a *force* applied to a body produces an *acceleration* proportional to the force. The constant of proportionality is the mass of the body. See also *rest mass*.

MASS ACTION LAW. The velocity of a chemical change is proportional to the *active masses* (*molecular concentrations*) of the reacting substances.

MASS DECREMENT. The difference between the *isotopic weight* of an *isotope* and its *mass number*.

MASS DEFECT. The difference beween the *mass* of a *nucleus* and the sum of the masses of its constituent *nucleons*. The *energy* equivalent of the mass defect, on the basis of the *mass-energy equation*, must be supplied to a nucleus to split it into its component nucleons.

MASS-ENERGY EQUATION. *Mass* and *energy* are mutually convertible under certain conditions. The equation connecting the two quantities in any such transformation is $E = mc^2$, where c is the velocity of *light* in cm./sec. and E is the energy, in *ergs*, released when a mass of m grams is completely converted into energy. See *annihilation radiation*, *conservation of mass and energy*.

MASS NUMBER. The *integer* which is nearest to the *atomic mass* of an *isotope*, i.e. the number of *nucleons* in the *nucleus* of an *atom*.

MASS SPECTROGRAPH. Apparatus for the determination of the exact *masses* of individual *atoms*, i.e. *isotopic weights*, by using the technique of *positive ray analysis*.

MASS SPECTRUM. See *positive ray analysis*.

MASSICOT. Yellow powder form of unfused lead monoxide, PbO.

MASURIUM. Former name of *element* of At. No. 43; replaced in 1949 by the name *technetium*.

MATCHES. The heads of safety matches usually contain antimony sulphide, *oxidizing agents* such as potassium chlorate, and some sulphur or *charcoal*; while the striking surface contains red phosphorus. Ordinary non-safety match-heads contain phosphorus sulphide, P_4S_3; very rarely red phosphorus.

MATTE. Mixture of the *sulphides* of iron and copper obtained as an intermediate stage in the *smelting* of copper.

MATTER. A specialized form of *energy* which has the attributes of *mass* and extension in *space* and time.

MAUVE, mauveine, aniline violet. Reddish-violet *dye*; complex *organic compound*, the first organic dye to be prepared artificially.

MAXIMUM (math.). A *function* $y=f(x)$ has a maximum value at $x=a$ if $f(a)$ is greater than the values of the function immediately preceding and immediately following $x=a$. The function has a minimum value at $x=b$ if $f(b)$ is less than the value of the function immediately preceding and immediately following $x=b$.

MAXIMUM AND MINIMUM THERMOMETER. See *thermometer*.

MAXIMUM PERMISSIBLE DOSE (OR LEVEL). See *dose*.

MAXWELL, THE. Unit of *magnetic flux*. The flux through 1 square centimetre *normal* to a *magnetic field* of intensity of 1 *gauss*.

MEAN (math.). Generally understood to be the arithmetic mean, i.e. the average. The geometric mean, M, between two quantities A and B is such a quantity that A, M and B are in *geometrical progression*; thus $M/A=B/M$, $AB=M^2$, and $M=\sqrt{AB}$.

MEAN FREE PATH. The average, or *mean*, distance travelled by a particle, *atom*, or *molecule* between collisions. In a *gas* the mean free path between molecules is inversely proportional to the *pressure*. See *Kinetic theory of gases*.

MEAN FREE TIME. The average, or *mean*, time that elapses between two collisions of a particle, *atom*, or *molecule*.

MEAN SOLAR DAY. See *solar day*.

MECHANICAL ADVANTAGE. In a *machine*, the ratio of the actual load raised to the *force* required to maintain the machine at constant speed.

MECHANICAL EQUIVALENT OF HEAT. If H units of *heat* are completely converted into W units of *work* then $W=JH$, where J is a constant called the mechanical equivalent of heat, or Joule's equivalent. J represents the amount of work obtainable by the complete conversion of unit quantity of heat into mechanical work. 1 *calorie* (15°) $\equiv 4 \cdot 185 \times 10^7$ *ergs*; 1 *British Thermal Unit* $\equiv$ 778 ft-lb.; i.e. J has the values of $4 \cdot 185 \times 10^7$ ergs/calorie and 778 ft-lb./B.Th.U. respectively for these two sets of units.

MECHANICS. Branch of physical science dealing with the behaviour of *matter* under the action of *force*. See *dynamics*; *statics*; *kinematics*.

MECHANISTIC THEORY. The view that all biological phenomena may be explained in mechanical, physical, and chemical terms; in opposition to the *vitalistic theory*.

MEDIAN. Line joining a vertex of a *triangle* to the mid-point of the opposite side.

MEDIAN LETHAL DOSE. (M)LD50. The *dose* of *ionizing radiation* which would kill 50% of a large batch of *organisms* within a specified period.

MEERSCHAUM. Natural *hydrated* magnesium silicate, $Mg_2Si_3O_8.2H_2O$. White *solid* used for tobacco pipes.

MEGA-. Prefix denoting one million times, in *metric units*; e.g. megohm, one million ohms; more loosely, denoting 'very large.'

MEGACYCLE. Measure of *frequency* of *high-frequency* electric *alternating current* or oscillatory discharge. One million cycles. Unit used in high-frequency alternating current measurement.

MEGATON BOMB. A *nuclear weapon* with an explosive power equivalent to one million tons of *T.N.T.* (approximately 10^{15} *calories*).

MEGOHM. One million *ohms*.

MEIOSIS. A process of *cell* division as a result of which a *diploid* cell produces four *haploid cells*. Consists of two successive cell divisions, each of which resembles *mitosis*, but the *chromosomes* are duplicated only once in the process. Meiosis occurs in the life cycle of all sexually reproducing *organisms*. In animals it is the process by which *gametes* are formed from *gametocytes*.

MELAMINE. $C_3H_6N_6$. Triaminotriazine. *Organic compound* which forms a *thermosetting* resin with *formaldehyde*.

MELANIN. $C_{17}H_{98}O_{33}N_{14}S$. A dark brown pigment produced in the skin *cells* called melanocytes. Skin and hair colours in many animals, including man, are due to melanin. People of different races have approximately the same number of melanocytes, colour differences being due to variations in the distribution of melanin in the skin. The *Sun* stimulates the production of melanin in melanocytes, and the function of the melanin is to absorb the Sun's harmful radiations.

MELTING POINT. The constant *temperature* at which the *solid* and *liquid phase* of a substance are in equilibrium at a given *pressure*. Melting points are normally quoted for standard atmospheric pressure, 760 mm. of mercury.

MENDELEVIUM. Md. *Transuranic element*, At. No. 101. Only known *isotope*, $^{256}_{101}$Md, has *half-life* of 30 minutes.

MENICUS. The curved surface of a *liquid* in a vessel. If the *contact angle* between the liquid and the wall of the vessel is less than 90°, the meniscus is *concave*; if greater, the meniscus is *convex*.

MENSURATION. Measurement of lengths, areas and volumes.

MENTHOL. $C_{10}H_{20}O$. One of a series of *organic compounds* of the *camphor* group. Occurs in natural *oils*. White *crystals*, m.p. 42° C., with a characteristic smell. Used in medicine.

MERCAPTANS. Thio-alcohols. *Organic compounds* with the general formula R.SH. Ethyl mercaptan $C_2H_5.SH$, is a *liquid*, b.p. 35° C., used in the manufacture of rubber *accelerators*.

MERCURIC. *Compound* of *bivalent* mercury.

MERCURIC CHLORIDE. See *corrosive sublimate*.

MERCURIOUS. *Compound* of *univalent* mercury.

MERCUROUS CHLORIDE. See *calomel*.

MERCURY (astr.). *Planet* with its orbit nearest the *Sun*. Mean distance from the Sun = 36 million miles. Sidereal period ('year') = 87·969 days. Mass 0·054 that of the *Earth*, diameter 3010 miles. Probably at a high *temperature* and without an atmosphere.

MERCURY. Quicksilver, Hydrargyrum. Hg. Element. A.W. 200·59. At. No. 80. *Liquid*, silvery-white *metal*, S.G. 13·6, m.p. −39° C., b.p. 357° C. Occurs as *cinnabar*, HgS. Extracted by roasting the ore in a current of air. Used in *thermometers*, *barometers*, *manometers*, and other scientific apparatus; *alloys* (called *amalgams*) used in dentistry. *Compounds* are poisonous; some are used in medicine.

MERCURY CELL. A *primary cell* consisting of a zinc *anode*, a *cathode* of mercuric oxide (HgO) mixed with graphite (about 5%), and an *electrolyte* of *potassium hydroxide* (KOH) saturated with *zinc oxide* (ZnO). The *EMF* is about 1·3 *volts* and by suitable design the cell can be made to deliver about 5 *ampere-hours* per cubic inch.

MERCURY VAPOUR LAMP. Lamp emitting a strong bluish *light* by the passage of an *electric current* through mercury *vapour* in a bulb. The light is rich in *ultra-violet radiations*; used in artificial sun-ray treatment and in street lighting.

MERIDIAN, CELESTIAL. The *great circle* of the *celestial sphere* passing through the *zenith* and the celestial poles, meeting the horizon at points called the North and South points.

MERIDIAN, MAGNETIC. See *magnetic meridian*.

MERIDIAN, TERRESTRIAL. Meridian of longitude. An imaginary *great circle* drawn round the *Earth*, which passes through both poles.

MESO-. A prefix indicating that a substance is optically inactive due to intra-molecular compensation.

MESONS. Group of unstable *elementary particles* with *rest masses* between those of the *electron* and the *proton*. Positive, negative, and neutral mesons exist; when charged the magnitude of the charge is equal to that of the electron. Mesons are found in *cosmic rays* and are emitted by *nuclei* under bombardment by high *energy* particles. They are believed to play a vital part in the cohesion of *nucleons* within nuclei, but no satisfactory explanation of the *exchange forces* with which they are associated has yet been given. Mesons are all extremely short-lived as will be seen from the table below which lists the three types of meson: μ-mesons or muons, π-mesons or pions, and K-mesons. The neutral K-meson can exist in states in which the *wave functions* of the K° and its *anti-particle* $\overline{K}^\circ$ are mixed. The symmetric mixture behaves like the particle designated K_1°, while the anti-symmetric mixture behaves like the particle designated K_2°.

Particle		Charge	Electron masses	Mean Life secs	Decay products
μ-mesons	μ^+	$+1$	$206 \cdot 77$	$2 \cdot 2 \times 10^{-6}$	$e^+ + \nu + \bar{\nu}$
(muons)	μ^-	-1	$206 \cdot 77$	$2 \cdot 2 \times 10^{-6}$	$e^- + \nu + \bar{\nu}$
π-mesons	π^+	$+1$	$273 \cdot 2$	$2 \cdot 5 \times 10^{-8}$	$\mu^+ + \nu$
(pions)	π^-	-1	$273 \cdot 2$	$2 \cdot 5 \times 10^{-8}$	$\mu^- + \bar{\nu}$
	π°	0	$264 \cdot 2$	$2 \cdot 0 \times 10^{-16}$	$2\gamma, \gamma + e^+ + e^-$
	K^+	$+1$	$966 \cdot 6$	$1 \cdot 2 \times 10^{-8}$	various
K-mesons	K^-	-1	$966 \cdot 6$	$1 \cdot 2 \times 10^{-8}$	various
	K_1°	0	$974 \cdot 2$	$1 \cdot 0 \times 10^{-10}$	$\pi^+ + \pi^-, \pi^\circ$
	K_2°	0	$974 \cdot 2$	$6 \cdot 1 \times 10^{-8}$	various

e^+ and e^- are positive and negative electrons.

ν and $\bar{\nu}$ are the *neutrino* and anti-neutrino.

γ is a *photon*.

META-. Prefix indicating that an *organic compound* contains a *benzene* ring substituted in the 1.3 positions.

METABOLISM. The chemical processes associated with living *organisms*. Usually divided into two parts: *catabolism*, as a result of which complex substances are decomposed into simple ones, with the release of *energy* which becomes available for the organism's activities; and *anabolism*, which comprises the building up of complex substances with the absorption or storage of energy. Metabolic reactions are usually under the control of *enzymes*, which are consequently of immense importance in the chemistry of life. Metabolic processes are very similar throughout the plant and animal kingdoms and there are therefore corresponding similarities between the enzymes which are manufactured by organisms.

METABOLITE. Any substance which takes part in the process of *metabolism*.

METAL. Substance having a 'metallic' lustre, malleable, ductile, of high *specific gravity*, and a good *conductor* of *heat* and *electricity*. *Elements* having such physical properties to a greater or less degree are generally *electropositive*, combine with oxygen to give *bases*; their *chlorides* are stable towards *water*. A number of elements normally regarded as metals have only some of the above properties. See *metalloid*.

METALDEHYDE, Meta. Solid *polymer* of *acetaldehyde*, CH_3CHO. Used as *fuel* in small heaters. White, *volatile*, inflammable, poisonous *solid*.

METALLIC CRYSTALS. The type of *crystal* formed by most *metals*, in which the outer *electrons* of the metallic *atoms* are shared by the crystal as a whole. Thus, the positively charged metal *ions* in the crystal *lattice* are surrounded by a 'gas' of *free electrons*. These free electrons account for the fact that most metals are good conductors of *heat* and *electricity*.

METALLOID. *Element* having some properties characteristic of *metals*, others of non-metals. Element giving rise to an *amphoteric oxide*. E.g. arsenic, antimony.

METALLURGY. Science and technology of *metals*; in particular, the extraction of metals from their ores.

METAMERISM. Type of *isomerism* exhibited by *organic compounds* of the same chemical class or type; caused by the attachment of different *radicals* to the same central *atom* or group. E.g. diethyl *ether*, $(C_2H_5)_2O$, and methyl propyl ether, $CH_3OC_3H_7$.

METASTABLE STATE. (chem.) State of supercooled *water* (see *supercooling*) or of supersaturated *solutions* (see *supersaturation*) in which the *phase* which is normally *stable* under the given conditions does not form unless a small amount of the normally stable phase is already present. Thus supercooled water will remain as *liquid* water below 0° C. until a small *crystal* of *ice* is introduced.

METASTABLE STATE (phys.). An excited state (see *excitation*) of an *atom* or *nucleus* which has an appreciable life-time.

METATHESIS (chem.). See *double decomposition*.

METEOR. *Solid* body from outer *space*. A meteor becomes incandescent ('shooting star') on entering the Earth's *atmosphere* owing to the frictional *forces* set up at its surface. Small meteors burn up completely in the atmosphere, but some of the larger ones survive and fall to Earth as meteorites. Meteorites are of two kinds, those which are predominantly stone and those which are predominantly iron. The largest meteorites can weight up to 100 tons. Every day some million meteors enter the Earth's atmosphere and some 10 tons of meteorite material are added to the planet's surface.

METEOR SHOWERS. Exceptionally heavy falls of *meteors* (about 20 times greater than the average) which enter the Earth's *atmosphere* when the Earth's *orbit* crosses the orbit of a *comet*, i.e. an orbit which contains either the material of which comets are made or into which they disintegrate.

METEORITE. See *meteor*.

METEOROLOGY. The science of the weather; the study of such conditions as atmospheric *pressure*, *temperature*, *wind* strength, *humidity*, etc., from which conclusions as to the forthcoming weather are drawn.

-METER. Suffix denoting measurer; e.g. *voltmeter*.

METHACRYLIC ACID. $CH_2:C(CH_3)COOH$. Corrosive *liquid*, m.p. 15° C., b.p. 163° C. The *polymer* of its methyl *ester*, methyl methacrylate, is an important *plastic* (Perspex*).

METHANE, marsh gas, fire-damp. CH_4. First *hydrocarbon* of the *paraffin series*. Odourless, invisible *gas*. B.p.—161·5° C. Inflammable, forms an explosive mixture with air. Formed from decaying *organic* matter and in coalmines; occurs in *coal-gas*.

METHANOL. See *methyl alcohol*.

METHYL ALCOHOL, wood spirit. CH_3OH. Colourless, poisonous *liquid* with a faint smell. B.p. 64·6° C. Obtained as wood naphtha by the *destructive distillation* of wood. Used to *denature methylated spirit*, as a *solvent*, and in chemical industry.

METHYL CARBINOL. See *ethyl alcohol*.

METHYL GROUP. The *univalent* organic *radical* CH_3—.

METHYLATED SPIRIT. *Liquid fuel* consisting, by *volume*, of 90% *ethyl alcohol*, 9·5% *methyl alcohol*, 0·5% *pyridine*, together with small amounts of *petroleum* and methyl violet dye.

METHYLATED SPIRIT, INDUSTRIAL. A variety of *methylated spirit* free from *pyridine*; consists of *ethyl alcohol* with 5% *methyl alcohol*.

METHYLENE BLUE. $C_{16}H_{18}N_{13}SCl$. *Soluble*, intense blue *dye*. Used as a dyestuff, in medicine, and as a stain in *biology*.

METOL, *p*-methylaminophenol. $CH_3NH.C_6H_4OH$. White crystalline *compound*, m.p. 87° C. Used as a developer in *photography*. Term also often applied to the *sulphate* of the compound.

METRE. Unit of length in the *metric system*. Redefined in 1960 as the length equal to 1,650,763·73 *wave lengths* in vacuo of the *radiation* corresponding to the transition between the levels $2p_{10}$ and $5d_5$ of the *isotope* $^{86}_{36}Kr$. This definition abrogated the platinum-iridium metre bar as the standard of length. One metre is equal to 39·37 inches.

METRE BRIDGE. See *Wheatstone bridge*.

METRE-CANDLE. See *lux*.

METRIC SYSTEM (UNITS). System of *weights* and measures originally based upon the *metre*. This was intended to be 1/10,000,000 of a quadrant of the Earth through Paris. See *weight, volume, length* (metric units of).

METRIC TON, tonne. 1000 *kilograms*; 2204·61 lb., 0·9842 ton.

MEV. Million *electron-volts*.

MHO, reciprocal ohm. Unit of *conductance*; ratio of the *electric current* flowing through a *conductor*, measured in *amperes*, to the *potential difference* between the ends of the conductor, measured in *volts*, gives the conductance in mhos.

MICA. A group of *minerals*, the most important of which are muscovite,

$H_2KAl_3(SiO_4)_3$, and phlogopite, $H_2KMg_3Al(SiO_4)_3$. Naturally occurring mica can be split along its cleavages into small thick pieces ('blocks') or thin sheets ('splittings'). Being an excellent insulator and being resistant to high *temperatures*, mica is used as a *dielectric* in *capacitors*, as a support for *electrodes* in *thermionic valves*, and for heating elements in irons etc. As mica is also transparent it is used for inspection windows of furnaces. Micanite* sheet is manufactured by bonding mica splittings with *shellac* or synthetic *resins*.

MICHELSON-MORLEY EXPERIMENT. An attempt to measure the *velocity* of the Earth through the *ether*, by measuring the effect which such a velocity would have upon the velocity of *light*. No such motion of the Earth relative to the ether was detected: a result of the greatest importance for the theory of *relativity*.

MICRO-. 1. Prefix denoting one-millionth, in *metric units*. 2. Prefix meaning 'very small'; on a small scale. See also *macro-*.

MICROBALANCE. *Balance* for weighing objects of very small *weight*, i.e. of the order of 10^{-3} to 10^{-6} gm.

MICROCOSMIC SALT. Sodium ammonium hydrogen phosphate, $NaNH_4HPO_4.4H_2O$. White crystalline *soluble salt*.

MICROFARAD. One-millionth of a *farad*.

MICROMETER. Instrument for the accurate measurement of small distances or *angles*.

MICRO-MICRON, $\mu\mu$. One-millionth of a *micron;* 10^{-12} *metre*, ·01 *Ångström units*.

MICRO-MILLIMETRE. One-millionth of a *millimetre*; 10^{-9} *metre*, 10 *Ångström units*.

MICRON, μ. One-millionth of a *metre*. 10,000 *Ångström units*.

MICRO-ORGANISM. *Unicellular organism* which can only be seen with the aid of a *microscope*.

MICROPHONE. Device for converting *sound*-waves into *electrical energy* which may then be reconverted into sound after transmission by wire or *radio*. One common type consists of a diaphragm in contact with, or close to, loosely packed carbon granules. The vibration of the diaphragm which is set up by sound disturbs the packing of the carbon granules and alters the electrical *resistance* of the carbon. Thus an *electric current* flowing through the carbon will vary in a manner which depends upon the *frequency* and intensity of the vibrations produced by the sound on the diaphragm. See also *condenser microphone*.

MICROPHOTOMETER. Special form of *densitometer* enabling density variations over a very small area of the image to be measured.

MICROSCOPE, COMPOUND. Instrument consisting essentially of two *converging lenses* or systems of lenses called the *objective* and the *eye-piece* respectively. The objective, which is nearest the viewed object, forms a real inverted magnified image of the object just inside the focal distance (see *focal length*) of the eyepiece. This image is viewed through the eyepiece, which then acts as a *simple microscope*. The useful *magnification* obtainable with an optical microscope is limited by the *wave-length* of visible *light* as two points on a microscopic specimen cannot be distinguished from each other if they are not as far apart as half the wave-length of the light used to illuminate them. Thus for magnifications in excess of about 1500, an *ultra-violet microscope*, or an *electron microscope* must be used.

MICROSCOPE, SIMPLE; magnifying glass. A *convex lens* which is used to produce a virtual *image* larger than the viewed object.

MICROTOME. Apparatus for cutting thin sections of material, for microscopical examination.

MICROWAVES. *Electromagnetic radiation* with *wave-lengths* ranging from very short *radio* waves almost to the *infra-red* region; i.e. wave-lengths from 30 cm. to 1 mm.

MICROWAVE SPECTROSCOPY. Measurement of the absorption or emission of *electromagnetic radiation* in the *waveband* 0·1 mm. to 10 cm. by atomic or molecular systems. See *electron spin resonance*.

MIL. One thousandth of an inch.

MILK OF LIME. *Suspension* of *lime* in *water*.

MILK SUGAR. See *lactose*.

MILKY WAY. Originally a description of the luminous band of *stars* encircling the heavens. It is now known that these stars are members of the *Galaxy* to which the *solar system* belongs, and the Galaxy is therefore often referred to as the Milky Way.

MILLI-. Prefix denoting one-thousandth, in *metric units*.

MILLIAMMETER. Sensitive *ammeter* graduated to measure *milliamperes*.

MILLIAMPERE. One-thousandth of an *ampere*.

MILLIBAR. Unit of atmospheric pressure, used in *meteorology*. 1000 *dynes* per square centimetre; approximately equal to 1/32 inch of mercury. See *pressure, units of*.

MILLICURIE. One-thousandth of a *curie*; that quantity of a *radioactive isotope* which decays at the rate of $3·7 \times 10^7$ disintegrations per second.

MILLIGRAM. 1/1000 *gram*; ·0154 *grain*.

MILLILITRE, ml. Unit of *volume*, used for *liquids*; 1/1000 *litre*. Very nearly equal to 1 cubic centimetre (c.c.).

MILLIMETRE, mm. 1/1000 *metre*; ·0394 inch. See *length, metric units*.

MILLIMICRON. 1/1000 *micron*; 10^{-7} cm.

MINERAL. Occurring naturally in the earth. The term, although applying mainly to *inorganic compounds*, also includes mineral *oil*, which consists chiefly of organic *hydrocarbons*.

MINERAL OIL. See *paraffin oil*.

MINIM. British fluid measure; 1/60 of a fluid drachm; ·0591 c.c. See *apothecaries' fluid measure*.

MINIMUM (math.). See *maximum*.

MINIUM. See *red lead*.

MINOR PLANETS. See *asteroids*.

MINORITY CARRIERS. In a *semiconductor*, the type of *carrier* which constitutes less than half the total number of carriers.

MIRROR. Surface which reflects regularly most of the *light* falling upon it, thus forming *images*. See *reflection*.

MIRROR IMAGE. *Image* of an object as viewed in a *mirror*; reversed in such a way that the image bears to the object the same relation as a right hand to a left.

MIRRORS, SPHERICAL. *Mirrors* the reflecting surfaces of which form a portion of a *sphere*. The surface of such a mirror may be regarded as being made up of an infinitely large number of very small plane mirrors, each at a *tangent to the curve* of the mirror. Thus a *ray* of incident *light* would be reflected at any point as if from such a small plane mirror. Spherical mirrors may be *convex*, with the reflecting surface on the outside of the sphere, or *concave*. The centre and radius of the sphere of which the mirror is considered to form a part, are termed the *centre* and *radius of curvature*; the centre of the mirror is the pole, and the line joining the centre of curvature to the pole is the axis. The principal focus (see *focus*) is at a point half-way between the pole and the centre of curvature. Regarding all distances as measured from the mirror and taking all distances in the direction opposite to that of the incident light as positive, the following relationship holds for spherical mirrors: $1/v + 1/u = 1/f = 2/r$, where u and v are the distances of object and image from the mirror, r the radius of curvature, and f the focal length.

MISCH METAL. *Alloy* of cerium with small amounts of other *rare earth metals*. Used for 'flints' in automatic lighters.

MISCIBLE. Capable of being mixed to form a *homogeneous* substance; usually applied to *liquids*; e.g. *water* and *alcohol* are completely miscible.

MISPICKEL, arsenical pyrites. Natural *sulphide* of iron and arsenic, $FeAsS$.

MIST. Droplets of *water*, formed by the *condensation* of *water-vapour* on dust particles.

MITOCHONDRIA. Minute rod-shaped or granular bodies, about $\frac{1}{2}$–1 *micron* in diameter or length, which occur in the *cytoplasm* of most *cells*. Mitochondria contain many of the *enzymes* of the cell, particularly those required by the *citric acid cycle*.

MITOSIS. Process by which the *nuclei* of *diploid cells* reproduce. After the *chromosomes* in the nucleus have duplicated the process of mitosis is divided into four stages. 1. Prophase, during which the chromosomes appear, shorten and thicken. 2. Metaphase, during which the nuclear membrane dissolves and a spindle forms, to the centre of which the chromosomes attach themselves. 3. Anaphase, during which the duplicates of the chromosomes separate and migrate to the ends of the spindle. 4. Telophase, during which two nuclear membranes form, each enclosing one set of chromosomes. The *cytoplasm* also divides in this stage, so that two new diploid cells are formed, each containing a set of chromosomes identical to that of the parent cell.

MIXED CRYSTALS. See *solid solutions*.

MIXTURES, mechanical mixtures. These differ from chemical *compounds* in the following respects: 1. The constituents may be separated by suitable physical or mechanical means. 2. Most mixtures may be made in all proportions; in the case of *solutions* which may be regarded as molecular mixtures, there are often limits of *solubility*. 3. No *heat* effect (except in the case of solutions) is produced on formation; the formation of chemical compounds is invariably accompanied by the evolution or absorption of *energy* in the form of heat. 4. The properties of a mixture are an aggregate of the properties of the constituents, whereas a compound has individual properties, often quite unlike those of the component *elements*.

M.K.S. SYSTEM. System of *units* derived from the *metre*, *kilogram*, and *second*.

MODERATOR. A substance used in *nuclear reactors* to reduce the speed of *fast neutrons* produced by *nuclear fission*. These substances consist of *atoms* of light *elements* (e.g. *deuterium* in *heavy water*, *graphite*, beryllium) to which the neutrons are able to impart some of their *energy* on collision, without being captured. Neutrons which have been slowed down in this way are much more likely to cause new fissions of $^{235}_{92}U$ than they are to be captured by $^{238}_{92}U$.

MODULATION. The process of varying some characteristic of one wave (usually a *radio-frequency carrier wave*) in accordance with some characteristic of another wave. The main types are *amplitude*, *frequency*, and *phase modulation*. See also *velocity modulation*.

MODULUS. Constant *factor* or multiplier for the conversion of *units* from one system to another. See also *elastic modulus*.

MOHS SCALE OF HARDNESS. A scale in which each *mineral* listed is softer than (i.e. is scratched by) all those below it. 1. *Talc*. 2. *Gypsum*. 3. *Calcite*. 4. *Fluorite*. 5. *Apatite*. 6. *Orthoclase*. 7. *Quartz*. 8. *Topaz*. 9. *Corundum*. 10. *Diamond*.

MOL, mole. *Gram-molecule* of a substance; the *weight* of it in grams numerically equal to its *molecular weight*.

MOLAR ELECTRODE POTENTIAL. See *electromotive series*.

MOLAR SOLUTION. *Solution* containing one *mol* or *gram-molecule* per *litre*.

MOLECULAR BIOLOGY. The study of the structure of the *molecules* which are of importance in *biology*.

MOLECULAR COMPOUNDS. Chemical *compounds* formed by the chemical combination of two or more complete *molecules*. E.g. the *hydrates* of *salts*.

MOLECULAR CONCENTRATION. *Concentration* of a *solution* expressed in terms of *gram-molecules* or *mols* in a given *volume*.

MOLECULAR DISTILLATION. The *evaporation* of *molecules* from a surface, at *pressures* of about 10^{-3} cm. of mercury, and their subsequent *condensation* under such conditions that their *mean free path* is of the same order as the distance between the heated and cooled surfaces. Used for *isotope separation* and distilling heat-sensitive *organic compounds*.

MOLECULAR FORMULA. *Formula* of a chemical *compound*, showing the kind and the number of *atoms* present in the *molecule*, but not their arrangement.

MOLECULAR ORBITAL. When two *atomic orbitals* overlap they coalesce to produce a single 'molecular orbital'.

MOLECULAR SPECTRUM. *Spectrum* emitted by *molecules*. Caused by transitions between different states of molecular rotation, vibration, etc.

MOLECULAR VOLUME. The *volume* occupied by one *mol* of a substance; equal to its *molecular weight* divided by its *density*.

MOLECULAR WEIGHT. The sum of the *atomic weights* of all the *atoms* which comprise a *molecule*.

MOLECULAR WEIGHT DETERMINATION. The following are amongst the available methods: Determination of the *vapour density*; applicable to *gases* and *volatile liquids*. Measurement of the *depression of freezing point, elevation of boiling point*, and *osmotic pressure* produced by a definite *concentration* of the substance in *solution*; used for *soluble* substances which do not dissociate or associate in solution. (See *dissociation, association.*) Determination of the *chemical equivalent* of the substance, with a knowledge of the *equation* for the reaction.

MOLECULE. Smallest portion of a substance capable of existing independently and retaining the properties of the original substance.

MOLYBDENUM. Mo. Element. A.W. 95·94, At. No. 42. Hard white *metal* resembling iron. S.G. 10·2, m.p. 2620° C. Occurs as molybdenite, MoS_2. Extracted by roasting the ore and reducing the *oxide* so formed in an electric furnace with carbon. Used for special *steels* and *alloys*.

MOMENT, MAGNETIC. See *magnetic moment*.

MOMENT OF FORCE. Measure of the tendency of a *force* to rotate the body to which it is applied. Measured by multiplying the magnitude of the force by the perpendicular distance from the line of action of the force to the *axis* of rotation.

MOMENT OF INERTIA. The moment of inertia *I* of a body about any *axis* is the sum of the products of the *mass dm* of each element of the body and the *square* of *r*, its distance from the axis. $I = \Sigma r^2 dm$.

MOMENTUM. The product of the *mass* and the *velocity* of a body. For speeds approaching that of *light*, the variation of mass with *velocity* must be taken into account, and the value of *m* appropriate to the velocity of the body must be used in the expression for the momentum. See *relativity, theory of*.

MOMENTUM, CONSERVATION OF. See *conservation of momentum*.

MONAD. *Element* having a *valency* of one.

MONATOMIC MOLECULE. *Molecule* of an *element*, consisting of a single *atom* of the element. E.g. the molecules of the *inert gases*.

MONAZITE. *Mineral* containing *compounds* of cerium, thorium, and other *rare earths*, with some occluded helium.

MOND PROCESS. Extraction of nickel by the action of *carbon monoxide*, CO, on the impure *metal*. This gives nickel carbonyl, $Ni(CO)_4$, a *gas* which decomposes when heated to 200° C. into pure nickel and carbon monoxide, the latter being used again.

MONEL METAL*. *Alloy* of copper (25%–35%), nickel (60%–70%) and small amounts of iron, manganese, silicon, and carbon. Used as an *acid*-resisting material in chemical industry.

MONO-. Prefix denoting one, single.

MONOBASIC ACID. An *acid* having one *atom* of *acidic* hydrogen in a *molecule*; acid giving rise to only one series of *salts*. E.g. *nitric acid*, HNO_3.

MONOCHROMATIC LIGHT. *Light* consisting of vibrations of the same or nearly the same *frequency*; light of one *colour*.

MONOHYDRIC. Containing one *hydroxyl group* in a *molecule*.

MONOMER. Chemical *compound* consisting of single *molecules*; as opposed to a *polymer*, the molecules of which are built up by the repeated union of monomer molecules. See *polymerization*.

MONOSACCHARIDES, simple sugars. Group of *carbohydrates* consisting chiefly of *sugars* having a *molecular formula*, $C_6H_{12}O_6$ (*hexoses*) or $C_5H_{10}O_5$ (*pentores*); unlike the *polysaccharides*, cannot be hydrolyzed to give simple sugars.

MONOTROPIC. Existing in only one *stable* physical form, any other form obtainable being unstable under all conditions.

MONOVALENT, univalent. Having a *valency* of one.

MOON, THE. *Satellite* of the *Earth*. Mean distance from the Earth, 238,800 miles; synodic month 29·5 days, sidereal month 27·3 days. Mass 0·0123 that of the Earth; diameter 2159·9 miles. Devoid of *water* or an *atmosphere*.

MORDANTS. Substances used in dyeing, especially fabrics of plant origin. The fabric is first impregnated with the mordant, which is generally a *basic metal hydroxide* for *acidic dyes*, or an acidic substance for basic dyes. The dye then reacts chemically with the mordant forming an insoluble *lake* which is firmly attached to the fabric.

MORPHIA. See *morphine*.

MORPHINE. $C_{17}H_{19}O_3N$. Member of the *alkaloids*; occurs in *opium*. White *solid*, m.p. 253° C. Powerful *narcotic*, used medically for relieving pain. Dangerous habit-forming drug.

MORPHOLOGY. The study of the form and structure of *organisms*.

MORTAR. Building material consisting mainly of *lime* and *sand;* hardens on exposure through chemical action between the ingredients and atmospheric *carbon dioxide*.

MOSAIC. 1. In television cameras (see *camera, television*) a device for the electrical storage of the optical image. Usually consists of a sheet of *mica* one side of which is covered with mutually insulated particles of a *photo-emissive* material, each of which is capacitively coupled through the mica to a conducting coating on the reverse side. This conducting coating, called the signal plate, is the output *electrode* from which the electrical signal representing the optical image is obtained.   2. In *nuclear physics*, a *photomicrograph* of a track in an *emulsion*, prepared from a number of photographs of consecutive fields of view and reconstructed as though the track lay in one *plane*.

MOSAIC GOLD. Crystalline stannic sulphide, SnS_2. Shining, golden-yellow scales.

MÖSSBAUER EFFECT. The discovery by R. L. Mössbauer in 1957 that in certain cases appreciable fractions of the *gamma-ray spectrum* emitted by some excited (see *excitation*) *nuclei* may be undisturbed by nuclear recoil or *lattice* vibrations and the consequent *Doppler effects*. The Mössbauer effect has been used to test the predictions of the theory of *relativity*, to investigate the properties of the *solid state* and the nature of *magnetism*.

MOTHER-LIQUOR. *Solution* from which substances are crystallized.

MOTION, EQUATIONS OF. *Equations* applying to bodies moving with uniform *acceleration*. If u = initial *velocity*, v = final velocity at the end of t seconds, f = acceleration, and s = distance moved in t seconds, (1) $v = u + ft$; (2) $s = ut + \frac{1}{2}ft^2$; (3) $v^2 = u^2 + 2fs$.

MOTION, LAWS OF. See *Newton's laws of motion*.

MOTOR. A device for converting other forms of *energy* into mechanical energy. Generally applied to the *internal-combustion engine* and the *electric motor*.

MOTOR, ELECTRIC. See *electric motor*.

MUCOPROTEINS. Glycoproteins. *Proteins* which contain a *carbohydrate* group.

MULTICELLULAR. Said of an *organism* which consists of more than one *cell*.

MULTIPLE PROPORTIONS, LAW OF. See *chemical combination, laws of*.

MULTIPLICATION CONSTANT (FACTOR). The 'effective' multiplication constant of a *nuclear reactor* is the ratio of the average number of *neutrons* produced by *nuclear fission* per unit time, to the total number of neutrons absorbed or leaking out in the same time. See *sub-critical* and *super-critical*.

MUMETAL*. An *alloy* of high *magnetic permeability* containing up to 78% nickel in addition to iron, copper, and manganese.

MUNTZ METAL*. Alloy containing 3 parts of copper and 2 parts of zinc.

MUON. μ-meson. See *meson*.

MURIATE. *Chloride*, *salt* of *hydrochloric acid*.

MURIATIC ACID. See *hydrochloric acid*.

MUSTARD GAS. Dichlorodiethyl sulphide, $(CH_2CH_2Cl)_2S$. Oily *liquid* which has been used as a 'war gas'. Destroyed by *oxidizing agents*, e.g. *bleaching powder*.

MUTAGEN. A substance which produces *mutations*.

MUTAROTATION. A change in the *optical rotation* of a substance.

MUTATION. A change in the chemical constitution of the *chromosomes* of an *organism*: the changes are normally restricted to individual *genes*, but occasionally involve serious alteration to whole chromosomes. When a mutation occurs in *gametes* or *gametocytes* an inherited change may be produced in the characteristics of the organisms which develop from them. It is due to the *natural selection* of strains of organisms which have become better adapted to their environment, as a consequence of genetic mutations, that the evolution of species has taken place. A *somatic* mutation is one which occurs to a body *cell*, and which is consequently passed on to all the cells which are derived from it by *mitosis*. Natural mutations are relatively rare events, and at this stage of biological evolution, when they occur in the cells of higher animals, almost always produce deleterious characteristics. Artificial mutations can be brought about by *ionizing radiations* (hence the genetic and *carcinogenetic* dangers of *nuclear weapons*) and by certain chemical substances.

MUTUAL INDUCTION. The induction of an *E.M.F.* in a circuit due to a changing current in a separate circuit with which it is magnetically linked. The induced E.M.F. is proportional to the rate of change of the current in the second circuit, the constant of proportionality being called the coefficient of mutual induction, or the mutual inductance. The unit of mutual inductance is the *henry*.

MYDRIATIC. Substance used to dilate the pupil of the eye.

MYOGLOBIN. A form of *haemoglobin* which occurs in muscle fibres.

MYOPIA, short sight. Defect of vision. Subject is unable to see distant objects distinctly. Corrected by the use of *concave* spectacle lenses.

N

NADIR (astr.). Lowest point; point opposite the *zenith* on the *celestial sphere*.

NANO-. Prefix indicating one thousand millionth. E.g. a nanosecond is 10^{-9} seconds.

NAPHTHA. General name for *mixtures* of *hydrocarbons* in various proportions, obtained from *paraffin oil*, *coal-tar*, etc. Wood naphtha is impure *methyl alcohol*, CH_3OH, produced by the *destructive distillation* of wood.

NAPHTHALENE. $C_{10}H_8$. *Cyclic hydrocarbon* occurring in *coal-tar*. White, shiny, crystalline *solid* with a penetrating smell. M.p. $80 \cdot 2°$ C. B.p. $218°$ C. Used in the manufacture of organic *dyes*.

NARCOTIC. Producing sleep, stupor, or insensibility.

NASCENT STATE. Certain *elements*, notably hydrogen, are more active when being set free in a *chemical reaction* than in their ordinary state; such 'nascent' elements are supposed to owe their activity to being composed of single *atoms* instead of *molecules*, or alternatively to some of the *chemical energy* liberated on the reaction being associated with the hydrogen instead of being released in the form of *heat*.

NATRIUM. See *sodium*.

NATRON. Natural sodium sesquicarbonate,

$$Na_2CO_3.NaHCO_3.2H_2O.$$

NATURAL (chem.). Occurring in nature; not artificially prepared.

NATURAL ABUNDANCE. The *abundance* of each different *isotope* in an *element* as it is normally found in nature.

NATURAL FREQUENCY. The *frequency* of free oscillation of any system.

NATURAL GAS. Mixture of gaseous *hydrocarbons* predominantly *methane*, often containing other *gases*, issuing from the earth in some localities, more particularly near deposits of mineral *oil*.

NATURAL LOGARITHM. See *logarithm*.

NATURAL SELECTION. The theory, first proposed by Charles Darwin, which explains the mechanism of biological evolution. According to this theory, the life-forms best adapted to their environment will survive and reproduce in the greatest numbers. As new characteristics arise as small uncontrolled variations (resulting from genetic *mutations*) nature selects for survival those strains of *organisms* which inherit distinctive characteristics best fitting them for their environment.

NAUTICAL MILE. 6082·66 feet; often used synonymously with the Admiralty mile, 6080 feet. Practically, may be taken as 1 minute of *latitude*.

NEAR INFRA-RED or **ULTRA-VIOLET.** The shortest *infra-red* or the longest *ultra-violet wave-lengths*; i.e. those wave-lengths of these two types of *radiation* which are 'nearest' in magnitude to those of visible *light*.

NEBULA (astr.). Cloudy, luminous patch in the heavens. Consists of a *galaxy* of *stars*, or of materials from which such galaxies are being formed.

NEGATIVE (math. and phys.). In any convention of signs, regarded as being counted in the minus, or negative direction, as opposed to positive.

NEGATIVE FEEDBACK. See *feedback*.

NEGATIVE, PHOTOGRAPHIC. See *photography*.

NEGATIVE POLE. The south-seeking pole of a *magnet*. See *magnetic pole*.

NEGATRON. Negaton. See *electron*.

NEODYMIUM. Nd. Element. A.W. 144·24. At. No. 60. See *lanthanides*.

NEON. Ne. Element. A.W. 20·183. At. No. 10. Colourless, odourless, invisible *gas* belonging to the *inert gases*. Occurs in the *atmosphere* (1 part in 55,000). Obtained by the *fractional distillation* of *liquid air*. A discharge of *electricity* through neon at low *pressures* produces an intense orange-red glow; used for neon signs.

NEOPRENE*. *Trans*-polychloroprene. $(CH_2.CH.CCl.CH_2)_n$. A synthetic *rubber* having a high *tensile strength* and better heat and *ozone* resistance than natural rubber.

NEPHASCOPE. Grid-like instrument for determining speed of celestial objects (including clouds) by observation of time of transit.

NEPTUNE (astr.). *Planet* with two *satellites*. *Orbit* lies between those of *Uranus* and *Pluto*. Mean distance from the *Sun*, 2794·1 million miles. *Sidereal period* ('year'), 164·8 years. Mass 17·46 times that of the *Earth*, diameter 27,840 miles. Surface temperature probably below $-200°$ C.

NEPTUNIUM. Np. *Transuranic element*, At. No. 93. Most stable *isotope*, $^{237}_{93}$Np, has a *half-life* of $2·2 \times 10^6$ years. *Metal* of silvery appearance, m.p. 640° C., produced as a *by-product* by *nuclear reactors* in the manufacture of plutonium.

NERNST EFFECT. If a *temperature* gradient is maintained across an electrical *conductor* (or *semiconductor*) which is placed in a transverse *magnetic field*, a *potential difference* will be produced across the conductor.

NERNST HEAT THEOREM. The *entropy* change for *chemical reactions* involving crystalline *solids*, is zero at the *absolute zero* of temperature. See also *thermodynamics, laws of.*

NESSLER'S SOLUTION. *Solution* of potassium mercuric-iodide, $KHgI_3$, in *potassium hydroxide* solution. Used as a test for *ammonia*, with which it forms a brown coloration or precipitate.

NEURON (E). Nerve cell. A special type of biological *cell*, being the unit of which the nervous systems of animals are composed. Consists of a *nucleus* surrounded by a *cytoplasm* from which thread-like fibres project. In most neurons impulses are received by numerous short fibres called *dendrites* and carried away from the cell by a single long fibre called an *axon*. Transfer of impulses from neuron to neuron takes place at junctions between axons and dendrites which are called *synapses*.

NEUTRAL (chem.). Neither *acid* nor *alkaline*. Containing equal numbers of *hydroxyl* and *hydrogen ions* and having a p_H of 7.

NEUTRAL (phys.). Having neither negative nor positive net *electric charge*.

NEUTRAL TEMPERATURE. The temperature of the hot junction of a *thermocouple* at which the *electromotive force* round the circuit is a maximum and the rate of change of E.M.F. with *temperature* is a minimum.

NEUTRALIZATION (chem.). Addition of *acid* to *alkali*, or vice versa, till neither is in excess and the *solution* is *neutral*.

NEUTRINO. *Elementary particle* with no *electric charge* or *rest mass*, but with spin $\frac{1}{2}$. Originally postulated to preserve the laws of *conservation of mass and energy* and *conservation of momentum*. The existence of the particle has since been established experimentally, and it is known to exist in two forms; the neutrino, which is emitted with *positrons*, and the anti-neutrino, which is emitted with negative *electrons* (e.g. in *neutron* decay). Both forms also appear in the decay of some *mesons*.

NEUTRON. *Elementary particle* which is a constituent of all atomic *nuclei* except that of normal hydrogen. The neutron has no *electric charge* and a *mass* only very slightly greater than that of the *proton* (1838·65 times heavier than an *electron* compared to 1836·12 times for the proton). Outside a nucleus a neutron decays, with a *half-life* of 12 minutes, into a proton, an electron, and an anti-*neutrino*. Neutrons and protons may be considered as different aspects of the same particles and the name *nucleon* is used to describe both of them.

NEUTRON EXCESS. See *isotropic number*.

NEUTRON FLUX. A measure of the number of *neutrons* passing through 1 sq. cm. in any direction in 1 second.

NEUTRON TEMPERATURE. The *energies* possessed by *neutrons* in thermal equilibrium with their surroundings may be expressed in terms of a *temperature*, if it is assumed that they behave as a *monatomic gas*. Under these conditions, the neutron temperature on the *Kelvin scale*, T, is given by: $E = \dfrac{3kT}{2}$, where E is the neutron energy and k is *Boltzmann's constant*.

NEW CANDLE. See *candela*.

NEWTON. A unit of *force* in the *M.K.S. system*. The force required to give a *mass* of one *kilogram* an *acceleration* of one *metre* per second per second.

NEWTON'S LAW OF COOLING. The rate at which a body loses *heat* to its surroundings is proportional to the *temperature* difference between the body and its surroundings (an *empirical* law, true only for small differences of temperature).

NEWTON'S LAWS OF MOTION. The fundamental laws on which classical *dynamics* is based. 1. Every body continues in its state of rest or uniform motion in a straight line except in so far as it is compelled by external *forces* to change that state. 2. Rate of change of *momentum* is proportional to the applied force, and takes place in the direction in which the force acts. 3. To every action there is an equal and opposite reaction.

NEWTON'S RINGS. Coloured rings which may be observed round the point of contact of a *convex lens* and a *plane* reflecting surface. Caused by the *interference* effects which occur between *light*-waves reflected at the upper and lower surfaces of the air film separating the lens and the flat surface.

NEWTONIAN MECHANICS. System of *mechanics* developed from *Newton's Laws of Motion*. Provides an accurate means of determining the motions of bodies possessing ordinary *velocities*. The motions of particles having very high velocities must be treated by relativistic mechanics, i.e. a system of mechanics based on the theory of *relativity*, as the change of *mass* of a particle with its velocity becomes important under such conditions.

NICHROME*. Trade name for a nickel-chromium *alloy* used for wire in electrical devices, owing to its high *resistance* and its ability to withstand high *temperatures*.

NICKEL. Ni. Element. A.W. 58·71. At. No. 28. Silvery-white magnetic *metal* resembling iron. S.G. 8·90, m.p. 1455° C. Resists *corrosion*.

Occurs combined with sulphur or arsenic in pentlandite, *kupfer-nickel*, smaltite and other ores. The ore is roasted to form the *oxide*, which is reduced to the metal by hydrogen, and the metal is then purified by the *Mond process*. Used for *nickel-plating*, in coinage, for *alloys* such as *nickel steel*, *nickel silver*, *platinoid*, *constantan*, *nichrome**, and as a *catalyst*.

NICKEL CARBONYL. See *Mond process*.

NICKEL-IRON ACCUMULATOR. See *accumulator*.

NICKEL PLATING. Depositing a thin layer of metallic nickel by an electrolytic process. See *electrolysis*.

NICKEL SILVER. Group of *alloys* of copper, nickel, and zinc in varying proportions, containing up to 30% nickel. A typical composition is 60% copper, 20% nickel, 20% zinc.

NICKEL STEEL. *Steel* containing up to 6% nickel.

NICOL PRISM. Optical device, constructed from a crystal of *calcite*, used for obtaining plane polarized light. See *polarization of light*.

NICOTINE. $C_{10}H_{14}N_2$. *Alkaloid* occurring in tobacco leaves. Colourless, intensely poisonous oily *liquid*, b.p. 247·3° C.

NICOTINIC ACID. Pyridine-3-carboxylic acid, $C_5H_4N.COOH$. *Vitamin* of the B complex. Colourless crystalline *solid*, m.p. 235° C.

NIOBIUM, columbium. Nb. Element. A.W. 92·906. At. No. 41. Grey *metal*, S.G. 8·4, m.p. 2500° C. Very rare. When added to *stainless steel* in small quantities it preserves its *corrosion* resistance at high *temperatures*.

NIT. A unit of *luminance* equal to one *candela* per square metre.

NITON. Obsolete name for *radon*.

NITRAMINES. *Nitro derivatives* of *amines* with the general formula $R.NH.NO_2$.

NITRATE. *Salt* of *nitric acid*.

NITRATION. Introduction of the nitro group, $-NO_2$, into *organic compounds* by the use of *nitric acid*. Of importance in the production of *explosives*, many *nitro derivatives* of organic compounds being chemically unstable.

NITRE, saltpetre. See *potassium nitrate*.

NITRIC ACID, aqua fortis. HNO_3. Colourless, corrosive, *acid liquid*, b.p. 86° C. Powerful *oxidizing agent*. Attacks most *metals* and many other substances with evolution of brown fumes of *nitrogen dioxide*, NO_2. Manufactured by the action of concentrated *sulphuric acid*, H_2SO_4, on *sodium* or *potassium nitrate*, and by the *oxidation* of *ammonia*, NH_3, by passing a mixture of ammonia and air over heated platinum which acts as a *catalyst*. Widely used in chemical industry.

NITRIC OXIDE. NO. Colourless *gas*, reacts with oxygen on contact to form *nitrogen dioxide*, NO_2.

NITRIDES. *Compounds* of *trivalent* nitrogen and *metals* (e.g. magnesium nitride, Mg_3N_2), formed by passing nitrogen over the red hot metal. Some non-metalic *elements* (e.g. boron and silicon) also from nitrides.

NITRIFICATION. 1. The treatment of a substance with *nitric acid*. 2. The process of conversion, by the action of *bacteria*, of nitrogen *compounds* from animal and plant waste and decay, into *nitrates* in the *soil*.

NITRILE RUBBERS. A group of synthetic *rubbers* which are co-polymers (see *polymerization*) of *butadiene* and *acrylonitrile*. These materials, which can be vulcanized in a similar manner to natural rubber, have a high resistance to *oil*, *fuels*, and *aromatic solvents*. Their properties can be modified by varying the proportions of the constituents; increasing the acrylonitrile content results in greater oil resistance.

NITRITE. A *salt* or *ester* of nitrous acid, HNO_2.

NITRO DERIVATIVES. *Aliphatic* or *aromatic compounds* which contain the group $-NO_2$. E.g. *nitrobenzene*.

NITROBENZENE. $C_6H_5NO_2$. Pale yellow, oily, poisonous *liquid*, b.p. $211°$ C., with an odour of bitter almonds. Produced by the action of *nitric acid* on *benzene*; reduction of nitrobenzene yields *aniline*.

NITROCELLULOSE. *Cellulose nitrate*, the *nitric acid ester* of *cellulose*. Although the term nitrocellulose is chemically incorrect for this compound, it is extensively used.

NITROCHALK. Mixture of *calcium carbonate*, $CaCO_3$, and *ammonium nitrate*, NH_4NO_3, used as a *fertilizer*.

NITROGEN. N. Element. A.W. 14·0067. At. No. 7. Odourless, invisible, chemically inactive *gas*, forming approximately $4/5$ of the *atmosphere*. Chief natural *compound* is *Chile saltpetre*. Compounds are used as *fertilizers* and in the manufacture of *nitric acid*. The element is vital to living *organisms*, forming an essential part of the *proteins* and *nucleic acids*. See *fixation of atmospheric nitrogen*; *nitrogen cycle*.

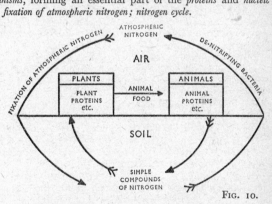

FIG. 10.

NITROGEN CYCLE. The circulation of nitrogen *compounds* in nature through the various *organisms* to which nitrogen is essential. *Inorganic* nitrogen compounds in the *soil* are taken in by plants, and are combined by the plants with other *elements* to form *nucleic acids* and *proteins*, the latter being the form in which nitrogen can be utilized by the higher animals. The result of animal waste and decay is to bring the nitrogen which the animals had absorbed back into the soil in the form of simpler nitrogen compounds. Bacterial action of various kinds converts these into compounds suitable for use by plants again. In addition to this main circulation, a certain amount of atmospheric nitrogen is 'fixed' (i.e. combined) by the action of *bacteria* associated with the roots of leguminous plants, and by the action of atmospheric *electricity*; while some combined nitrogen is set free by the action of *denitrifying bacteria*. See Fig. 10, page 203.

NITROGEN DIOXIDE, nitrogen peroxide, NO_2. Dark brown *gas* with a pungent smell, formed by the *reduction* of *nitric acid* and in the decomposition, by *heat*, of some *nitrates*. On cooling to a low *temperature* becomes paler in colour, owing to the *association* of the *molecules* to form N_2O_4.

NITROGLYCERIN, glyceryl trinitrate. $C_3H_5(NO_3)_3$. Pale yellow, heavy, oily *liquid*. Explodes with great violence when subjected to sudden shock or detonation. Used as an *explosive*, either alone or in the form of *dynamite*.

NITROLIME. See *calcium cyanamide*.

NITROUS ETHER. See *ethyl nitrite*.

NITROUS OXIDE, N_2O. See *laughing-gas*.

NOBELIUM. No. Tentative name given to the *transuranic element* of At. No. 102. Also known as Element 102. Only known *isotope*, $^{254}_{102}$No, has *half-life* of 10 minutes.

NOBLE METALS. *Metals* such as silver, gold, and platinum, which do not corrode or tarnish in air or *water*, and are not easily attacked by *acids*. From the chemical point of view, unreactive metals are low in the *electromotive series*.

NODAL POINTS. Two points on the axis of a *lens* system, such that if the incident *ray* passes through one, travelling in a given direction, the emergent ray passes through the other in a parallel direction.

NODES. Points of zero displacement in a system of stationary waves. See also *antinodes*.

NOISE (elec.). 1. Effect observed in amplifying circuits due to the amplification, together with the input signal, of spurious *voltages* arising from such causes as the vibration of certain components, the random motion of the *electrons* constituting the *current* in the *conductors*, etc. 2. A term used in *information theory* to indicate a disturbance which does not represent any part of a message from a specified source.

NOMOGRAM. Nomograph. An alignment chart arranged so that the value of a *variable* can be found, without calculation, from the values of one or two other variables which are known.

NON-CONSERVATION OF PARITY. See *parity*.

NON-ELECTROLYTES. Substances which do not yield *ions* in *solution* and which therefore form solutions of low electrical *conductivity*. See *electrolysis*.

NON-METALLIC ELEMENTS. Chemical *elements* not possessing the properties of the *metals*.

NORDHAUSEN ACID, fuming *sulphuric acid*, pyrosulphuric acid.

$H_2S_2O_7$. Oily, fuming *liquid* made by the action of *sulphur trioxide*, SO_3, on ordinary sulphuric acid, H_2SO_4.

NORMAL (math.). A line *perpendicular* to a surface.

NORMAL SOLUTION (chem.). A *solution* containing 1 *gram-equivalent* per *litre*. Term used in *volumetric analysis*.

NORMAL STATE of atom. See *ground state*.

NORMALITY (chem.). Method of expressing *concentrations* of *solutions*; number of *gram-equivalents* of *reagent* per *litre* of solution. Thus, a solution containing 2 gram-equivalents per litre is a twice-*normal* or 2N solution.

NORMALIZING. A *heat* treatment applied to *steel* in order to relieve internal *stresses*. Involves heating above a critical *temperature* and cooling in air.

NOTATION. Representation of numbers, quantities, or other entities by symbols; a system of symbols for such a purpose.

NOVA. A *star* which ejects a small part of its material in the form of a *gas* cloud. During the process the star becomes 5000 to 10,000 times more luminous than it was before the outburst. 'Dwarf' novae increase their *luminosity* by a factor of only 10–100. Novae appear to be one of a pair of *binary stars*. See also *supernovae*.

N-P-N TRANSISTOR. See *transistor*.

N.T.P.; S.T.P. Normal (standard) *temperature* and *pressure*. A pressure of 760 mm. of mercury and a temperature of 0° C.; standard conditions under which *volumes* of *gases* are compared.

N-TYPE CONDUCTIVITY. The *conductivity* in a *semiconductor* caused by a flow of *electrons*, whereas p-type conductivity is caused by a flow of *holes*.

NUCLEAR BARRIER. Potential Barrier. The region of high *potential energy* through which a charged particle must pass on entering or leaving an atomic *nucleus*.

NUCLEAR CHARGE. The positive *electric charge* on the *nucleus* of an *atom*. When expressed in units equal to the charge on the *electron*, this is numerically equal to the *atomic number* of the *element*, to the number of *protons* in the nucleus, and to the number of electrons surrounding the nucleus in the *neutral* atom. See *atom, structure of*.

NUCLEAR ENERGY. Atomic energy. *Energy* released during a *nuclear reaction* as the result of the conversion of *mass* into *energy* (see *mass-energy equation*). Nuclear energy is released in *nuclear reactors* and *nuclear weapons*.

NUCLEAR FISSION. A *nuclear reaction* in which a heavy atomic *nucleus* (e.g. uranium) splits into two approximately equal parts, at the same time emitting *neutrons* and releasing very large amounts of *nuclear energy*. Fission can be spontaneous or it may be caused by the impact of a neutron (see *chain reaction*), an energetic charged particle or a *photon* (*photofission*). See also *nuclear reactor* and *nuclear weapon*.

NUCLEAR FORCE. The attractive *force* which acts between *nucleons* when they are extremely close together (closer than 10^{-13} cm.). The nuclear force replaces the repulsive electromagnetic interaction between *protons* at such proximities and holds the nucleons together in the atomic *nucleus* (see *exchange forces*). The precise nature of the nuclear force is not known.

NUCLEAR FUEL. A substance which undergoes *nuclear fission* in a *nuclear reactor*.

NUCLEAR FUSION. A *nuclear reaction* between light atomic *nuclei* as a result of which a heavier nucleus is formed and a large quantity of *nuclear energy* is released. E.g. the fusion of two *deuterium* nuclei to form a *tritium* nucleus and a *proton* is accompanied by an energy release of 4 *Mev*. $(D+D=T+p+4$ Mev$)$. For fusion to be possible the reacting nuclei must possess sufficient *kinetic energy* to overcome the *electrostatic field* which surrounds them. The *temperatures* associated with fusion reactions are therefore extremely high. Fusion reactions occur on *Earth* during the explosion of a hydrogen bomb (see *nuclear weapons*) and during controlled *thermonuclear reactions*. Fusion reactions are believed to be the source of the energy of the *stars* (including the *Sun*).

NUCLEAR ISOMERS. *Atoms* of an *element* of the same *mass* but possessing different rates of *radioactive decay*.

NUCLEAR MAGNETIC RESONANCE. NMR. All atomic *nuclei*, except *even-even nuclei*, have *magnetic moments* associated with them, which tend to be aligned by an externally applied *magnetic field*, but because nuclei possess *angular momentum*, they precess (see *precessional motion*) about the direction of the applied field. The *energy* of the interaction between the applied and the nuclear magnetic fields is *quantized* (see *quantum mechanics*), so that only certain orientations of the nucleus relative to the applied field are permitted: a transition from one orientation to another involves the absorption or emission of a *quantum* of *electromagnetic radiation*, the *frequency* of which can be shown to equal the precessional frequency. With the magnetic field strengths customarily used (up to about 20 kilo*gauss*) the energies involved are small, and the radiations fall in the *radio frequency* band, i.e. 1–100 *megacycles* per second. Transitions from one *energy level* to another can be induced by applying a second magnetic field, at right angles to the first, which rotates in *phase* with the nuclear precession. NMR spectroscopy (also called 'radio frequency spectroscopy') consists of observing the point of resonance at which such transitions are induced. Data obtained in this way provides valuable information concerning nuclear properties. As the *orbital electrons* 'shield' the nucleus to a certain extent from the applied magnetic field, at a given frequency nuclei in different electronic (i.e. chemical) environments will resonate at slightly different values of the applied field. This phenomenon, known as the 'chemical shift' enables NMR spectroscopy to be of great value in working out the configuration of complex *molecules*.

NUCLEAR PHYSICS. The study of the *physics* of the atomic *nucleus* and of sub-atomic particles.

NUCLEAR POWER. Electric or motive power produced from a unit in which the primary *energy* source is a *nuclear reactor*.

NUCLEAR REACTION. Any reaction which involves a change in the *nucleus* of an *atom*, as distinct from a *chemical reaction* which only involves the *orbital electrons*. Such reactions occur naturally, on the *Earth* in *radioactive elements*, and in *stars* as *thermonuclear reactions*. They are also produced artificially in *nuclear reactors*, *nuclear weapons*, and controlled thermonuclear reactions. See also *nuclear fission* and *nuclear fusion*.

NUCLEAR REACTOR. Atomic pile. An assembly in which a *nuclear fission chain reaction* is maintained and controlled for the production of *nuclear energy*, *radioactive isotopes*, or artificial *elements*. The *nuclear fuel* used in a reactor consists of a *fissile* material (e.g. $^{235}_{92}$U) which undergoes fission, as a consequence of which two *nuclides* of approximately equal *mass* are produced together with between two and three *neutrons* and a considerable quantity of *energy*. These neutrons cause further fissions so that a chain reaction develops; in order that the reaction should not get out of control, its progress is regulated by neutron absorbers (see *control rods*), only sufficient free neutrons being allowed to exist in the reactor to maintain the reaction at a constant level. The fissile material is usually mixed with a *moderator* which slows down (see *thermalize*) the *fast neutrons* emitted during fission, so that they are more likely to cause further fissions of the fissile material than they are to be captured by the $^{238}_{92}$U *isotope*. In a 'heterogeneous reactor' the fuel and the moderator are separated in a geometric pattern called a *lattice*. In a 'homogeneous reactor' the fuel and the moderator are mixed so that they present a uniform medium to the neutrons (e.g. the fuel, in the form of a uranium *salt*, may be dissolved in the moderator).

Besides this classification, reactors may be described in a number of ways. They may be described in terms of neutron energy (see *fast reactor*, *thermal reactor*) or in terms of function, e.g. a 'power reactor' for generating useful *electric power*, a 'production reactor' for manufacturing fissile material (see also *breeder reactor* and *converter reactor*) and a 'propulsion reactor' for supplying motive power to ships or submarines. Reactors are also described in terms of their fuel (e.g. 'plutonium reactor'), their moderator (e.g. 'graphite-moderated reactor') or their coolant (e.g. *boiling-water reactor*).

The term nuclear reactor may also be applied to a device in which a controlled *thermonuclear reaction* takes place, in this case it is referred to as a 'fusion reactor'.

NUCLEAR TRANSMUTATIONS. The changing of *atoms* of one *element* into those of another by suitable *nuclear reactions*.

NUCLEAR WEAPONS. Weapons in which the explosive power is derived from *nuclear fission* or a combination of nuclear fission and *nuclear fusion*. The fission bomb (atom[ic] bomb or A-bomb) consists essentially of two or more *masses* of a suitable *fissile* material (e.g. $^{235}_{92}$U or $^{239}_{94}$Pu) each of which is less than the *critical mass*. When the bomb is detonated the sub-critical masses are brought rapidly together to form a super-critical assembly, so that a single fission at the instant of contact sets off an uncontrolled *chain reaction*. The resulting release of *nuclear energy* produces a devastating *explosion* the effect of which is comparable to the explosion of tens of *kilotons* of *T.N.T.* The fusion bomb (thermo-nuclear bomb, hydrogen bomb, or H-bomb) consists of a fission bomb surrounded by a layer of hydrogenous material (e.g. lithium deuter-ide). At the *temperature* resulting from the explosion of the fission bomb, fusion of the hydrogen nuclei to form helium nuclei takes place (see *thermonuclear reaction*) with the evolution of even greater quantities of energy. The explosive effect of a fusion bomb (or fission-fusion bomb) is comparable to the explosion of tens of *megatons* of T.N.T. See also *fall-out*.

NUCLEIC ACIDS. Large *molecules* consisting of chains of *nucleotides*. Present in all living matter in which they are responsible for storing and transferring the *genetic code*. See *deoxyribonucleic acid* and *ribonucleic acid*.

NUCLEOLUS. Small dense body containing *nucleo-protein*, one or more of which occur in the *nucleus* of biological *cells*.

NUCLEON. A constituent of the atomic *nucleus*, i.e. a *proton* or a *neutron*.

NUCLEONICS. The practical applications of *nuclear physics*, and the techniques associated with these applications.

NUCLEOPHILIC REAGENTS. *Reagents* which react at centres of low *electron* density (e.g. *hydroxyl ions*). Nucleophilic reagents behave as electron donors, either transferring electrons or sharing their electrons with outside *atoms* or *ions*. *Molecules* or ions containing an atom with an unshared electron pair often act as nucleophilic reagents.

NUCLEO-PROTEIN. Compounds of *nucleic acids* and *proteins* which are found in *cell nuclei* principally in the form of *chromosomes*. *Viruses* consist almost entirely of nucleo-proteins. Life is based on the self-replicating properties of nucleo-proteins.

NUCLEOR. The 'core' of a *nucleon*, which according to recent views consists of a nucleor surrounded by a cloud of *pions*.

NUCLEOSIDE. A *compound* formed from a nitrogenous base (*purine* or *pyrimidine*) and a *pentose sugar*, e.g. adenosine which consists of *adenine* and D-ribofuranose. The phosphorylated *derivative* of a nucleoside is called a *nucleotide*.

NUCLEOTIDE. A most important type of *compound* found in all living matter. Nucleotides consist of a nitrogenous base (*purine* or *pyrimidine*), a *pentose sugar* and a phosphate group. Found free in *cells* as *adenosine triphosphate* and as part of various *coenzymes*; found in the form of *poly-nucleotide* chains as *nucleic acids*.

NUCLEUS. Vital central point; particle of *matter* acting as centre; e.g. a particle of dust will act as a nucleus for the *condensation* of *water vapour* in mist.

NUCLEUS, ATOMIC. The positively charged core of an *atom*, consisting of one or more *protons* and, except in the case of hydrogen, one or more *neutrons*. The number of protons in the nucleus is given by the *atomic number* and the number of neutrons by the difference between the *mass number* and the *atomic number*. Nearly the whole of the *mass* of an atom is concentrated in its nucleus, which occupies only a tiny fraction of its *volume*. See *atom, structure of*.

NUCLEUS OF CELL. Membrane-bounded body found within the *cytoplasm* of most biological *cells* of both plants and animals. The nucleus contains the *chromosomes* which become visible under a *microscope* during *mitosis* or *meiosis*. The nucleus is therefore the repository of the substances which control the characteristics of cells and their progeny.

NUCLIDE. Nucleide. An *atom* of a specific *isotope*, characterized by its *atomic number*, *mass number*, and its *energy* state.

NUMERATOR. Number above the line in a vulgar fraction. E.g. 3 in $\frac{3}{16}$.

NUTATION. An oscillation of the *Earth*'s poles about the mean position.

NYLON. Officially defined as 'a generic term applied to any long-chain synthetic *polyamide* which has recurring *amide* groups as an integral part of the main *polymer* chain, and which is capable of being formed into a filament in which the structural elements are oriented in the direction of the axis'. The familiar commercial form of nylon, is a substance formed by the *condensation polymerization* of adipic acid with hexamethylene diamine. The *solid* polymer is melted and forced through fine jets to make filaments which are then collected in the form of yarn.

O

OBJECTIVE (phys.). *Lens* or system of lenses nearest the object in a *telescope* or compound *microscope*.

OBLATE SPHEROID. See *spheroid*.

OBTUSE ANGLE. *Angle* greater than 90°.

OCCLUSION. Certain *solids* have the property of absorbing or occluding some *gases*, either by the formation of a chemical *compound*, or by forming a *solid solution*, or by the *condensation* of the gas on the surface of the solid.

OCCULTATION. The cutting off of the *light* or *radio* emission from one celestial body when another is interposed between it and the observer. E.g. a *star* may become invisible to an *optical* or *radio telescope* when it is hidden behind the *Moon*.

OCHRE. Natural *hydrated* form of *ferric oxide*, Fe_2O_3, containing various impurities. Used as a red or yellow *pigment*.

OCTA-, OCTO-. Prefix denoting eight, eightfold.

OCTACALCIUM PHOSPHATE. OCP. $Ca_4H(PO_4)_3$. $2.5H_2O$. Crystalline substance of importance in the chemistry of bones, teeth, and precipitated calcium phosphates.

OCTANE. C_8H_{18}. *Hydrocarbon* of the *paraffin series*. Exists in several isomeric forms (see *isomerism*). *Liquid*, b.p. 126° C., S.G. 0·704.

OCTANE NUMBER OF A FUEL. Defined as the percentage by *volume* of *iso*-octane, C_8H_{18} (2:2:4-trimethylpentane) in a mixture of *iso*-octane and normal *heptane*, C_7H_{16}, which is equal to the *fuel* in knock characteristics (see *knocking*) under specified test conditions.

OCTANT. Portion of a *circle* cut off by an arc and two radii at 45°; one-eighth of the area of a circle.

OCTAVE. The interval between two musical notes, the fundamental components (see *quality of sound*) of which have *frequencies* in the ratio two to one. This use of the word has been extended to include the interval between two frequencies of any type of oscillation which are in the ratio two to one.

OCTAVES, LAW OF. An incomplete statement of the *Periodic Law* made by Newlands independently of Mendeleev.

OCTET. A stable group of eight *electrons* which constitutes the outer electron *shell* of an *atom* of an *inert gas* (except helium whose only electron shell contains two electrons). When the atoms of the *elements* (except hydrogen) combine to form *compounds*, they do so by donating or sharing electrons so that each combining atom has a completed octet in its outer shell. See *valency, electronic theory of*.

ODD-EVEN NUCLEUS. *Nucleus* which contains an odd number of *protons* and an even number of *neutrons*.

ODD-ODD NUCLEUS. *Nucleus* which contains an odd number of both *protons* and *neutrons*.

OERSTED, THE. The unit of *magnetic field strength* or *magnetic intensity* in *C.G.S. electromagnetic units*, i.e. the *force* in *dynes* which a unit *magnetic pole* would experience at any point in a magnetic field.

OESTROGENS. Female sex *hormones* of which the most important are the *sterols* oestradiol ($C_{18}H_{24}O_2$), oestrone ($C_{18}H_{22}O_2$), and oestriol ($C_{18}H_{24}O_3$).

OHM, THE. Unit of electrical *resistance*. The 'absolute ohm' is 10^9 *electromagnetic units* of resistance, and is that resistance in which *energy* is dissipated at the rate of 1 *watt* by the flow of one absolute *ampere* of current. The former 'international ohm' ($= 1\cdot00049$ absolute ohms) was defined as the resistance, at 0° C., of a column of mercury 106·3 cm. in length, of *mass* 14·4521 gm., and of uniform cross-sectional area.

OHM'S LAW. The ratio of the *potential difference* between the ends of a *conductor* and the *current* flowing in the conductor is constant. This ratio is termed the *resistance* of the conductor. For a potential difference of E *volts* and a current of I *amperes*, the resistance, R, in *ohms* is equal to E/I.

OIL, MINERAL. General name given to various *mixtures* of natural *hydrocarbons*. See *paraffin oil*.

OIL OF VITRIOL. Concentrated *sulphuric acid*.

OIL, SYNTHETIC. Natural mineral *oils* are composed of various *hydro-*

carbons. It is possible to make similar products artificially from *coal*, etc., by combining carbon or *carbon monoxide* with hydrogen. See *Bergius process; Fischer-Tropsch process*.

OIL-IMMERSION LENS. See *immersion objective*.

OILS. See *fats and oils*.

OLEATES. *Salts* or *esters* of *oleic acid*.

OLEFIANT GAS. See *ethylene*.

OLEFINES, olefins. *Ethylene* series of *unsaturated hydrocarbons*, having the general formula C_nH_{2n}.

OLEIC ACID. $C_{17}H_{33}COOH$. *Unsaturated organic acid*. Occurs in the form of *glycerides* in many *fats and oils*. *Liquid*, m.p. 14° C. A high proportion of *triolein*, the glyceride of oleic acid, in a fat or oil makes it more liquid.

OLEIN. See *triolein*.

OLEUM. Fuming sulphuric acid; concentrated *sulphuric acid*, H_2SO_4, containing extra *sulphur trioxide*, SO_3.

OLFACTORY. Pertaining to the sense of smell.

OMEGATRON. An instrument in which *ions* are caused to move in spiral paths by the application of an *electric field* at right angles to a constant *magnetic field*. As the angular frequency of rotation of the ions depends upon their charge to mass ratio, it is possible by this means to separate ions of different *isotopes*. The instrument may be used for the absolute determination of atomic *masses* and for isotopic and chemical analysis.

ONTOGENY (bio.). The history of the development of an individual member of a species, as opposed to 'phylogeny' which is the history of the evolution of the species (or other biological group).

OOCYTE. A female *gametocyte* which undergoes *meiosis* to form an *ovum*.

OPACITY. The extent to which a medium is *opaque*. Numerically the *reciprocal* of the *transmittance*.

OPAQUE. Not permitting a *wave-motion* (e.g. *light*, *sound*, *X-rays*) to pass. Usually applied to light; not *transparent* or *translucent*. See *opacity*.

OPEN-CHAIN COMPOUNDS. *Organic compounds* not derived from ring compounds; *aliphatic compounds*.

OPEN CLUSTERS. Clusters of *stars* which have a common motion through *space*. The open clusters are much less densely populated with stars than the *globular clusters*, containing only some hundreds of stars interspersed with *gas* and dust clouds.

OPEN-HEARTH PROCESS, Siemens-Martin process. Process for *steel* manufacture. *Pig-iron* and steel scrap or iron ore in calculated amounts are heated together by *producer gas* on a hearth in a furnace.

OPIUM. The dried, milky juice from unripe fruits of the opium poppy, Papaver somniferum. Contains several *alkaloids*, including *morphine* and *codeine*.

OPPOSITION (astr.). A *planet* having its *orbit* outside that of the *Earth* is in opposition when the Earth is in a line between the *Sun* and the planet.

OPTIC AXIS. The direction in a doubly refracting *crystal* in which *light* is propagated without *double refraction*.

OPTICAL ACTIVITY, optical rotation. The property possessed by some substances and their *solutions* of rotating the plane of vibration of polarized light (see *polarization of light*). The amount of this rotation is proportional to the distance the light travels in the medium, and to the *concentration* of the solution. The amount of rotation also depends upon the *wave-length* (i.e. the *colour*) of the light used. This last phenomenon is termed 'rotatory dispersion'.

OPTICAL AXIS. Line passing through the *optical centre* and the *centre of curvature* of a spherical *mirror* or *lens*.

OPTICAL CENTRE of thin lens. A point, situated for all practical purposes at the geometrical centre of the *lens*, through which an incident *ray* passes without being deviated.

OPTICAL ISOMERISM. Form of *isomerism* in which the isomers differ in their *optical activity*. See *stereoisomerism*.

OPTICAL MASER. See *laser*.

OPTICAL ROTATION. See *optical activity*.

OPTICAL TELESCOPE. An astronomical *telescope* which is used to observe celestial bodies by the *light* which they emit, as compared to a *radio telescope* which is used to observe their *radio frequency* emissions.

OPTICS. The study of *light*.

OPTICS, GEOMETRICAL. Branch of *optics* built up on the laws of *reflection* and *refraction*, and assuming the *rectilinear propagation of light*; it involves no consideration of the physical nature of light. Mainly concerned with the formation of images by *mirrors* and *lenses*.

ORBIT. 1. The path of one heavenly body around another as a result of their mutual gravitational attraction. Particularly the path of the *planets* around the *Sun*, or the *Moon* (or *artificial satellites*) around the *Earth*. 2. The path of an *electron* around the *nucleus* of an *atom*. See *orbital electron* and *atom, structure of*.

ORBITAL. See *atomic orbital* and *molecular orbital*

ORBITAL ELECTRON. Planetary electron. An *electron* contained within an *atom* which may be thought of as orbiting around the *nucleus*, in a manner analogous to the *orbit* of a *planet* around the *Sun*. See *atom, structure of*, and *Bohr theory*.

ORDINARY RAY. When a *ray* of *light* is incident upon a *crystal* which exhibits *double refraction* so that the direction of the ray makes an angle with the *optic axis* of the crystal, the ray splits into two rays. One of these obeys the ordinary laws of *refraction* and is called the ordinary ray. The other is the 'extraordinary ray'.

ORDINATE. In *analytical geometry*, the ordinate of a point is the perpendicular distance of the point from the x-axis. See Fig. 5, page 70.

ORGANIC ACID. An *organic compound* which is able to give up a *proton* to a *base*; i.e. one which contains one or more *carboxyl groups* or in some cases *hydroxyl groups* (e.g. *phenol*).

ORGANIC BASE. *A molecule* or *ion* possessing a *lone pair of electrons* which can be used for co-ordination (see *valency, electronic theory of*) with a *proton.* The common *organic compounds* which fulfil this condition owe their basic character to an oxygen or nitrogen *atom.*

ORGANIC CHEMISTRY. *Chemistry* of the *organic compounds;* chemistry of carbon compounds excluding the *metal carbonates* and the *oxides* and *sulphides* of carbon. Originally, the chemistry of substances produced by living *organisms,* as distinct from the *inorganic chemistry* of substances of *mineral* origin.

ORGANIC COMPOUNDS. Chemical *compounds* containing carbon combined with hydrogen, and often also with oxygen, nitrogen, and other *elements.* The *molecules* of organic compounds are often very complex, and contain a large number of *atoms.* They are not usually ionized in *solution* (see *dissociation*), and frequently show the phenomenon of *isomerism.*

ORGANISM. A living animal or plant.

ORGANOMETALLIC COMPOUND. A *compound* in which one or more organic *radicals* are attached to an *atom* of a *metal;* e.g. $Na(CH_3)$.

ORIGIN (math.). The point of intersection of two or more axes (see *co-ordinates, cartesian* and *polar co-ordinates*).

ORMOLU. *Alloy* of copper, zinc, and tin in various proportions; generally containing at least 50% copper.

ORPIMENT. Natural arsenic trisulphide, As_2S_3. Yellow mineral.

ORSAT APPARATUS. A portable apparatus for determining the amount of *carbon dioxide,* oxygen, and *carbon monoxide* in flue or exhaust *gases.* A measured *volume* of the gas is successively passed through three tubes, the first of which contains *potassium hydroxide* to absorb the CO_2, the second alkaline *pyrogallol* to absorb oxygen, and the third cuprous chloride in *hydrochloric acid* to absorb the CO. The diminution of volume after the gas has been passed through each tube indicates the quantity of each constituent gas.

ORTHO-. 1. Prefix denoting right, straight, correct. 2. Prefix indicating that an *organic compound* contains a *benzene* ring substituted in the 1.2 positions.

ORTHOCHROMATIC FILM. Photographic *film* sensitive to green in addition to blue and violet *light,* thus giving a more accurate representation of *colours* in monochrome than ordinary film. See *photography.*

ORTHOCLASE FELSPAR. Natural potassium aluminium silicate, $K_2O.Al_2O_3.6SiO_2$. Constituent of *granite.*

ORTHO-HYDROGEN. Hydrogen *molecules* in which the *spins* of the two constituent *atoms* are parallel.

OSCILLATOR. 1. A device for producing sonic or *ultrasonic* pressure waves in a medium. 2. A device with no rotating parts for converting *direct current* into *alternating current;* usually consists of *thermionic valves* or *transistors* coupled with a suitable *resonant circuit.*

OSCILLOSCOPE. See *cathode ray oscilloscope.*

OSMIC ACID. Osmium tetroxide, OsO_4. Colourless, crystalline *solid,* m.p. 40° C.; *solution* used as a stain for *fat* globules in microscopy.

OSMIRIDIUM. Natural *alloy* of osmium, iridium, with smaller amounts of platinum, rhodium, and ruthenium. Hard and resistant to *corrosion*; used for tipping pen-nibs.

OSMIUM. Os. Element. A.W. 190·2. At. No. 76. Hard, white crystalline *metal*. S.G. 22·48, m.p. 2700° C. Heaviest substance known. Occurs together with platinum (see *osmiridium*); used in *alloys* with platinum and iridium.

OSMOMETER. An instrument for measuring *osmotic pressures*.

OSMOSIS. The flow of *water* (or other *solvent*) through a *semi-permeable membrane*; i.e. a membrane which will permit the passage of the solvent but not of dissolved substances. There is a tendency for *solutions* separated by such a membrane to become equal in *molecular concentration*; thus water will flow from a weaker to a stronger solution, the solutions tending to become more nearly equal in concentration.

OSMOTIC PRESSURE of a solution. The *pressure* which must be applied to a *solution* in order to prevent the flow of *solvent* through a *semipermeable membrane* separating the solution and the pure solvent. When a solvent is allowed to flow through such a membrane into a vessel or cell containing a solution, the solvent will flow into the cell (see *osmosis*) until such a pressure is set up as to balance the pressure of the solvent flowing in. The osmotic pressure of a dilute solution is analogous to gaseous pressure; a substance in solution, if not dissociated (see *dissociation*), exerts the same osmotic pressure as the gaseous pressure it would exert if it were a *gas* at the same *temperature*, and occupying the same *volume*. The osmotic pressure, temperature, and volume of a dilute solution of a *non-electrolyte* are connected by laws exactly similar to the *gas laws*.

OSTWALD'S DILUTION LAW. A law relating the dissociation constant, K, (see *dissociation*) and the degree of dissociation (or *ionization*), a, of a weak *electrolyte* of *concentration* c gram-molecules per *litre*. This law states that for a binary electrolyte $K = \dfrac{ca^2}{1-a}$, an equation which applies with a fair degree of accuracy to weak *organic acids* and *bases*.

OUNCE, AVOIRDUPOIS. 437½ *grains*; 28·3 *grams*.

OUNCE, FLUID. 8 fluid *drachms*; 28·41 c.c.

OUNCE, TROY. 480 *grains*; 31·1 *grams*.

OVERTONES. Notes of lesser intensity and higher *pitch* (i.e. of higher *frequency*) than the *fundamental note*, and superimposed upon the latter to give a note of characteristic *quality*.

OVUM. A female *gamete* produced by *meiosis* from an *oocyte*.

OXALATE. *Salt* of *oxalic acid*.

OXALIC ACID. (COOH)₂.2H₂O. White crystalline poisonous *soluble solid*, m.p. 101° C. *Salts* occur in wood sorrel and other plants. Used in dyeing, *bleaching*, *ink* manufacture, metal polishes, and for removing ink stains.

OXIDANT. Oxydant. The substance which supplies the oxygen in an *oxidation* reaction. The term is frequently used with reference to the substance which supplies the oxygen in a *combustion* process, particularly in a *rocket*. The oxidant used in rockets is usually liquid oxygen, *hydrogen peroxide*, or *nitric acid*.

OXIDASE. *Enzyme* which catalyses *oxidation* of the *substrate*.

OXIDATION. The combination of oxygen with a *substance*, or the removal of hydrogen from it. The term is also used more generally to include any reaction in which an *atom* loses *electrons*; e.g. the change of a *ferrous* ion, Fe^{++}, to a *ferric ion*, Fe^{+++}.

OXIDE. *Binary compound* with oxygen.

OXIDIZING AGENT. A substance which brings about an *oxidation* reaction.

OXY-ACETYLENE BURNER. Device for obtaining a very high-*temperature flame* (3300° C.) for *welding*, by burning a mixture of oxygen and *acetylene* in a special jet.

OXYGEN. O. Element. A.W. 15·9994, At. No. 8. Odourless, invisible *gas*; the most abundant of all the *elements* in the *Earth's crust* including the seas and the *atmosphere*; forms approximately one-fifth of the atmosphere. Chemically very active; *combustion* and *respiration* both involve combination with oxygen. Essential to most forms of life. *Compounds* (*oxides*) are very widely distributed. The pure element is made by the *fractional distillation* of *liquid air*. Used for *welding* and metal-cutting.

OXY-HAEMOGLOBIN. Unstable *compound* formed by the action of oxygen on *haemoglobin* in *respiration*.

OXY-HYDROGEN BURNER. Device similar to the *oxy-acetylene burner* except that hydrogen instead of *acetylene* is burnt in oxygen; gives a *flame* temperature of about 2400° C.

OZOKERITE, earth-wax. Natural *mixture* of *solid hydrocarbons*. Brownish or greyish mass, resembling *paraffin wax*.

OZONE. O_3. *Allotropic form* of oxygen, containing three *atoms* in the *molecule*. Bluish *gas*, very active chemically, powerful *oxidizing agent*. Formed when oxygen or air is subjected to a silent electric discharge. Occurs in ordinary air in very small amounts only; the health-giving effects sometimes attributed to it in sea-air are probably due to other causes. Ozone in the *atmosphere* is mainly present at altitudes of between 15 and 30 *kilometres*, and it is responsible for absorbing a large proportion of the Sun's *ultra-violet radiation*. Without the absorption by ozone the Earth would be subjected to a degree of *ultra-violet radiation* lethal to plants. Used for purifying air.

P

PACKING FRACTION. The difference between the *mass* of an *isotope* (on the physical scale of *atomic weights*) and its *mass number*, divided by the mass number. E.g. one chlorine isotope has a mass of $32 \cdot 9860$ and a mass number of 33, its packing fraction is therefore:

$$\frac{32 \cdot 9860 - 33 \cdot 000}{33} = -0 \cdot 00042$$

Packing fractions are often multiplied by 10^4 for convenience, and in this example the packing fraction would be given as $-4 \cdot 2$.

PAINT. *Liquid* containing a coloured material (*pigment*) in *suspension*. The application of the paint to a surface and the *evaporation* or hardening of the liquid cover the surface with the pigment in the form of a skin. The liquid generally consists of *linseed oil*, a 'thinner' of *turpentine* or other *volatile* liquid, and a 'drier' to accelerate drying or hardening of the linseed oil. Paints may also be based on *water* in the form of an *emulsion*, and are then called 'emulsion paints'. Such paints usually consist of an emulsion of *butadiene* and *styrene*, *polyvinyl acetate*, or *acrylic resins* in water.

PAIR PRODUCTION. The creation of a negative *electron* and *positron* as a result of the interaction between a *photon* or a fast particle (usually an electron) and the *field* of an atomic *nucleus* (see also *showers*). 'Internal pair production' occurs as the result of the de-*excitation* of an excited nucleus. Pair production, which is sometimes extended to mean the creation of any elementary *particle* and its *anti-particle*, is an example of the creation of *matter* from *energy* in accordance with the *mass-energy equation*.

PALAEONTOLOGY. The branch of *geology* which is concerned with the study of *fossils* and their relationship to the evolution of the *Earth's crust* and life upon Earth.

PALLADIUM. Pd. Element. A.W. $106 \cdot 4$. At. No. 46. Silvery-white *metal* which occurs with and resembles platinum. S.G. $11 \cdot 40$, m.p. $1549°$ C. Used in *alloys* and as a *catalyst*.

PALMITIC ACID. $C_{15}H_{31}COOH$. *Organic fatty acid*; occurs in the form of *tripalmitin* in palm oil and many natural *fats*. Wax-like *solid*, m.p. $64°$ C.

PALMITIN. See *tripalmitin*.

PANCHROMATIC FILM. Photographic *film* sensitive to *light* of all *colours* including red, thus giving a more accurate representation of colours in monochrome than *orthochromatic film*. See *photography*.

PANTOTHENIC ACID. $C_9H_{17}NO_5$. White *insoluble solid*: member of the *vitamin* B complex, of importance to many *organisms*.

PAPAIN. An *enzyme*, found in the fruit and leaves of the paw-paw tree, which is capable of digesting *proteins*. Used for softening meat for human consumption.

PAPER. Paper normally consists of sheets of *cellulose*, mainly obtained from wood pulp from which *lignin* and other non-cellulosic materials have been removed.

PAPER CHROMATOGRAPHY. A method of analysing *mixtures* of *com-

pounds, depending upon the different rates at which compounds in *solution* will migrate across a sheet of porous paper specially prepared with *indicators*.

PARA-. 1. Prefix denoting beside, beyond; or wrong, irregular. 2. Prefix indicating that an *organic compound* contains a *benzene* ring substituted in the 1.4 positions.

PARABOLA. Curve traced out by a point which moves so that its distance from a fixed point, the focus, is equal to its distance from a fixed straight line, the directrix.

PARABOLIC REFLECTOR. Paraboloid reflector. A *concave* reflector, the section of which is a *parabola*. Used for producing a parallel *beam* of *electromagnetic radiation* when a source is placed at its focus, or for collecting and focusing an incoming parallel beam of radiation. If the radiation is *light* the reflector is usually called a parabolic mirror, but with *microwave* or *radio frequency* radiation (see *radio telescope*) it may be called a 'dish aerial'.

PARABOLOID OF REVOLUTION. The surface obtained by rotating a *parabola* about its *axis of symmetry*.

PARACHOR. A relation showing the influence of *temperature* upon the *surface tension* of a *liquid*; interpreted as the *molecular volume* measured at a standard internal *pressure*. The value is composed, approximately, of a sum of terms for separate *atoms*, and of constants for various types of linkage between the atoms, thus giving a method for the determination of the constitution and structure of *molecules*.

PARAFFIN (chem.). *Hydrocarbon* of the *paraffin series*.

PARAFFIN OIL, kerosine. Mixture of *hydrocarbons* obtained in the *distillation* of *petroleum*. The boiling range of the kerosines is 150°–300° C. Used for paraffin lamps, oil-burning engines, domestic heaters.

PARAFFIN SERIES. *Homologous series* of *hydrocarbons* having the general formula C_nH_{2n+2}. Chemically inert, *stable*, inflammable. The first four members of the series (*methane*, *ethane*, *propane*, *butane*) are *gases* at ordinary *temperatures*; the next eleven are *liquids*, and form the principal constituents of *paraffin oil*; the higher members are *solids*, forming the chief constituents of *paraffin wax*.

PARAFFIN WAX. White, translucent *solid* melting to a colourless *liquid* in the range 50°–60° C. Consists of a *mixture* of the higher *hydrocarbons* of the *paraffin series*. Used for candles, waxed paper, polishes.

PARAFORM, paraformaldehyde. Solid *polymer* of *formaldehyde*, readily converted into formaldehyde on heating. Used in fumigation.

PARA-HYDROGEN. Hydrogen *molecules* in which the *spins* of the two constituent *atoms* are anti-parallel.

PARALDEHYDE. $(CH_3CHO)_3$. *Polymer* of *acetaldehyde*. *Liquid*, b.p. 124° C. Used in medicine as a *hypnotic*.

PARALLAX. Difference in direction, or a shift in the apparent position, of a body, due to a change in position of the observer.

PARALLAX, ANNUAL, OF A STAR. The *angle* between the direction in which a *star* appears as observed from the *Earth*, and the direction in which it would appear from the centre of the *Sun*.

PARALLEL BEAM OF LIGHT. A *beam* of *light* which neither converges nor diverges; theoretical concept of a beam of light from an infinitely great distance, so that the *rays* composing the beam may be considered to be parallel; e.g. light from the *Sun*.

PARALLEL, CONDUCTORS IN. Electrical *conductors* joined in parallel between two points A and B, so that each conductor joins A to B. If R_1, R_2, R_3, etc., are the *resistances* of the separate conductors, the total resistance R between A and B is given by the formula:

$$\frac{1}{R} = \frac{1}{R_1} + \frac{1}{R_2} + \frac{1}{R_3} \dots \text{ etc. See Fig. 11.}$$

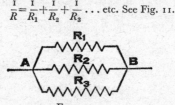

FIG. 11.

PARALLELEPIPED. Solid figure having six faces, all *parallelograms*; all opposite pairs of faces being similar and parallel.

PARALLELOGRAM. Plane, four-sided, *rectilinear* figure having its opposite sides parallel. It may be proved that in all parallelograms the opposite sides and *angles* are equal; the *diagonals* bisect each other; and the diagonals bisect the parallelogram. The *area* of a parallelogram is given by (*a*) the product of the base and the vertical height, and (*b*) the product of two adjacent sides and the *sine* of the angle between them. See *trigonometrical ratios*.

PARALLELOGRAM OF FORCES. If a particle is under the action of two *forces* which are represented in direction and magnitude by the two sides of a *parallelogram* drawn from a point, the *resultant* of the two forces is represented by the *diagonal* of the parallelogram drawn from that point.

PARALLELOGRAM OF VELOCITIES. If a body has two component *velocities*, represented in magnitude and direction by two adjacent sides of a *parallelogram* drawn from a point, the *resultant* velocity of the body is represented by the *diagonal* of the parallelogram drawn from that point.

PARAMAGNETISM. Substances possessing a *magnetic permeability* slightly greater than unity, i.e. possessing a small positive *magnetic susceptibility*, are said to be paramagnetic. The *atoms* of a paramagnetic substance possess a permanent *magnetic moment* due to unbalanced *electron spins* or unbalanced orbital motions of the electrons around the *nucleus* (see *atom, structure of*). Application of a *magnetic field* to such a substance tends to align the magnetic axes of the atoms in the direction of the field, giving the substance a resultant magnetic moment.

PARAMETER. A *variable*; the term is used in at least two different senses. 1. In two-dimensional *analytical geometry* it is often convenient to express the variables (x, y) each in terms of a third variable t, such that x and y are functions of t; $x = f(t), y = g(t)$. The equations are termed parametric equations, and t is a parameter. 2. A variable which may be kept constant while the effect of other variables is investigated.

PARAMETRIC AMPLIFIER. An *amplifier* of *microwaves* which depends on the periodic variation, by an alternating *voltage*, of the *reactance* of a *thermionic valve* or *semiconductor* device.

PARASITIC CAPTURE. The absorption of a *neutron* by a *nuclide*, which does not result in a *nuclear fission* or the production of a useful artificial *element*.

PARIS GREEN, Schweinfurt green. Double *salt* of copper arsenite and acetate, $Cu(CH_3COO)_2 \cdot 3Cu(AsO_2)_2$.

PARITY. Space-reflection symmetry. Mirror symmetry. The principle of space-reflection symmetry, or conservation of parity, states that no fundamental distinction can be made between left and right; that the laws of *physics* are the same in a right-handed system of co-ordinates as they are in a left-handed system. This law holds for all the phenomena described by *classical physics*, but in 1957 it was shown to be violated by certain interactions between *elementary particles*. Interactions between elementary particles are of three types: *strong nuclear interactions*, electromagnetic interactions and *weak nuclear interactions*. For all strong nuclear interactions and electromagnetic interactions parity is conserved, that is to say, if a left-polarized particle exists (i.e. one which *spins* in an opposite sense to its direction of motion) there will be an approximately corresponding number of right-polarized particles. It has been found, however, that for weak nuclear interactions parity is not conserved. Thus, in a typical weak interaction, such as the *decay* of a *neutron*, the emitted *electron* is always left-polarized. As a result of non-conservation of parity in weak interactions it is now possible to make a fundamental distinction between left and right.

If parity is conserved, it is said to be even (or positive) when the *wave function* of a definite state of a system is left unchanged by reversing the sign of all the co-ordinates; it is said to be odd (or negative) if the sign of the wave function is thereby changed. If parity is not conserved the wave functions bear no simple relation to each other under these circumstances.

PARSEC. Astronomical unit of distance, corresponding to a *parallax* of one second of arc. 19×10^{12} miles, $3 \cdot 3$ *light-years*.

PARTHENOGENESIS. The development of an *ovum* into a new individual without *fertilization* by a male *gamete*. Occurs naturally in some plants (e.g. dandelion) and some animals (e.g. aphids); can be induced artificially in others.

PARTIAL PRESSURES, Dalton's law of. The total *pressure* of a *mixture* of two or more *gases* or *vapours* is equal to the sum of the pressures that each component would exert if it was present alone and occupied the same *volume* as the whole mixture.

PARTICLE ACCELERATOR. See *accelerator*.

PASCAL'S LAW OF FLUID PRESSURES. *Pressure* applied anywhere to an enclosed body of *fluid* is transmitted equally in all directions. This pressure acts at right angles to every portion of the surface of the container, the *force* per unit *area* being uniform throughout.

PASCHEN SERIES. A series of lines which occurs in the *infra-red* region of the *spectrum* of hydrogen.

PASCHEN'S LAW. The breakdown or 'sparking potential' for a pair of parallel *electrodes* situated in a *gas*, i.e. the *potential* which must be applied between them for sparking to occur, is a *function* only of the product of the *pressure* of the gas and the separation of the electrodes.

PASSIVE IRON. Iron made chemically unreactive by the surface action of concentrated *nitric acid* or other powerful *oxidizing agent*, which produces a protective film of iron oxide on the surface of the metal.

PASTEURIZATION. Partial sterilization, especially of milk; heating to a *temperature* sufficiently high to kill *bacteria*, but not spores of bacteria.

PATHOGENIC. Causing disease.

PAULI EXCLUSION PRINCIPLE. Each *electron* moving round the *nucleus* of a *neutral atom* can be characterized by values of four so-called *quantum numbers*. The principle states that no two electrons in a neutral atom can have the same set of four quantum numbers. The principle is of great importance in the theoretical building-up of the *periodic table*.

PEARL. Secretion consisting mainly of *calcium carbonate*, $CaCO_3$, produced by various molluscs.

PEARL ASH. *Potassium carbonate*, K_2CO_3, made from wood *ashes*.

PEARL SPAR. See *dolomite*.

PEAT. Early stage in the formation of *coal* from vegetable matter. Accumulation of partly decomposed plant material, used as *fuel*.

PECTINS. Class of complex *polysaccharides* occurring in plants, particularly fruits. *Solutions* have the power of setting to a jelly; this is probably responsible for the 'setting' of jams.

PELTIER EFFECT. When an *electric current* flows across the junction between two different *metals* or *semiconductors*, a quantity of *heat*, proportional to the total *electric charge* crossing the junction, is evolved or absorbed, depending on the direction of the current. This effect is due to the existence of an *electromotive force* at the junction.

PENCIL LEAD. A mixture of *graphite* with *clay* in various proportions, to give different degrees of hardness.

PENCIL OF LIGHT (phys.). A collection of *rays* proceeding from or towards a point.

PENDULUM, SIMPLE. Device consisting of a weight or 'bob' swinging on the end of a string or wire. In the case of an ideal pendulum, when the *angle* described by the pendulum is small, the string has negligible *weight,* and the *mass* of the pendulum is concentrated at one point, the time of one complete swing, T, is given by the formula $2\pi\sqrt{l/g}$, where l is the length of the string, and g the *acceleration due to gravity*.

PENETRATION FACTOR. The *probability* that an incident particle, in a *nuclear reaction*, will pass through the *nuclear barrier*.

PENICILLIN. Class of chemically related *antibiotics* produced by the Penicillium mould. A very powerful agent for preventing the growth of several types of disease *bacteria*.

PENNYWEIGHT. 24 grains, 1/20 troy ounce. See *troy weight*.

PENTA-. Prefix denoting five, fivefold.

PENTANE. C_5H_{12}. Fifth member of the *paraffin series*. Exists in three isomeric forms (see *isomerism*). Contained in light *petroleum*; n-pentane has b.p. 36° C. and S.G. 0·62.

PENTODE. *Thermionic valve* containing five *electrodes*: a *cathode*, an *anode* or plate, a *control grid*, and (between the two latter) two other grids called the screen grid and the suppressor grid.

PENTOSE. *Monosaccharide sugar* containing five carbon *atoms* and having the general formula $C_5H_{10}O_5$. The most important pentose is *ribose* which is an essential constituent of the *nucleic acids*.

PENUMBRA. Half-shadow, formed when an object in the path of *rays* from a large source of *light* cuts off a portion of the light. See *shadow*.

PEPSIN. Digestive *enzyme* produced in the stomach. Converts *proteins* into *peptones*; acts only in an *acid* medium.

PEPTIDASE. An *enzyme* which attacks *peptide* linkages and splits off *amino acids*. See also *proteinase*.

PEPTIDE. A *compound* of two or more (see *polypeptide*) *amino acids* formed by *condensation* of the -NH₂ group of one acid and the *carboxyl group* of another. The peptide linkage, —NH—CO—, results.

PEPTONES. Organic substances produced by the *hydrolysis* of *proteins* by the action of *pepsin* in the stomach. *Soluble* in *water*, absorbed by the body.

PER-. Prefix denoting, in chemical nomenclature, an excess of the normal amount of an *element* in a *compound*; e.g. *peroxide*.

PERCHLORATES. *Salts* of perchloric acid, $HClO_4$.

PERCUSSION CAP. Device used in fire-arms. A small copper cylinder containing *fulminate of mercury* or other violent *explosive* which will explode on being struck, thus initiating the explosion of the main charge.

PERFECT GAS, ideal gas. Theoretical concept of a *gas* which would obey the *gas laws* exactly. Such a gas would consist of perfectly elastic *molecules*, the *volume* occupied by the actual molecules, and the *forces* of attraction between them, being zero or negligible.

PERI-. Prefix denoting around, about.

PERICLASE. Natural magnesium oxide, MgO.

PERIGEE. The *Moon*, the *Sun*, or an artificial Earth *satellite*, are said to be in perigee when they are at their least distance from the Earth.

PERIHELION. The time of, or the point of, the nearest approach of a *planet* to the *Sun*.

PERIMETER. The distance all round a plane figure; e.g. the perimeter of a *circle* is its circumference.

PERIOD (phys.). If any quantity is a *function* of the time, and this function repeats itself exactly after constant time intervals T, the quantity is said to be periodic, and T is called the period of the function.

PERIODIC LAW. The statement that 'the properties of the *elements* are in periodic dependence upon their *atomic weights*', published by Mendeleev in 1869. The law is brought out clearly when the elements are arranged in the *periodic table*.

PERIODIC SYSTEM. Arrangement of the chemical *elements* in the *periodic table*.

PERIODIC TABLE. An arrangement of the chemical *elements* in order of their *atomic numbers* in such a way as to demonstrate the *periodic law*. In such an arrangement elements having similar properties occur at regular intervals and fall into groups of related elements. From the position of an element in the periodic table its properties may be predicted with a fair measure of success; Mendeleev was able to forecast the existence and properties of then undiscovered elements by means of his original table. The periodic law has since been shown to reflect the grouping of *electrons* in the outer *shells* of the *atoms* of the elements. Elements with the same numbers of electrons in their outer shells have similar chemical properties, as these electrons determine the valencies (see *valency, electronic theory of*) of the atoms. See Table 5, page 335.

PERIPHERY. The external surface or boundary of a body; the circumference or *perimeter* of any closed figure.

PERISCOPE. Device for viewing objects which are above the eye-level of the observer, or are placed so that direct vision is obstructed. Essentially consists of a long tube, at each end of which is a right-angled *prism*, so situated that, by *total internal reflection* at the longest faces, *light* is turned through an angle of 90° by each prism. Thus light from a viewed object enters the observer's eye in a direction parallel to, but below, the original direction of the object.

PERMALLOY*. Class of iron-nickel *alloys* with high *magnetic permeability*. Used in parts of electrical machinery which are subject to alternating *magnetic fields*; causes only low losses of *energy* due to *hysteresis*.

PERMANENT GAS. *Gas* which cannot be liquefied by *pressure* alone; gas above its *critical temperature*.

PERMANENT HARDNESS OF WATER. Hardness which is not destroyed by *boiling* the *water*. See *hard water*.

PERMANENT MAGNETISM. Magnetic properties of substances (especially *steel*) possessed without the influence of an external *magnetic field*.

PERMANGANATE. *Salt* of permanganic acid, $HMnO_4$. Term commonly applied to *potassium permanganate*.

PERMEABILITY. A body is said to be permeable to a substance if it allows the passage of the substance through itself.

PERMEABILITY, MAGNETIC. See *magnetic permeability*.

PERMITTIVITY. The 'absolute permittivity' of a *dielectric* medium is the ratio of the *electric displacement* to the strength of the *electric field* at the same point. For 'relative permittivity' see *dielectric constant*.

PERMUTATION (math.). An arrangement of a specified number of different objects. E.g. the six possible permutations of the digits 123 are 123, 132, 213, 231, 312, 321, The number of possible permutations of n objects if all are taken each time, denoted by ^nP_n, is *factorial n*. The number of permutations of n different objects taken r at a time,

$$^nP_r, \text{ is } \frac{\lfloor n}{\lfloor n-r}.$$

PEROXIDE. *Oxide* which yields *hydrogen peroxide* with an *acid*; term also applied to an oxide which contains more oxygen than the normal oxide of an *element*.

PEROXIDE OF HYDROGEN. See *hydrogen peroxide*.

PERPENDICULAR. At right angles; a straight line making an *angle* of 90° with another line or *plane*.

PERPETUAL MOTION. Concept of a machine which, once set in motion, will go on for ever without receiving *energy*. It is impossible to make a machine which will go on for ever and be able to do *work*, i.e. create energy without receiving energy from outside.

PERSISTENCE OF VISION. The sensation of *light*, as interpreted by the brain, persists for a brief interval after the actual light stimulus is removed; successive images, if they follow one another sufficiently rapidly, produce a continuous impression. Use is made of this in the cine-projector and in *television*.

PERSONAL EQUATION. Time interval or lag peculiar to a person between the perception and recording of any event. In many physical observations an error is introduced by the time-lag between the actual occurrence of the observed event, its perception by the observer, and its recording.

PERSPEX*. See *polymethyl methacrylate*.

PERTURBATIONS. Deviations in the motions of the *planets* from their true elliptical *orbits*, as a result of their gravitational attractions for each other.

PETRIFACTION. Turning of *organic* structures, such as trees, into a stony or *mineral* structure. Generally caused by dissolved *hydrated silica*, SiO_2, penetrating into the pores and gradually losing its *water*.

PETROL, gasoline. Complex *mixture* consisting mainly of *hydrocarbons*, such as *hexane*, *heptane*, and *octane*; other *fuels* and special ingredients are often added.

PETROLATUM, petroleum jelly, Vaseline*. Purified mixture of *hydrocarbons*; semi-solid whitish or yellowish mass.

PETROLEUM, mineral oil. Natural *mixture* of *hydrocarbons* and other *organic compounds*. Composition of various petroleums varies according to source; e.g. American petroleum contains a high proportion of *paraffins* while Russian petroleum is rich in *cyclic hydrocarbons*. *Fractional distillation* yields *petrol*, *paraffin oil*, lubricating oil, *petrolatum*, and *paraffin wax*.

PETROLEUM ETHER. *Mixture* of the lower *hydrocarbons* of the *paraffin series* consisting mainly of *pentane* and *hexane*. B.p. 30°–70° C.

PETROLOGY. The study of the origin, structure, and composition of rocks.

PEWTER. *Alloy* of approximately 4 parts of tin to 1 of lead, with small amounts of antimony.

P$_H$ VALUE. See *hydrogen ion concentration*.

PHAGE. See *bacteriophage*.

PHARMACOGNOSY. Knowledge or study of *drugs*.

PHARMACOLOGY. Study of the action of chemical substances upon animals and man.

PHARMACOPHORE. The portion of a *molecule* of a substance which is regarded as determining the special physiological action of the substance.

PHARMACY. The preparation and dispensing of *drugs* and medicines.

PHASE (chem.). Separate part of a *heterogeneous* body or system. E.g. a *mixture* of *ice* and *water* is a two-phase system, while a *solution* of *salt* in water is a system of one phase.

PHASE (phys.). 1. Points in the path of a *wave motion* are said to be points of equal phase if the displacements at those points at any instant are exactly similar; i.e. of the same magnitude and varying in the same manner. 2. One of the circuits in a system or apparatus in which there are two or more alternating *voltages* displaced in phase (meaning as 1) relative to one another. In a 'two-phase' system the displacement is one quarter of a *period*, in a 'three-phase' system it is one third of a period.

PHASE ANGLE. The *angle* between the *vectors* representing two harmonically varying quantities (e.g. *current* and *voltage*) which have the same *frequency*.

PHASE MODULATION. *Modulation* of the *phase angle* of a *sinusoidal carrier wave*. The *phase* of the modulated wave differs from that of the carrier by an amount proportional to the instantaneous value of the modulating wave.

PHASE RULE. $F+P=C+2$. For a *heterogeneous* system in equilibrium, the sum of the number of *phases* plus the number of *degrees of freedom* is equal to the number of *components*, plus two. E.g. with *ice*, *water*, and *water vapour* in equilibrium, the number of phases is 3, the number of components 1, and hence the number of degrees of freedom is 0; the system is said to be invariant, since no single variable can be changed without causing the disappearance of one phase from the system.

PHASES OF THE MOON. The various shapes of the illuminated surface of the *Moon* as seen from the *Earth* (new moon, first quarter, full moon, third quarter); due to variations in the relative positions of Earth, *Sun*, and Moon.

PHENOBARBITONE. Luminal. Phenylethylbarbituric acid. $C_6H_5.C_2H_5.C:(NHCO)_2:CO$. White crystalline powder, m.p. 174° C.; used as a sedative and *hypnotic* drug usually in the form of the *soluble* sodium *salt*.

PHENOL, carbolic acid. C_6H_5OH. White crystalline *solid*, m.p. 41° C., with a characteristic 'carbolic' smell. *Soluble* in *water*, corrosive, and poisonous. Used as a *disinfectant* and in the manufacture of *plastics* and *dyes*.

PHENOL-FORMALDEHYDE RESIN. Phenolic resin. A very widely used type of synthetic *resin* produced by the *condensation* of *phenols* with *formaldehyde*: forms the basis of *thermosetting* moulding materials, also used in *paints*, varnishes, and *adhesives*.

PHENOLPHTHALEIN. $C_{20}H_{14}O_4$. Colourless crystalline *solid*, m.p. 261° C. Solution in *alcohol* turns a deep purple-red in the presence of *alkalis*, and is used as an *indicator*. Also used in *dye* manufacture and as a laxative.

PHENOLS. Class of *aromatic organic compounds* containing one or more *hydroxyl groups* attached directly to the *benzene* ring. They correspond to the *alcohols* in the *aliphatic* series, forming *esters* and *ethers*, but they also have weak *acidic* properties and form *salts*. See *phenol*.

PHENYL. The *univalent radical* C_6H_5—.

PHLOGISTON THEORY. A theory of *combustion* which was generally accepted during the eighteenth century until refuted by Lavoisier. All combustible substances were supposed to be composed of phlogiston, which escaped on burning, and a calx or ash, which remained. Replacement of phlogiston into the calx would restore the original substance.

PHON. A unit of loudness, used in measuring the intensity of *sounds*. The loudness, in phons, of any sound is equal to the intensity in *decibels* of a sound of *frequency* 1000 which seems as loud to the ear as the given sound.

PHOSGENE, carbonyl chloride. $COCl_2$. Colourless, poisonous *gas* with a penetrating smell resembling musty hay. Used extensively as a poison gas during 1915-18.

PHOSPHATE. *Salt* of *phosphoric acid*, H_3PO_4. Phosphates are used as *fertilizers* to rectify a deficiency of phosphorus in the *soil*.

PHOSPHINE. PH_3. Colourless, inflammable poisonous *gas* with an unpleasant smell.

PHOSPHITE. *Salt* of phosphorous acid, H_3PO_3.

PHOSPHOLIPIDS. Phosphatides. Compound *lipids* which contain *phosphoric acid* groups and nitrogenous *bases*. Found in brain tissue and in egg yolk.

PHOSPHOR. A substance which is capable of *luminescence*, i.e. storing *energy* (particularly from *ionizing radiation*) and later releasing it in the form of *light*. If the energy is released after only a short delay (between 10^{-10} and 10^{-4} seconds) the substance is called a 'scintillator'.

PHOSPHOR BRONZE. *Alloy* of copper (80%–95%), tin (5%–15%), and phosphorus (0·25%–2·5%). Hard, tough, and elastic.

PHOSPHORESCENCE. A form of *luminescence* in which a substance emits *light* of one *wave-length* after having absorbed *electromagnetic radiation* of a shorter wave-length. Unlike *fluorescence*, phosphorescence may continue for a considerable time after *excitation*.

PHOSPHORIC ACID. H_3PO_4. Crystalline, very *soluble solid*; m.p. 41° C.; commonly met with as a thick, syrupy *liquid*. Strong *tribasic acid*.

PHOSPHORUS. P. Element. A.W. 30·9738. At. No. 15. Occurs in several *allotropic forms*, white phosphorus and red phosphorus being the commonest. The former is a waxy white, very inflammable and poisonous *solid*, m.p. 44° C. Red phosphorus is a non-poisonous, dark red powder, not very inflammable. The *element* occurs only in the combined state, mainly as calcium phosphate, $Ca_3(PO_4)_2$. Extracted by heating with *coke* and *silica* (sand) in an electric furnace, and distilling off the phosphorus. Essential to life; calcium phosphate is the main constituent of animal bones. *Compounds* are used as *fertilizers* and *detergents*.

PHOSPHORUS PENTOXIDE. P_2O_5. *Deliquescent*, colourless, crystalline *solid*, m.p. 563° C. Used as a drying agent.

PHOT. Unit of *illumination*; an illumination of one *lumen* per square centimetre.

PHOTOCHEMICAL REACTIONS. *Chemical reactions* which are initiated, assisted, or accelerated by exposure to *light*. E.g. hydrogen and chlorine combine explosively on exposure to sunlight but only slowly in the dark.

PHOTOCHROMISM. Phototropism. The property of certain *dyes*, or other *compounds*, as a result of which they undergo a reversible change in the *colours* which they absorb when exposed to *light* of different *wavelengths*. Thus some photochromic materials will darken in bright light, but will revert to their original colour when the source of light is removed.

PHOTO-CONDUCTIVE EFFECT. A *photo-electric effect* in which the electrical *conductivity* of certain substances, notably selenium, increases with the intensity of the *light* to which the substance is exposed.

PHOTODISINTEGRATION. 1. A *nuclear reaction* caused by a *photon* in which the *nucleus* emits charged fragments or *neutrons*. 2. See *photodissociation*.

PHOTODISSOCIATION. Photodisintegration. The *dissociation* of a chemical *compound* as the result of the absorption of *radiant energy*.

PHOTO-ELECTRIC CELL. Photocell. Device used for the detection and measurement of *light*. The cell may depend for its action upon (1) the normal *photo-electric effect*; the cell is then called a *photo-emissive* cell; (2) the *photo-voltaic effect (rectifier* or *barrier layer* cell); or (3) the *photo-conductive effect* (conductivity cell). Photo-emissive cells consist of two *electrodes*, a plane *cathode* coated with a suitable *photo-sensitive* material, and an *anode* which is maintained at a positive *potential* with respect to the cathode and which attracts the *photo-electrons* liberated by the latter. These electrodes are arranged in an envelope which is either evacuated, or, for greater sensitivity, contains a *gas* at low *pressure*. The *electric current* passing through the cell is a measure of the *light* intensity incident on the cathode. For rectifier or barrier cells, the *potential difference* developed across the boundary gives rise to a current when the faces of the cell are connected externally. This current can be measured directly by suitable means such as a *galvanometer*. Rectifier cells require no external source of *E.M.F.* and are very convenient for photographic *exposure meters*, etc. The conductivity cell is simply an arrangement for measuring the *resistance* of a layer of material, usually selenium, which shows the photo-conductive effect.

PHOTO-ELECTRIC EFFECT. In general, any effect arising as a result of a transfer of *energy* from *light* incident on a substance to *electrons* in the substance. The term is normally restricted to one type of the effect, namely the emission of electrons by substances when irradiated with light of a *frequency* greater than a certain minimum *threshold frequency*. Electrons liberated in this way are called photo-electrons, and constitute a photo-electric current when the system is included in a suitable circuit.

PHOTO-ELECTRONS. See *photo-electric effect*.

PHOTO-EMISSIVE. A substance is described as being photo-emissive if it is capable of emitting *electrons* when it is subjected to *electromagnetic radiation*. The *wave-length* of the radiation which will provoke such emission depends upon the nature of the substance: *light* provokes some *metals* into photo-emission, other materials require *ultra-violet radiation* or *X-rays*.

PHOTOFISSION. *Nuclear fission* caused by *photons* (of *gamma-rays*).

PHOTOGRAPHY. By means of a system of *lenses* in the *camera* an image of the object to be photographed is thrown for a definite length of time on to a plate or *film* made of *glass, celluloid,* or other *transparent* material and covered with an *emulsion* containing *silver bromide*, AgBr, or silver chloride, AgCl. The effect of this exposure of the film is to make the silver compound easily reduced (see *reduction*) to metallic silver by the chemical action of *developing*; developers produce a black deposit of fine particles of metallic silver on those portions of the film which had been exposed to *light*, thus giving a negative image. *Fixing* consists of the chemical action of *sodium thiosulphate*, $Na_2S_2O_3$, ('hypo'), and other *reagents* on the unchanged silver *salts* to give a *soluble compound*, which is then washed out with *water*, leaving a negative which is free of light-sensitive silver salts. By placing the finished negative over a piece of sensitive paper similar to film, and exposing to light, the silver salts in the paper are affected in a similar way to those in the original film; those portions of the negative which were darkest let through least light, and thus give the whitest portions on the developed paper. The negative image is thus again reversed, and a correct image or photograph is obtained on the paper, which is then fixed and washed as before.

PHOTOLYSIS. The *decomposition* of a chemical *compound* as the result of *irradiation* by *light* or *ultra-violet radiation*. 'Flash photolysis' is a method of identifying the free *radicals* formed when the *vapour* of a compound at low *pressure* is exposed to an intense, but very brief, flash of radiation. A second flash, following shortly after the first, is used to photograph the *absorption spectrum* of the *gases* which records the free radicals present. Subsequent flashes at regular intervals may be used to calculate the lifetimes of the radicals so formed.

PHOTOMESON. A *meson* produced by the interaction between a *photon* and an atomic *nucleus*.

PHOTOMETER. Instrument for comparing the *luminous intensity* of sources of *light*.

PHOTOMICROGRAPH. A photograph obtained with the aid of a *microscope*.

PHOTOMULTIPLIER. Electron multiplier. *Photo-electric cell* of high sensitivity used for detecting very small quantities of *light* radiation. Consists of a system of *electrodes* suitably arranged in an evacuated envelope. Light falling on the first electrode ejects *electrons* from this surface (see *photo-electric effect*). These electrons are accelerated to the second electrode, where they each produce further electrons by the process of *secondary emission*. This process continues until the secondary emission from the final electrode is sufficient to produce a useful *electric current*, permitting measurement or the operation of a *relay*.

PHOTON. A *quantum* of *electromagnetic radiation* which has zero *rest mass*, and *energy* equal to the product of the *frequency* of the radiation and *Planck's constant*. Photons are generated when a particle possessing an *electric charge* changes its *momentum*, in collisions between *nuclei* or *electrons*, and in the *decay* of certain nuclei and particles. In some contexts it is convenient to regard a photon as an *elementary particle*.

PHOTO-SENSITIVE. Substances are said to be photo-sensitive if they produce a *photo-conductive*, *photo-electric*, or *photo-voltaic effect* when subjected to suitable *electromagnetic radiation*.

PHOTOSPHERE. The visible, intensely luminous portion of the *Sun* which has an estimated *temperature* of 6000° K.

PHOTOSYNTHESIS. The process by which green plants manufacture their *carbohydrates* from atmospheric *carbon dioxide* and *water* in the presence of sunlight. The reaction, which is highly complex in detail,

may be summarized by the equation:
$$6CO_2 + 6H_2O = C_6H_{12}O_6 + 6O_2.$$

When *light* falls upon green plants the greater part of the *energy* is absorbed by small particles called chloroplasts, which contain a variety of pigments, amongst them *compounds* called *chlorophylls*. The chlorophylls transform the energy of the light into *chemical energy* by a process which is not fully understood, but which is known to involve the *photolysis* of water and the activation of *adenosine triphosphate* (ATP). The energy-rich ATP subsequently energizes the fixation of the CO_2, after a series of reactions, so that *sugar molecules* are formed. As animals are unable to fix atmospheric CO_2 in this way, they depend for their carbon on the plants (or other animals) which they consume. Photosynthesis is therefore essential to all the higher life forms, either directly or indirectly.

PHOTO-VOLTAIC EFFECT. A *photo-electric effect* in which *light* falling on a specially prepared boundary between certain pairs of substances (e.g. copper and *cuprous oxide*) produces a *potential difference* across the boundary.

PHTHALIC ACID. $C_6H_4(COOH)_2$. *Water soluble organic compound*, m.p. 207° C.; on heating above its melting point yields phthalic anhydride which is used in the manufacture of *glyptal resins*.

PHYLOGENY. See *ontogeny*.

PHYSICAL CHANGE. Any change in a body or substance which does not involve an alteration in its chemical composition.

PHYSICAL CHEMISTRY. The study of the *physical changes* associated with *chemical reactions* and the dependence of physical properties on chemical composition.

PHYSICAL STATES OF MATTER. The physical state in which *matter* exists, at a particular *temperature* and *pressure*, depends upon the *kinetic energy* of, and interaction between, its component *atoms*, *molecules*, or *ions*. In *gases* the distance between the fast moving atoms or molecules is such that the interaction between them is very small (see *Van der Waals' forces*); they are therefore free to move about the space which contains them almost independently of each other (see *kinetic theory of gases*). In the *solid state* the atoms, molecules, or ions have insufficient kinetic energy to overcome the strong *forces* which act between them, they therefore vibrate about the fixed positions of a *crystal lattice*. *Liquids* represent an intermediate state between gases and solids. Raising the temperature of a solid increases the kinetic energy of its components so that they are able to overcome the forces between them, the solid then becomes a liquid and eventually a gas. Increasing the pressure of a gas increases the number of collisions between the components and thus facilitates their interactions: for this reason increased pressure causes, or assists in, the *liquefaction of gases*. A hot ionized *plasma* has sometimes been referred to as the fourth state of matter.

PHYSICS. The study of the properties of *matter* and *energy*.

PHYSIOLOGICAL SALINE. An *isotonic solution* of *salts* in *distilled water* used for preserving *cells*. Such solutions contain no food for the cells and their survival in them is therefore restricted.

PHYSIOLOGY. The study of the functioning of the various organs of living beings.

PHYTAMINS. See *auxins*.

PI, π. Symbol for the ratio of the circumference of any *circle* to its diameter. $3 \cdot 14159 \ldots$ (Approximately $22/7$.)

PICO-. Prefix denoting one million millionth. E.g. a picofarad is 10^{-12} *farad*.

PICRIC ACID, trinitrophenol. $C_6H_2(NO_2)_3OH$. Bright yellow crystalline *solid*, m.p. $122°$ C. *Explosive*, poisonous. Formerly used as an explosive (see *lyddite*), as a *dye*, and (in *solution*) for treating burns.

PIEZO-ELECTRIC EFFECT. A property of certain *asymmetric crystals*. When such crystals are subjected to a *pressure*, positive and negative *electric charges* are produced on opposing faces; the signs of these charges are reversed if the pressure is replaced by a tension. The inverse piezo-electric effect occurs if such crystals are subjected to an *electric potential*, an alteration in size of the crystal taking place.

PIG-IRON, cast iron. Impure form of iron obtained from iron ores by the *blast furnace* process.

PIGMENT. Coloured substance which, when applied to a surface, colours the surface. Distinct from a *dye*, which penetrates the fibres or tissues of the surface; in general, pigments are *insoluble* materials which may be removed by mechanical means.

PIGMENT COLOUR, body colour. The *colour* of most natural objects is due to the differential absorption by the substance of the different *wave-lengths* (i.e. colours) present in the incident white *light*. The incident light penetrates a small distance into the substance, undergoes this absorption and is then diffusely reflected out again. The colour the body appears is determined by the wave-lengths absorbed the least. Thus, a substance which absorbs chiefly the red and yellow will appear blue. See also *surface colour*.

PILE, VOLTAIC. See *voltaic pile*.

PINCH EFFECT. 1. The constriction of a *liquid conductor* of *electricity* (e.g. mercury or molten *metal*) which occurs when a substantial *current* is passed through it. 2. The constriction of a *plasma* due to the *magnetic field* of a high current within the plasma. See *thermonuclear reactions*.

PINK SALT. Ammonium chlorostannate, $(NH_4)_2SnCl_6$. Used as a *mordant* in dyeing.

PINKING. See *knocking*.

PINT. Unit of capacity equal to one eighth of a *gallon*.

PION. See *meson*.

PIPETTE. Glass tube with the aid of which a definite *volume* of *liquid* may be transferred.

PITCH. Name given to numerous hard, dark substances which melt to viscous, tarry liquids; applied to the residue from the *destructive distilla-tion* of wood and *coal-tar*, to *asphalt*, various *bitumens*, etc.

PITCH OF A NOTE. Measure of the *frequency* of vibration of the source producing the note; a high frequency produces a note of high pitch. See *sound*.

PITCH OF A SCREW. The distance between adjoining crests of the thread, measured parallel to the *axis* of the screw.

PITCHBLENDE. Natural ore consisting mainly of uranium oxide, U_3O_8. Occurs in Saxony, Bohemia, East Africa, and Colorado. Contains small amounts of radium, of which it is the principal source.

PLANCK'S CONSTANT. h. The universal constant relating the *frequency* of a *radiation*, ν, with its *quantum* of *energy*, E; i.e. $E = h\nu$. Planck's con-stant has the dimensions of *action* (energy $\times$ time) and its value is $6 \cdot 625 \times 10^{-27}$ *erg* seconds. The symbol $\hbar$ is often used for $\dfrac{h}{2\pi}$.

PLANE (math.). A flat surface; mathematically defined as a surface con-taining all the straight lines passing through a fixed point and also intersecting a straight line in space.

PLANE-POLARIZED LIGHT. See *polarization of light*.

PLANETOIDS. See *asteroids*.

PLANETS. Heavenly bodies revolving in definite *orbits* about the *Sun*. In order of increasing distance from the Sun they are *Mercury, Venus, the Earth, Mars, Jupiter, Saturn, Uranus, Neptune*, and *Pluto*. See Table 2, page 333.

PLASMA (bio.). See *blood plasma*.

PLASMA (phys.). 1. The region in a *discharge in gases* in which the numbers of positive and negative *ions* are approximately equal. 2. The term has been extended to include the very hot ionized gas in which controlled *thermonuclear reaction* experiments are carried out. In such a plasma, which has been described as the fourth state of matter, the *ionization* is virtually complete. Again the numbers of positive ions and electrons are approximately equal and the plasma is therefore virtually electrically *neutral* and highly conducting. See also *containment*.

PLASMOLYSIS. The effect of *osmosis* on *cells* of living *organisms*. A cell placed in a *solution* which is of a greater *molecular concentration* than (i.e. is *hypertonic* to) the contents of the cell becomes plasmolyzed; the *water* in the cell flows out through the cell wall and the cell contents contract.

PLASTER OF PARIS. Powdered calcium sulphate, $2CaSO_4.H_2O$, obtained by heating *gypsum* to 120° C.–130° C. With *water*, sets and hardens.

PLASTICIZER. 1. A non-*volatile liquid* added to *paints* and varnishes to prevent brittleness of the dried film. 2. A liquid or *solid* substance added to synthetic or natural *resins* to modify their flow properties.

PLASTICS. Many different definitions have been given. In general, the term may be taken to cover materials which are *stable* in normal use, but which at some stage of their manufacture are plastic, and can be shaped or moulded by *heat*, *pressure*, or both. Most plastics are polymers (see *polymerization*), and are classified into *thermoplastic* and *thermosetting* materials.

PLATELET. See *blood platelet*.

PLATINIZED ASBESTOS. *Asbestos* in the fibres of which a black deposit of finely-divided platinum has been formed. Used as a *catalyst*.

PLATINOID. *Alloy* of 60% copper, 24% zinc, 14% nickel, and 2% wolfram.

PLATINUM. Pt. Element. A.W. 195·09. At. No. 78. Hard, silvery-white, ductile, and malleable *metal*. S.G. 21·45. M.p. 1773·5° C. Very resistant to *heat* and *acids*. Coefficient of *expansion* very nearly equal to that of *glass*. Occurs as the metal, alloyed with osmium, iridium, and similar metals. Used for electrical contacts, scientific apparatus, as a *catalyst* (see *platinized asbestos*) and in jewellery.

PLUMBAGO, black-lead, *graphite*. Natural *allotropic form* of carbon.

PLUTO. Planet with its *orbit* outside that of *Neptune*. Discovered in 1930. Mean distance from the *Sun*, 3666·1 million miles. *Sidereal period* ('*year*') 248·4 years. *Mass* approximately one tenth that of the *Earth*, diameter approximately 3600 miles. Surface temperature probably below −200° C.

PLUTONIUM. Pu. At. No. 94. *Transuranic element*. Different *isotopes* of plutonium can be produced by suitable *nuclear reactions*. The isotope $^{239}_{94}$Pu is produced in *nuclear reactors* and is of considerable importance since it undergoes *nuclear fission* when bombarded by *slow neutrons*. This isotope, which has a *half-life* of 24,400 years, is also used in *nuclear weapons*, one pound having an *energy* equivalent of about 10^7 *kilowatt-hours*.

PNEUMATIC. Operated by, or filled with, compressed air.

P-N-P TRANSISTOR. See *transistor*.

POINT SOURCE OF LIGHT. Theoretical concept of a source of *light* in which all the light is emitted from a single point.

POISE. A unit of *viscosity* in *C.G.S. units*. Defined as the tangential *force* per unit area (*dynes* per sq. cm.) required to maintain unit difference in *velocity* (cm. per second) between two parallel *planes* separated by one centimetre of *fluid*.

POISEUILLE'S EQUATION. The *volume V* of a *liquid* flowing through a cylindrical tube per second is given by the equation $V = \dfrac{\pi p a^4}{8 l \eta}$, where p is the *pressure* difference between two points on the *axis* of the tube at a distance l apart, η is the coefficient of *viscosity* and a is the radius of the tube. The result assumes uniform *streamline* flow, and also that the liquid in contact with the walls of the tube is at rest.

POISON, NUCLEAR. Reactor poison. A substance which absorbs *neutrons* in a *nuclear reactor*. Poisons may be deliberately added to reduce the reactivity, or they may be *fission products*, such as xenon, which have to be periodically removed.

POISSON'S RATIO. The ratio of the *lateral strain* to the *longitudinal* strain in a stretched wire. Given by the ratio of d/D to l/L, where $D =$ original diameter, $L =$ original length, $d =$ decrease in diameter, and $l =$ increase in length.

POLAR BOND. An electrovalent bond. See *valency, electronic theory of*.

POLAR CO-ORDINATES. The position of any point P lying in a *plane* can be completely determined by (1) its distance, r, from any selected point O in the plane, termed the *origin*, and (2) the *angle* θ which the line joining P and O (called the *radius vector*) makes with any co-planar reference line passing through O. The angle is taken as positive when measured anti-clockwise from the reference line. The polar co-ordinates of the point P are r and θ, denoted by (r, θ).

POLAR MOLECULE. A *molecule*, the configuration of *electric charge* in which constitutes a permanent electric *dipole*.

POLARIMETER. Apparatus for measuring the rotation of the plane of vibration of polarized light by optically active substances. See *polarization of light* and *optical activity*.

POLARISCOPE. See *polarimeter*.

POLARIZATION, ANGLE OF. The *angle* of reflection from a *dielectric* medium, e.g. *glass*, at which the reflected *ray* is completely polarized, the plane of vibration being at right angles to the plane of incidence. See *polarization of light*.

POLARIZATION, ELECTRIC. See *electric polarization*.

POLARIZATION, ELECTROLYTIC. Increase in the electrical *resistance* of an *electrolyte* due to various causes; chiefly associated with the accumulation of gaseous *molecules* on the *electrodes* at which they are liberated.

POLARIZATION OF LIGHT. Ordinary *light* consists of electric (E) and magnetic (H) vibrations taking place in all possible *planes* containing the *ray*, the vibrations themselves being at right angles to the direction of the light path; i.e. light is a *transverse wave* motion. For each E vibration the associated H vibration takes place in a plane at right angles to it. In plane-polarized light, the E vibrations are confined to one plane, called the plane of vibration, and hence the associated H vibrations are also confined to one plane, the plane at right angles to this, called the plane of polarization. See also *circularly* and *elliptically polarized light*.

POLAROID*. Trade name of thin *transparent films* which produce plane-polarized light (see *polarization of light*) on transmission. Consist of thin sheets of *cellulose nitrate* packed with ultra-microscopic doubly-refracting *crystals* (see *double refraction*) with their *optic axes* parallel. The crystals produce plane-polarized light by differential absorption of the *ordinary* and *extraordinary rays*.

POLE, MAGNETIC. See *magnetic pole*.

POLE OF MIRROR. See *mirrors, spherical*.

POLE STRENGTH. See *magnetic pole strength*.

POLONIUM. Po. Radium-F. *Radioactive element* decaying by *alpha-particle* emission. At. No. 84. Forms a stage in the radio-active *disintegration* of radium. The principal *isotope* has a *mass number* of 210 and a *half-life* of 138 days.

POLY-. Prefix denoting many, several, numerous.

POLYAMIDE. A *polymer* in which the units are linked by *amide* or *thio*-amide groupings. See *nylon*.

POLYBASIC. *Acid* containing more than one *atom* of *acidic hydrogen* in a *molecule*.

POLYGON. *Plane* figure bounded by straight lines.

POLYGON OF FORCES. If any number of *forces*, acting on a particle, can be represented in magnitude and direction by the sides of a *polygon* taken in order, the forces will be in *equilibrium*.

POLYHEDRON. A solid figure having *polygons* for its faces. A regular polyhedron has all its faces equal in all respects; the five possible types of regular polyhedra are: (1) *tetrahedron*, 4 triangular faces; (2) *cube*, 6 square faces; (3) octahedron, 8 triangular faces; (4) dodecahedron, 12 five-sided faces; (5) icosahedron, 20 triangular faces.

POLYHYDRIC ALCOHOLS. *Alcohols* containing two or more *hydroxyl groups* in the *molecule*. E.g. *glycols* are dihydric alcohols and *glycerin* is a trihydric alcohol.

POLYMER. Product of *polymerization*.

POLYMERIZATION. Originally understood to be the chemical union of two or more *molecules* of the same *compound* to form larger molecules, resulting in the formation of a new compound of the same *empirical formula* but of greater *molecular weight*. E.g. *paraldehyde*, $(CH_3CHO)_3$, is formed by the polymerization of *acetaldehyde*, CH_3CHO, and each molecule of the *polymer* is made up of three molecules of the acetalde-hyde *monomer*. The meaning of the term has been extended to cover (1) 'addition polymerization', in which the molecule of the polymer is a multiple of the monomer molecule, as in the case of paraldehyde; (2) 'condensation polymerization', in which the monomer molecules are joined by *condensation* into a polymer molecule, which differs in empirical formula from the monomer; and (3) 'co-polymerization', in which the polymer molecule is built up from two or more different kinds of monomer molecules. Many important products, such as *plastics* and textile fibres, consist of polymeric substances, either *natural* (e.g. *cellulose*), or *synthetic* (e.g. *nylon*).

POLYMETHYL METHACRYLATE. A colourless, *transparent, solid thermo-plastic*, produced by the *polymerization* of methyl methacrylate (see *methacrylic acid*), which is widely used because of its optical properties in place of *glass*. (Trade name 'Perspex'.)

POLYMORPHISM. The existence of the same substance in more than two different crystalline forms.

POLYNUCLEOTIDE. A chain of *nucleotides* linked together as in a *nucleic acid*. *Ribonucleic acid* consists of a single chain, while *deoxyribonucleic acid* usually consists of a double *helix* comprising two polynucleotide chains.

POLYPEPTIDE. A chain of three or more *amino acids* each of which is joined to its neighbours by the *peptide* linkage. Polypeptide chains may consist of up to several hundred amino acid units. *Proteins* consist of polypeptide chains cross-linked together in a variety of ways.

POLYPLOIDY. Having more than twice the normal *haploid* number of *chromosomes* in a *cell*. Artificial polyploidy can be induced (e.g. by *colchicine*) and is used to produce fertile hybrids with desired characteristics.

POLYPROPYLENE. A colourless, *transparent thermoplastic* material produced by the *polymerization* of *propylene*. Used where a flexible *plastic* material is required. Similar to *polythene* but of greater strength.

POLYSACCHARIDES. Large class of natural *carbohydrates*. *Molecules* are derived from the *condensation* of several, frequently very many, molecules of simple *sugars* (*monosaccharides*). Class includes *cellulose* and *starch*.

POLYSTYRENE. A *thermoplastic* material, produced by the *polymerization* of *styrene* ($C_6H_5CH:CH_2$), possessing good electrical insulating properties.

POLYTHENE, polyethylene, Alkathene*. Tough, waxy *thermoplastic* material, made by the addition *polymerization* of *ethylene*, C_2H_4. Used as an insulating material and for many other purposes where a flexible, chemically resistant *plastic* material is required.

POLYVINYL ACETATE. A colourless *thermoplastic* material, produced by the *polymerization* of *vinyl* acetate ($CH_2:CHOOC.CH_3$), used in *adhesives*, *inks*, and lacquers and for coating paper and fabric.

POLYVINYL CHLORIDE. PVC. A colourless *thermoplastic* material, produced by the *polymerization* of vinyl chloride (see *vinyl group*), with good resistance to *water*, *acids*, *alkalis*, and *alcohols*.

POLYVINYLIDENE CHLORIDE. A white *thermoplastic* material, produced by the *polymerization* of vinylidene chloride ($CH_2:CCl_2$). Also used as a co-polymer with *acrylonitrile* or *vinyl* chloride giving products with a wide range of flexibilities.

PORCELAIN. Hard, white material made by the firing of a *mixture* of pure kaolin (*china clay*) with *felspar* and *quartz*, or with other materials containing *silica*.

POSITION CIRCLE. *Circle* with centre at an observed point and radius such that the circumference passes through the place of observation. The portion of the circumference near the place of observation approximates to a *position line* if the radius is large.

POSITION LINE. A line of position on which the observer is situated at a given time. The intersection of two position lines, determined at the same time, fixes the position of the observer.

POSITIVE (math., phys.). In any convention of signs, regarded as being counted in the plus, or positive direction, as opposed to *negative*.

POSITIVE COLUMN. Luminous region in a *discharge in gases* near to the positive *electrode*.

POSITIVE FEEDBACK. See *feedback*.

POSITIVE MAGNETIC POLE. The north-seeking pole of a *magnet*. See *magnetic pole*.

POSITIVE RAY ANALYSIS. *Positive rays* may be separated out into a mass spectrum by means of suitably disposed *magnetic* and *electric fields*. The deflection of any one *ion* in these fields is a *function* of the ratio of its *mass* to its *electric charge*, m/e. Such a spectrum can be made to affect a photographic plate, and will appear as a number of lines, each corresponding to a definite value of m/e. *Isotopes* were first discovered in this way.

POSITIVE RAYS. Streams of *ions* bearing positive *electric charges*. May be produced by means of an electric discharge in a rarefied gas. See *discharge in gases*.

POSITRON. Positive *electron*. *Elementary particle* with the same *mass* as the electron and an *electric charge* of equal magnitude but opposite sign. Positrons are produced during several *decay* processes and during *pair production*; they do not themselves decay spontaneously but on passing through matter they collide with negative electrons as a result of which both particles are annihilated. See *annihilation radiation*.

POSITRONIUM. An unstable unit, resembling an *atom* of hydrogen, which consists of a *positron* (instead of a *proton*) and an *electron*. Decays by annihilation in less than 10^{-7} seconds into two or three *photons*.

POTASH. *Potassium carbonate*, K_2CO_3. Term also applied to *potassium hydroxide*, KOH (caustic potash) and, loosely, to potassium *salts* in general.

POTASSIUM, kalium. K. Element. A.W. 39·102. At. No. 19. Silvery-white, soft, highly reactive *metal*, strongly resembling sodium. S.G. 0·86, m.p. 62·3° C. Widely distributed in the form of various *salts* (e.g. *carnallite*); essential to life; found in all living matter. Salts used as *fertilizers*.

POTASSIUM BICARBONATE, bicarbonate of potash. $KHCO_3$. White, *soluble* salt.

POTASSIUM BROMIDE. KBr. White, crystalline *salt*, m.p. 730° C., used in medicine and *photography*.

POTASSIUM CARBONATE, potash, carbonate of potash. K_2CO_3. White, very *soluble, deliquescent salt*, m.p. 891° C.

POTASSIUM DICHROMATE, dichromate or bichromate of potash. $K_2Cr_2O_7$. Red, crystalline, *soluble salt*, m.p. 398° C., prepared from *chrome iron ore*. Used as an *oxidizing agent*, and in the *paint* and *dye* industries.

POTASSIUM HYDROXIDE, caustic potash. KOH. White, *deliquescent solid*, m.p. 360·4° C., dissolves in *water* to give an *alkaline solution*.

POTASSIUM NITRATE, nitre, saltpetre. White, *soluble* crystalline *salt*, m.p. 336° C. When hot, acts as an *oxidizing agent*. Used in medicine, for pickling meat, and in *gunpowder*.

POTASSIUM PERMANGANATE, permanganate of potash. $KMnO_4$. Deep purple, crystalline, *soluble salt*, dissolves in *water* to give a purple *solution* which acts as a powerful *oxidizing agent*. Used as a *disinfectant* and in *volumetric analysis*.

POTENTIAL. See *electric potential*.

POTENTIAL BARRIER. See *nuclear barrier*.

POTENTIAL DIFFERENCE. If two points have a different *electric potential* there is said to be a potential difference (P.D.) between them; if the points are joined by an electric *conductor*, an *electric current* will flow between them. Defined as the *work* performed when a unit positive *electric charge* is moved from one of the points to the other. Also referred to as *electromotive force*, E.M.F. The practical unit of P.D. and E.M.F. is the *volt*.

POTENTIAL ENERGY. *Energy* which a body possesses by virtue of its position. E.g. a coiled spring, or a vehicle at the top of a hill, possesses potential energy. Measured by the amount of *work* the body performs in passing from that position to a standard position in which the potential energy is considered to be zero. The potential energy of a *mass*, m, raised through a height, h, is mgh, where g is the *acceleration due to gravity*. The energy will be in *ergs* if m is in *grams*, h in centimetres and g in cm./sec².

POTENTIAL SERIES. See *electromotive series*.

POTENTIOMETER. An instrument for measuring *direct current E.M.F.* or *potential differences*, which does not draw current from the circuit containing the E.M.F. to be measured. In its simplest form consists of a uniform *resistance AB* (see Fig. 12) in the form of a single wire, connected to a source of E.M.F., *E*. A slide wire contact *C* is connected in series with a sensitive *galvanometer G*, to one terminal of the E.M.F. to be measured. The other terminal is connected to *A*, so that the E.M.F.s across *XY* and *AC* are in opposition through *G*. Contact *C* is then adjusted until no current flows through the galvanometer. The required E.M.F. is then given by El_1/L, where L is the total length of the resistance *AB*, and l_1 is the length *AC* for zero current through *G*.

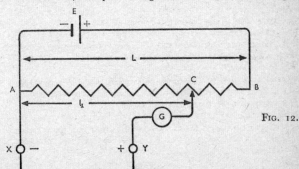

FIG. 12.

POUND. British unit of *weight*. Formerly defined as the weight, in vacuo, of a platinum cylinder called the Imperial Standard Pound. Redefined by statute in 1963 as 0.453,592,37 *Kilogram*. Used as a unit of *force*, i.e. the force of attraction of the *Earth* upon a *mass* of one pound, and as a unit of mass.

POUNDAL. Unit of *force* in the *F.P.S. system* of units. That force which, acting on a *mass* of 1 *pound*, will impart to it an *acceleration* of 1 foot per second per second. Approximately 1/32 of a force of 1 pound weight.

POWER (math.). A quantity successively multiplied by itself is said to be raised to a power, the magnitude of the power being the number of times that the quantity occurs in the multiplication. Thus $2 \times 2 \times 2 \times 2$ is 2 raised to the fourth power, 2 to the fourth, denoted as 2^4, 4 being the *index* or *exponent*.

POWER (phys.). Rate of doing *work*. Measured in units of work per unit time. See *watt*, *horse-power*.

POWER ALCOHOL. Industrial *ethyl alcohol* used as a *fuel*.

POWER FACTOR. In an electrical *circuit*, the ratio of the *power* dissipated, P, to the product of the *electromotive force*, E, and the *current*, I. In single-*phase* and three-phase circuits the power factor is given by cos ϕ, where ϕ is the *phase angle* between the E.M.F. and the current. i.e. $P = EI \cos \phi$.

POWER REACTOR. See *nuclear reactor*.

PRASEODYMIUM. Pr..Element. A.W. 140.907. At. No. 59. See *lanthanides*.

PRECESSIONAL MOTION. A rotating body is said to precess when, as a result of an applied *couple*, the *axis* of which is at right angles to the rotation axis, the body turns about the third mutually perpendicular axis.

PRECIPITATE (chem.). An *insoluble* substance formed in a *solution* as the result of a *chemical reaction*.

PRECIPITATION (chem.). The formation of a *precipitate*. A common type of precipitation, much used in chemical analysis and preparations, occurs by *double decomposition* when two *solutions* are mixed if each of the solutions contains one *radical* of an *insoluble compound*.

PRESBYOPIA. Long sight. Defect of vision normally occurring in elderly people. Subject is able to see distant objects clearly, but is unable to accommodate the eye to see near objects distinctly. Corrected by the use of *convex* spectacle *lenses*.

PRESSURE. The *force* per unit *area* acting on a surface. 'Absolute pressure' is the pressure measured with respect to zero pressure. 'Gauge pressure' is the pressure measured by a gauge in excess of the pressure of the *atmosphere*.

PRESSURE, ATMOSPHERIC. See *atmosphere, the normal or standard*.

PRESSURE, UNITS OF. In the *C.G.S. system*, 1 bar = 10^6 *dynes*/sq. cm. See also *atmosphere, the normal or standard*.

PRESSURIZED WATER REACTOR. PWR. A *nuclear reactor* in which *water* is the coolant and the *moderator*, but in which the water is maintained at a high *pressure* in order to prevent it *boiling*. The pressurized water is passed through a heat exchanger to generate *steam* which may be used for producing *electric power* in a conventional *turbo-generator*.

PRIMARY CELL. Voltaic cell. Device, usually irreversible, for producing an *electromotive force* and delivering an *electric current* as the result of a *chemical reaction*. See *Daniell cell, Leclanché cell, Weston cell, Mercury cell.*

PRIMARY COIL. The input coil of a *transformer* or *induction coil*.

PRIMARY COLOURS (phys.). Red, green, and a bluish-violet. Any *colour* may be obtained by suitably combining *light* producing these (see *colour vision*). Term also used for the *pigment colours* red, yellow, and blue, which cannot be imitated by mixing any other pigment colours.

PRIME NUMBER (math.). Number possessing no *factors* (i.e. divisible by no whole number, other than itself and one).

PRINCIPAL FOCUS. See *mirrors, spherical; lens.*

PRINCIPAL PLANE (phys.). In a *crystal* exhibiting *double refraction*, a principal plane is a plane containing the *optic axis* and either the *ordinary ray* (principal plane of ordinary ray) or the *extraordinary ray* (principal plane of extraordinary ray).

PRINCIPAL POINTS (phys.). Two points on the *axis* of a thick *lens* or combination lens system, such that if the object distance is measured from one and the image distance from the other, the *equations* obtained relating object-image distance, etc., are similar to those obtained for a thin lens.

PRINCIPAL SECTION (phys.). A principal section of a *crystal* exhibiting *double refraction* is a *plane* passing through the *optic axis* and at right angles to one of the crystal surfaces.

PRINCIPLE OF SUPERPOSITION. See *Huygens' principle of superposition.*

PRINTED CIRCUIT. A method of manufacturing parts of *electronic* equipment in which the wiring between components, and certain fixed components themselves, are printed on to an insulating board. The board is coated with copper and the portion of the metal which represents the wiring or components is photographically covered with a protective film, the rest of the metal being etched away in an *acid* bath.

PRISM (math.). Solid figure having two identically equal faces (bases) consisting of *polygons* in parallel *planes*; the other faces being *parallelograms* equal in number to the number of sides of one of the bases.

PRISM, optical. Triangular *prism* made of material *transparent* to the *light* being used; e.g. *glass* for visible light, *quartz* for *ultra-violet* and near *infra-red radiation.*

PRISMATIC. In the shape of a *prism*.

PRISMATIC OPTICAL INSTRUMENTS. Instruments (field-glasses, etc.) in which a right-angled *prism* is used to invert the inverted image produced by the *objective*.

PROBABILITY DISTRIBUTION OF ELECTRONS. The *probability* that an *electron* within an *atom* will be at a certain point in *space* at a given time; determined by the magnitude of the square of the *wave function*.

PROBABILITY, MATHEMATICAL. If an event can happen in *a* ways and fail in b ways, and, except for the numerical difference between a and b, is as likely to happen as to fail, the mathematical probability of its happening is $\dfrac{a}{a+b}$ and of its failing, $\dfrac{b}{a+b}$.

PROCESS CONTROL. The control of complex industrial or chemical processes by *electronic* means.

PRODUCER GAS. A *fuel gas* produced by the partial *combustion* of *coke* or *coal* in a restricted supply of air, to which *steam* may have been added. The principal constituents of the gas are *carbon monoxide* (25%–30%), nitrogen (50%–55%), and hydrogen (10%–15%). *Hydrocarbons* and *carbon dioxide* will also be present.

PRODUCT (math.). The product of two or more quantities is the result of multiplying them together.

PRODUCTION REACTOR. See *nuclear reactor*.

PROGESTERONE. $C_{21}H_{30}O_2$. *Steroid hormone* responsible for preparing the reproductive organs of mammals for pregnancy and for protecting the embryo.

PROJECTILE. Body thrown or projected. If the projectile is discharged with a *velocity v* at an *angle a* to the horizontal, the following formulae hold true if the resistance of the air is neglected (*g* being the *acceleration due to gravity*):

$$\text{Time to reach highest point of flight} = \frac{v \sin a}{g}$$

$$\text{Total time of flight} = \frac{2v \sin a}{g}$$

$$\text{Maximum height} = \frac{v^2 \sin^2 a}{2g}$$

$$\text{Horizontal range} = \frac{v^2 \sin 2a}{g}$$

PROLATE SPHEROID. See *spheroid*.

PROMETHIUM. Pm. *Radioactive element* of the *lanthanide* series. At. No. 61. Occurs as a fission product of uranium in *nuclear reactors*. The most stable *isotope*, $^{145}_{61}$Pm, has a *half-life* of about thirty years.

PROMPT CRITICAL. Capable of sustaining a *nuclear fission chain reaction* on the *prompt neutrons* alone, without contribution from *delayed neutrons*.

PROMPT NEUTRONS. *Neutrons* resulting from *nuclear fission* (either during the fission process or from freshly formed fission fragments) which are emitted without measurable delay, i.e. less than a millionth of a second. See *delayed neutrons*.

PRONTOSIL. *Organic compound* derived from chrysoidine (an *azo dye*) which has been used for destroying certain types of disease *bacteria* in the living body. The earliest used of the *sulphonamide* group of drugs.

PROOF SPIRIT. *Ethyl alcohol* containing 49·28% alcohol by *weight*, or 57·10% by *volume*, and having a *specific gravity* of 0·91976 at 60° F.

Formerly defined as the weakest solution of alcohol which would fire *gunpowder* when brought into contact with it and ignited.

PROOF SPIRIT, DEGREES. The number of degrees under proof is the *volume* percentage of *water* in a *solution* regarded as containing *proof spirit* and water; degrees over proof is the volume increase obtained when 100 volumes of the spirit are diluted with sufficient water to obtain proof spirit.

PROPANE. C_3H_8. Third *hydrocarbon* of the *paraffin series*. Inflammable *gas*. B.p. $-42\cdot17°$ C.

PROPELLANT. The explosive substance used to fill cartridges, shell cases, and *solid fuel rockets*. The term is also used to include the fuel and *oxidant* of rockets when these are separate.

PROPER MOTION OF A STAR. The component of a *star*'s motion in *space* relative to the *Sun*, which is perpendicular to the line of sight.

PROPORTION (math.). An equality between two *ratios*. If $a/b = c/d$, the four quantities a, b, c, d are in proportion.

PROPULSION REACTOR. See *nuclear reactor*.

PROPYL. The *univalent alkyl radical*. C_3H_7—.

PROPYLENE. Propene. $CH_2{:}CH.CH_3$. Second member of the *olefine* series of *hydrocarbons*. Colourless *gas*. B.p. $-47°$ C.

PROSTHETIC GROUP. A non-*protein* group which is combined to a protein, e.g. the haem group in *haemoglobin* or the *nucleic acid* in *nucleo-protein*.

PROTARGOL. Powder containing finely-divided silver and *protein*; with *water*, forms a *colloidal solution* of silver.

PROTEASES, proteinases. Group of *enzymes* capable of breaking up *proteins* into *amino acids*, of building up amino acids into proteins, and of substituting one amino acid for another in protein *molecules*. Occur in all living tissues; conduct the processes of protein *metabolism* in the living *organism*.

PROTECTIVE FOODS. Foods which protect against *deficiency diseases*.

PROTEINS. A class of complex nitrogenous *organic compounds* of high *molecular weight* (18,000–10,000,000) which are of great importance to all living matter. Protein *molecules* consist of hundreds or thousands of *amino acids* joined together by the *peptide* linkage into one or more inter-linked *polypeptide* chains, which may be folded in a variety of different ways. Some twenty different amino acids occur in proteins and each protein molecule is likely to contain all of them arranged in a variety of sequences. It is the sequence of the different amino acids which give individual proteins their specific properties. The particular sequence of the amino acids in proteins, which are synthesized in the *cytoplasms* of *cells*, is determined by the sequence of the *nucleotides* in the *nucleic acids* of the *chromosomes*, three nucleotides coding for each amino acid. Most proteins form *colloidal solutions* in water or dilute *salt* solutions, but some (notably the fibrous proteins) are *insoluble*. Proteins may be simple, i.e. yielding only amino acids on *hydrolysis*, others are 'conjugated', i.e. combined with other substances (see *prosthetic groups*). *Enzymes* are a particularly important group of proteins as they determine the *chemical reactions* which will take place in a cell, and therefore the characteristics which it will have.

PROTEIN-SPARERS. *Proteins* may be used by the body to supply *energy* by being oxidized, in the same way as *carbohydrates* and *fats*; this, however, causes the proteins so used to be lost for their more important function of body-building. Carbohydrates and fats when eaten with proteins in a food thus act as *protein-sparers*, providing energy while the proteins are utilized for building tissue.

PROTEOLYTIC, proteoclastic. Having the power of decomposing or *hydrolyzing proteins*.

PROTIUM. The hydrogen *isotope* with *mass number* of one.

PROT(O)ACTINIUM. Pa. *Radioactive* element. At. No. 91. The most abundant natural *isotope* has a *mass number* of 231 and a *half-life* of 34,300 years.

PROTON. Stable *elementary particle* with *electric charge* equal in magnitude to that of the *electron* but of opposite sign, and with *mass* $1836 \cdot 12$ times greater than that of the electron (i.e. $1 \cdot 00727$ *atomic mass units*). The proton is a *hydrogen ion* (i.e. a normal hydrogen atomic *nucleus*) and is a constituent of all other atomic nuclei. See *atom, structure of*.

PROTOPLASM. The *matter* of which biological *cells* consist. Usually divided into two parts, the *cytoplasm* and the *nucleus*.

PROTYLE. Primary 'element' from which *atoms* of all other *elements* were supposed to be formed; considered by Prout (1816) to be hydrogen.

PRUSSIAN BLUE. Potassium *ferric* ferrocyanide, $KFe[Fe(CN)_6]$. Deep blue substance obtained by the action of a ferric *salt* on potassium ferrocyanide.

PRUSSIC ACID. Solution of *hydrocyanic acid*, HCN. Intensely poisonous.

PSEUDO-SCALAR. A *scalar quantity* which changes sign in the transition from a right-handed to a left-handed system of co-ordinates.

PSEUDO-VECTOR. Axial vector. A *vector* quantity which changes sign in the transition from a right-handed to a left-handed system of co-ordinates.

PSYCHROMETRY. Measurement of the *humidity of the atmosphere*.

PTOMAINES. Name given to a class of extremely poisonous *organic compounds* formed during the putrefaction of *proteins* of animal origin. Food poisoning, frequently misnamed ptomaine poisoning, is almost invariably due to causes other than the ptomaines.

PTYALIN. *Enzyme* in the saliva; serves to convert *starch* into *sugar*.

P-TYPE CONDUCTIVITY. See *N-type conductivity*.

PUDDLING PROCESS. Preparation of nearly pure *wrought iron* from *cast iron* which contains a high percentage of carbon. The cast iron is heated with *haematite*, Fe_2O_3, the oxygen in which oxidizes the carbon.

PULSE. A brief increase in the magnitude of a quantity whose value is usually constant (e.g. *current* or *voltage*).

PULSE HEIGHT ANALYSER. An instrument incorporating an *electronic* circuit which permits only *voltage pulses* of predetermined *amplitudes* to be passed to succeeding circuits. The range of amplitudes which are passed through such circuits is referred to as the 'channel width' or 'window'. In a single-channel analyser the channel width is usually pre-set and the *threshold* varied to scan the amplitude spectrum of incoming pulses. In a multi-channel instrument, often called a 'kicksorter', the incoming pulses are sorted and recorded according to their amplitudes. The kicksorter is used for distinguishing between *isotopes* by sorting the characteristic 'kicks' which their *radiations* give.

PULSE-JET. A type of *ram-jet* in which the *combustion* process is not continuous, but is arranged to occur at intervals between which the *pressure* in the combustion chamber is allowed to build up. The German 'flying bombs' of World War II were powered by pulse-jets fitted with air intake valves which opened when the pressure resulting from the passage of the projectile through the air exceeded the pressure in the combustion chamber: each new charge being separately fired.

PURINES. Class of *organic compounds* derived from *uric acid*. Purines are of great importance biologically as they occur in *adenosine triphosphate* and *nucleic acids*. *Adenine* and *guanine* are typical purines.

PURPLE OF CASSIUS. A purple *pigment*, consisting of a *mixture* of colloidal gold and *stannic* acid. Used for making ruby *glass*.

PUTREFACTION. Chemical *decomposition*, by the action of *bacteria*, of the bodies of dead animals and plants; especially the *decomposition* of *proteins* with the production of offensive substances.

PUTTY. Material composed of powdered *chalk* mixed with *linseed oil*.

PUTTY POWDER. Impure tin oxide, SnO_2.

PYKNOMETER. Apparatus for determining the *density* and coefficient of *expansion* of a *liquid*. A glass vessel which is graduated to hold a definite *volume* of liquid at a given *temperature*. By weighing it full of liquid at different temperatures, the variations in density, and therefore the apparent expansion, may be found.

PYRAMID (math.). Solid figure having a *polygon* for one of its faces (termed the base), the other faces being *triangles* with a common vertex. The *volume* of a pyramid is one-third of the *product* of the area of the base and the vertical height.

PYRENE. 1. The *hydrocarbon* $C_{16}H_{10}$, yellow *crystals*, m.p. 149° C., found in *coal-tar*. 2. Trade name for a *fire extinguisher* consisting of *carbon tetrachloride*, CCl_4.

PYRIDINE. C_5H_5N. *Heterocyclic organic compound*. Colourless *liquid* with an unpleasant smell. B.p. 115° C. Occurs in *bone-oil* and *coal-tar*. Used for making *methylated spirit* unpalatable; *compounds* derived from it are used in medicine.

PYRIDOXINE. Vitamin B_6. $C_8H_{11}NO_3$. A *pyridine derivative* which is a member of the *vitamin* B complex; believed to be of importance in the utilization of *unsaturated fatty acids* by many *organisms*.

PYRIMIDINES. Class of *heterocyclic compounds* comprising a six-membered ring containing two nitrogen *atoms*. Pyrimidines are of great biological importance as they occur in *nucleic acids*. *Uracil*, *thymine*, and *cytosine* are typical pyrimidines.

PYRITES. Natural *sulphides* of certain *metals*. Iron pyrites is FeS_2; copper pyrites ('fools' gold') is $CuFeS_2$.

PYRO-. Prefix denoting fire, strong heat. In chemical nomenclature denotes a substance obtained by heating; e.g. pyroboric acid, obtained by heating *boric acid*.

PYROELECTRICITY. The property of certain *crystals*, e.g. *tourmaline*, of acquiring *electric charges* on opposite faces when the crystals are heated.

PYROGALLOL, pyrogallic acid, 1, 2, 3-trihydroxybenzene. $C_6H_3(OH)_3$. White, crystalline *soluble solid*, m.p. 132° C. Powerful *reducing agent*; *alkaline solution* rapidly absorbs oxygen. Used in photographic *developing* and in gas analysis for the estimation of oxygen. See *Orsat apparatus*.

PYROLIGNEOUS ACID. Watery *liquid* obtained by the *destructive distillation* of wood. Contains *acetic acid*, CH_3COOH, *methyl alcohol*, CH_3OH, *acetone*, $(CH_3)_2CO$, and small amounts of other *organic compounds*.

PYROLUSITE. Natural *manganese dioxide*, MnO_2. Black crystalline *solid*, S.G. 4·8; principal ore of manganese.

PYROLYSIS. Chemical *decomposition* by the action of *heat*.

PYROMETERS. Instruments for measuring high *temperatures*. The four main types are: (1) platinum resistance *thermometers*, which make use of the increased electrical *resistance* of platinum wire with rise in temperature; (2) thermo-electric thermometers, using the principle of the *thermocouple*; (3) optical pyrometers, in which the temperature is estimated by the intensity of the *light* emitted by the body in a narrow *wave-length* range; and (4) *radiation* pyrometers, which detect the *heat* radiation from the hot body (see *radio-micrometer*).

PYROPHORIC ALLOYS. *Alloys* which emit sparks when scraped or struck, and are therefore used as 'flints' in lighters. See *misch metal*; *Auer metal*.

PYROTECHNICS. Fireworks.

PYRUVIC ACID. $CH_2.CO.COOH$. *Organic acid*, m.p. 13° C., of importance in the metabolic (see *metabolism*) breakdown of *glucose*. Pyruvic acid is itself broken down in the *citric acid cycle*.

PYTHAGORAS, THEOREM OF. In a right-angled *triangle* the square on the *hypotenuse* is equal to the sum of the squares on the other two sides.

Q

Q-VALUE, nuclear energy change, nuclear heat of reaction. The net amount of *energy* released in a *nuclear reaction*; usually expressed in million *electron-volts*, *Mev*, per individual reaction.

Q. S. G. Quasi stellar galaxy. A *quasar* which is not a radio source.

QUADRANT, quarter-circle. *Sector* of a *circle* bounded by an arc and two radii at right angles.

QUADRATIC EQUATION. An *equation* involving the *square* or second *power* of the unknown quantity; satisfied by two values (known as *roots*) of the unknown quantity. Any quadratic equation may be written in the form $ax^2+bx+c=0$; the roots of this equation are given by the expression $x=\dfrac{-b\pm\sqrt{b^2-4ac}}{2a}$.

Thus any quadratic equation may be solved by substitution of the appropriate values in the above expression.

QUADRATURE. The position of the *Moon* or outer *planet* such that a line between it and the *Earth* makes a right angle with a line joining the Earth to the *Sun*.

QUADRILATERAL. *Plane* figure bounded by four straight lines.

QUALITATIVE. Dealing only with the nature, and not the amounts, of the substances under consideration.

QUALITATIVE CHEMICAL ANALYSIS. Determination of the chemical nature of substances; identification of substances present in a *mixture*.

QUALITY CONTROL. The application of the theory of mathematical *probability* to sampling the output of an industrial process, with the object of detecting and controlling any variations in quality.

QUALITY OF SOUND. Most sounds are not 'pure'; i.e. they are composed of vibrations of more than one *frequency*. A note consists of a 'fundamental', of greatest intensity and lowest *pitch*; and several *overtones*, of much lesser intensity and of frequencies which are simple multiples of that of the fundamental. The various overtones produce a characteristic quality or timbre in the note.

QUANTITATIVE. Dealing with quantities as well as the nature of the substances under consideration.

QUANTITATIVE CHEMICAL ANALYSIS. Determination of the amounts of substances present, by chemical means.

QUANTIZED. A quantity is said to be quantized if, in accordance with *quantum mechanics*, it can only have certain discrete values (each of which is called a *quantum*). Such a quantity cannot vary continuously, differences in value being separated by 'jumps'.

QUANTUM. According to the *quantum theory*, *energy* exists in discrete units, only whole numbers of which can exist: each unit is called a quantum (plural 'quanta'). The quantum of *electromagnetic radiation* is the *photon*; in certain contexts the quantum of energy associated with *nuclear forces* may be taken as the *meson*.

QUANTUM ELECTRONICS. The study of the generation or amplification of *microwave power* in *solid crystals*, in accordance with the laws of *quantum mechanics*.

QUANTUM MECHANICS. The system of mechanics which, during the present century, has replaced *Newtonian mechanics* as a method of interpreting physical phenomena occurring on a very small scale (e.g. the motion of *electrons* and *nuclei* within *atoms*; see *atom, structure of*).

Quantum theory originated with the discovery by Max Planck that the *heat radiation* from a black-body (see *black-body radiation*) is *quantized*, i.e. emitted in discrete *quanta* of *energy*, the magnitude of which are given by the product of the *frequency* of the radiation and a universal constant, now known as *Planck's constant*. It was soon realized that all *electromagnetic radiations* are quantized (see *photon*) and the theory was developed by Niels Bohr so that the *spectrum* of hydrogen could be accounted for *quantitatively* (see *Bohr theory*). This early version of quantum mechanics was refined by Sommerfeld to take into account the elliptical *orbits* of electrons. More recently quantum mechanics has been developed in a specialized form, known as *wave mechanics*, which is more versatile and involves fewer arbitrary assumptions than the original theory.

QUANTUM NUMBERS. One of several *integral* or half-integral numbers which specify the state of a system or its components in *quantum mechanics*. An *electron* within an *atom* is specified by four quantum numbers: (1) the principal quantum number, n, defining the quantum *shell* in which the electron occurs; (2) the azimuthal quantum number, l, defining the shape of the *orbit* and the *energy* sub-level; (3) the magnetic orbital quantum number, m_l, which determines the orientation of the orbit with reference to a fixed direction; and (4) the magnetic *spin* quantum number, m_s, which distinguishes between the clockwise and anticlockwise spin of an electron: this number is either $\pm \frac{1}{2}$. See also *Pauli's exclusion principle*.

QUANTUM THEORY. The theory which grew up around Planck's introduction into *physics* of the concept of the discontinuity of *energy*. The system of *quantum mechanics* evolved from this theory during the first half of the twentieth century.

QUART. Unit of capacity equal to one quarter of a *gallon*.

QUARTER-WAVE PLATE. Plate of doubly refracting material (see *double refraction*) cut parallel to the *optic axis* of the *crystal*, and of such a thickness that a *phase* difference of $\pi/2$ or $90°$ is introduced between the *ordinary* and *extraordinary rays* for *light* of a particular *wave-length* (usually sodium light). Plane-polarized light (see *polarization of light*) incident normally upon such a plate, with its plane of vibration making an angle of $45°$ with the optic axis, emerges from the plate *circularly polarized*. A quarter-wave plate is often used in the analysis of polarized light.

QUARTZ. Natural crystalline *silica*, SiO_2. Sometimes occurs in clear, colourless *crystals* (*rock crystal*); more frequently as a white, *opaque* mass. Quartz crystals exhibit the *piezo-electric effect* to a marked extent.

QUARTZ CLOCK. A clock regulated by a *quartz crystal* which vibrates with a definite constant *frequency* under the effect of an alternating *electric field* tuned to this *resonance* frequency of the crystal. (See *piezo-electric effect*.) Much more accurate than a pendulum-regulated clock; used for astronomical and other very precise work.

QUASARS. Quasi stellar radio sources. Recently discovered extra-galatic sources of high energy *electromagnetic radiation*. Originally located by radio astronomers (see *radio astronomy*) because of their powerful *radio frequency* emissions.

QUATERNARY AMMONIUM COMPOUNDS. *Compounds* of the general formular NR_4OH; theoretically derived from *ammonium hydroxide*, NH_4OH, by replacement of the hydrogen *atoms* by *organic radicals*.

QUENCHING. The process of terminating the discharge in a *Geiger counter* by preventing re-ignition.

QUENCHING OF STEEL. Rapid cooling by immersion into *water* or *oil*, to harden the *steel*.

QUICKLIME. Calcium oxide, CaO. Combines with water, with evolution of *heat*, to give *slaked lime*, calcium hydroxide, $Ca(OH)_2$. Used in *mortar*, etc.

QUICKSILVER. See *mercury*.

QUININE. $C_{20}H_{24}O_2N_2.3H_2O$. *Alkaloid* occurring in Cinchona bark. Colourless, crystalline *solid*, m.p. 57° C., with a bitter taste. *Basic* in chemical character. Used in medicine.

QUINOL. Hydroquinone. $C_6H_4(OH)_2$. *Aromatic organic compound* obtained by the *reduction* of *quinone*; m.p. 170° C. Being a powerful *reducing agent*, it is widely used in photographic *developing*.

QUINONES. *Aromatic organic compounds* containing a *benzene* ring in which two *atoms* of hydrogen are replaced by two atoms of oxygen. Quinones are used in *photography* and in *dye* manufacture, they are also widely distributed in plants. *Para*-quinone, or para-benzoquinone, $O:C_6H_4:O$ is a crystalline *solid*, m.p. 116° C., with a pungent odour.

QUINQUEVALENT. Having a *valency* of five.

QUOTIENT. See *division*.

R

RACEMIC ACID, racemic tartaric acid, *dl*-tartaric acid. *Racemic form of tartaric acid.*

RACEMIC FORM. Isomeric form of a substance which exhibits *stereoisomerism*. Consists of an *equimolecular mixture* of the two *optically active* forms. Such a racemic form is denoted by the letters *dl.*, e.g. *dl*-tartaric acid; it is optically inactive and is said to be externally compensated.

RAD. The unit of absorbed *dose* of *ionizing radiation*. One rad is equal to the *energy* absorption of 100 *ergs* per gram of *irradiated* material.

RADAR. An abbreviation of the words RAdio Detection And Ranging. A general term now used to include any system employing *microwaves* for the purpose of locating, identifying, navigating, or guiding such moving objects as ships, aircraft, missiles, or artificial *satellites*. The system consists essentially of a generator of *electromagnetic radiation* of centimetric *wave-lengths*, the output of which is *pulse* modulated (see *modulation*) at a *radio frequency* and fed to a movable *aerial* whence it is radiated as a *beam*. Distant objects which cross the path of the beam reflect the pulses back to the transmitter, which also acts as a receiver. A *cathode-ray tube* indicator displays the received signal in the correct time sequence so that the time taken for a pulse to travel to the object and back can be measured. Thus the distance of the object from the transmitter can be calculated, and its direction can be ascertained from a knowledge of the direction of the aerial. This fundamental technique has been extended so that automatic guidance and navigation can be effected by *computers* without the necessity of a display.

RADIAL VELOCITY. See *line of sight velocity*.

RADIAN. Measure of *angle*; the angle subtended at the centre of a *circle* by an arc equal in length to the radius of the circle. 2π radians $= 360°$, and 1 radian $= 57 \cdot 296°$.

RADIANT ENERGY. *Energy* that is transmitted in the form of *radiation*, particularly *electromagnetic radiation*. Radiant energy is the only form in which energy can exist in the absence of *matter*.

RADIANT HEAT. See *infra-red radiation*.

RADIATION. In general, the emission of any *rays*, *wave motion*, or particles (e.g. *alpha particles*, *beta particles*, *neutrons*) from a source; usually applied to the emission of *electromagnetic radiation*.

RADIATION HAZARD. The potential danger to health resulting from exposure to *ionizing radiation* or the consumption of *radioactive* substances.

RADIATION POTENTIAL, resonance potential. The *energy* (expressed in *electron-volts*) necessary to transfer an *electron* from its normal position in an *atom* to some other possible position; i.e. to an *energy level* of greater energy.

RADIATIVE CAPTURE. See *capture*.

RADIATIVE COLLISION. A collision between charged particles in which part of the *kinetic energy* is converted into *electromagnetic radiation*.

RADICAL, radicle (chem.). A group of *atoms*, present in a series of *compounds*, which maintains its identity through chemical changes which affect the rest of the *molecule*, but which is usually incapable of independent existence. E.g. the *ammonium* radical, NH_4—; ethyl, C_2H_5—. See also *free radical*.

RADIO. The use of *electromagnetic radiation* to communicate electrical signals without wires ('wireless' transmission). In the widest sense the term incorporates sound broadcasting (including *radio telephony* and *radio telegraphy*), *television*, and *radar*. Transmission by radio involves a transmitter feeding a transmitting *aerial*, from which electromagnetic energy is broadcast, either as *ground waves* or *sky waves*, to a receiving aerial which feeds a receiver. The transmitter in sound broadcasting consists of a generator of a *radio frequency carrier wave* which is modulated (see *modulation*) in accordance with the *electric currents* provided by the amplified output of a *microphone*. The modulated carrier wave is fed to the transmitting aerial and if the receiving aerial is tuned to the *fre-

quency of the carrier wave (see *resonant circuit*) it will enable the receiver selectively to amplify and demodulate the transmitted signal. *Demodulation* is achieved by *rectification* of the signal by a *thermionic valve* or *transistor*. In this way a current is produced in the output stage of the receiver which varies in *amplitude* in accordance with the frequency of the sound wave fed to the microphone at the transmitter. This current may then be used to operate a loudspeaker which reproduces the original sound.

RADIO-. See *radioactive*.

RADIO ASTRONOMY. The study of heavenly bodies by the reception and analysis of the *radio frequency electromagnetic radiation* which they emit or reflect. In general, electromagnetic radiations from extra-terrestrial sources are either absorbed by the Earth's *atmosphere* or reflected away from the Earth by the *ionosphere*. The two exceptions, which allow us to experience the rest of the Universe, are the optical *wave-lengths* which are able to penetrate the atmosphere, and the radio wave-lengths in the band 1 cm–10 metres which are too long to be absorbed by the atmosphere and too short to be reflected by the ionosphere. The radiations which pass through this 'radio window' onto the Universe come from a variety of sources, ranging from objects within the *solar system* (e.g. the *Sun* and the *planet Jupiter*) to *galaxies* which are too distant to be observed by *optical telescopes*. In general radio frequency emission may be due to thermal, or non-thermal causes: emission from the 'quiet' Sun is of thermal origin for example, whereas the radiation from *sunspots* is of unexplained non-thermal origin. The method by which radio astronomy attempts to make sense out of the apparently incoherent radio 'noise' from the Universe, is to construct maps of the sky in terms of radio emission, at several different *frequencies*. The intensities of the sources thus located are then compared with optical observations. In this way *radio stars* and *radio galaxies* have been identified. See also *radio telescope*.

RADIO FREQUENCY. The *frequency* of an *electromagnetic radiation* which falls within the range used in *radio*, i.e. 10 *kilocycles* to 100,000 *megacycles* per second.

RADIO FREQUENCY HEATING. A general term which includes industrial *induction* or *dielectric heating*, particularly when the *frequency* of the alternating field is above about 25 *kilocycles* per second.

RADIO FREQUENCY WELDING. See *high frequency welding*.

RADIO GALAXIES. *Galaxies* which emit *electromagnetic radiation* of *radio frequencies* as observed by the techniques of *radio astronomy*. The exact source of this galactic radiation is not always understood, but radiation has been received from galaxies which have been observed optically to be in collision. See also *radio stars* and *synchrotron radiation*.

RADIO INTERFEROMETER. A type of *radio telescope* which consists of two or more separate *aerials*, each receiving *electromagnetic radiation* of *radio frequencies* from the same source, and each joined to the same receiver. The instrument works on the same principle as the optical *interferometer*, but as the *wave-lengths* of the incident radiation is much greater, the distance between aerials has to be correspondingly increased. The chief advantage of radio interferometers, over single aerial *parabolic reflectors*, is that they can be made more sensitive to radiation from sources of small angular diameter. See also *radio astronomy*.

RADIO STAR. A discrete source of *electromagnetic radiation* of *radio frequencies* outside the *solar system*. Such sources have been discovered by the techniques of *radio astronomy*, both within the *Galaxy* and outside it, but only a small number have been identified with *stars* which can be located with *optical telescopes*. Other sources are *supernovae* explosions and remnants, colliding *galaxies* and gas clouds; some sources, however, remain unexplained.

RADIO TELEGRAPHY. The transmission of coded messages (e.g. in Morse code) by *radio*.

RADIO TELEPHONY. The use of *radio*, rather than wires or cables, for all or part of a *telephone* system.

RADIO TELESCOPE. An instrument used in *radio astronomy* to pick up and analyse the *radio frequency electromagnetic radiations* of extra-terrestrial sources. The two principal types of radio telescope are: (1) *parabolic reflectors*, which are usually steerable so that they can be pointed at any part of the sky, and which reflect the incoming radiation on to a small *aerial* at the *focus* of the *paraboloid*; and (2) fixed *radio interferometers*. The latter have greater position-finding accuracy and greater ability to distinguish a small source against an intense background, while the former are more versatile owing to their mobility.

RADIOACTIVE. Possessing, or pertaining to, *radioactivity*. Sometimes only the prefix 'radio-' is used to describe radioactive *nuclides* or the substances containing them, e.g. radiocarbon is an abbreviation for radioactive carbon.

RADIOACTIVE AGE. The age of a *mineral*, *fossil*, or wooden object as estimated from its content of *radioactive isotopes*. This method assumes that the content of radioactive isotopes has remained unchanged except for radioactive *decay*. See also *dating* and *radiocarbon dating*.

RADIOACTIVE EQUILIBRIUM. A state ultimately reached when a *radioactive* substance of slow *decay* (see *radioactivity*) yields a radioactive product on *disintegration*. This product may also decay to give a further radioactive substance, and so on. The amount of any of the daughter radioactive products present after equilibrium has been reached remains constant, the loss due to decay being counterbalanced by gain from the decay of the immediate parent.

RADIOACTIVE SERIES. Radioactive family. A series of *radioactive isotopes*, each except the first being the *decay* product of the previous one. The final member of the series, usually an isotope of lead, is stable. See *radioactivity*.

RADIOACTIVE STANDARD. A specimen of a material containing a *radioactive isotope* of precisely known rate of *decay*, which is used for the calibration of instruments measuring *radiation*.

RADIOACTIVE TRACING. Any two *isotopes* of an *element* are chemically identical. Thus, by introducing a small amount of a *radioactive* isotope, called a tracer, the course taken by the stable isotope of the same element can be followed or traced by detecting the course of the accompanying radioactive isotope by suitable means. This can be done in various ways; e.g. *Geiger counter*. See *labelled compound*.

RADIOACTIVITY. The property of spontaneous *disintegration* possessed by certain unstable types of atomic *nuclei*. The disintegration is accompanied by the emission of either *alpha-* or *beta-particles* and/or *gamma rays*. The most common type of disintegration involves beta-particle emission and occurs either: (1) when a *neutron* present in the unstable nucleus is converted into a *proton* with the emission of an *electron* and an anti-*neutrino*, or more rarely (2) when a proton is converted into a neutron with the emission of a *positron* and a neutrino. These *beta transformations* are accompanied by unit change of *atomic number* but no change in *mass number*. Alpha particles are only emitted by certain radioactive *isotopes* of the heavier *elements*; when this occurs the atomic number of the daughter nucleus is two less than that of the parent and its mass number is reduced by four units. Gamma-ray emission accompanies alpha or beta emission when the daughter nucleus is formed in an excited state (see *excitation*).

Natural radioactivity is due to the disintegration of naturally occurring radioactive isotopes, which may be arranged in three *radioactive series*. The rate at which radioactive isotopes disintegrate is uninfluenced by any chemical changes, any normal changes of *temperature* or *pressure*, or by the effects of *electric* or *magnetic fields*. However 'induced' or 'artificial' radioactive isotopes of most elements can be formed by bombardment with particles (e.g. neutrons) or *photons* in a *nuclear reactor* or *accelerator*.

Radiations emitted by radioactive isotopes are used in the treatment of disease (see *radiotherapy*) and in *radioactive tracing*.

RADIOBIOLOGY. The branch of *biology* which is concerned with the effects of *radiation* on living *organisms* and the behaviour of *radioactive* materials, or the use of *radioactive tracing*, in biological systems.

RADIOCARBON DATING. The estimation of the age of wooden archaeological objects by measuring their content of the *radioactive isotope* of carbon, $^{14}_{6}C$. The impact of *cosmic rays* on the Earth's *atmosphere* causes a very small proportion of nitrogen *atoms* to transform into $^{14}_{6}C$ atoms. Some of these radioactive carbon atoms find their way, via *carbon dioxide* and *photosynthesis*, into living trees. When a tree is cut down, however, it ceases to acquire further $^{14}_{6}C$ atoms. Therefore by comparing the *radioactivity* of a modern piece of wood with that of a specimen of unknown age, the length of time that has elapsed since the latter ceased to be living can be estimated (provided that it is not more than about 6000 years). This method has been checked by comparison with specimens of wood of known age from the tombs of the Pharaohs and has been found to be fairly reliable.

RADIOCHEMISTRY. The study and application of chemical techniques to the purification of *radioactive* materials, and the formation of *compounds* containing radioactive *elements*.

RADIODIAGNOSIS. The branch of medical *radiology* which is concerned with the application of *X-rays* to diagnosis.

RADIOGENIC. Resulting from *radioactive decay*.

RADIOGRAPHY. The formation of images on *fluorescent* screens or photographic material by short *wave-length radiation*, such as *X-rays* and *gamma rays*.

RADIOLOGY. The science of *X-rays* and *radioactivity*, including *radiodiagnosis* and *radiotherapy*.

RADIOLYSIS. The chemical *decomposition* of substances as a result of *irradiation*.

RADIOMICROMETER. Extremely sensitive instrument for measuring *heat radiations*. Consists of a *thermocouple* connected directly into a single copper loop forming the coil of a sensitive *galvanometer*.

RADIOTHERAPY. The treatment of disease by means of *radiation*, particularly *X-rays* and techniques involving *radioactivity*.

RADIUM. Ra. Naturally occurring *radioactive element*. At. No. 88. The most stable *isotope*, $^{226}_{88}$Ra, has a *half-life* of 1620 years. Very rare *metal*, chemically resembling barium; m.p. 700° C., S.G. 5. See *radioactivity*.

RADIUM EMANATION. See *radon*.

RADIUS. See *circle*.

RADIUS OF CURVATURE. Consider any point P on a curve S lying in a *plane*. A *circle* can be drawn with centre at a unique point O on the *normal* to S at P, such that the curve and the circle are tangential at P. The radius of this circle, OP, is the radius of curvature of the curve at P. The concept may be extended to a point on a three-dimensional curved surface. In this case, an infinite number of radii of curvature exist, corresponding to the infinite number of plane curves which can form the line of intersection of the curved surface and the plane containing the normal at P. Of these curves, two are unique, one having a maximum radius of curvature at P and the other a minimum. These two are called the principal radii of curvature at P.

RADIUS OF GYRATION. The *moment of inertia I*, of a body of *mass M* about a given *axis* can be expressed in the form $I = Mk^2$. k is called the radius of gyration about that axis.

RADIUS VECTOR (astr.). A line drawn from a central body (the focus) to a *planet* in any position in its *orbit*.

RADIUS VECTOR (math.). The position of any point P in space with respect to a given origin O may be completely defined by the direction and length of the line OP. This line is called the radius vector of the point P. See *polar co-ordinates*.

RADON. Rn. Radium emanation, niton. Element. At. No. 86. The most stable *isotope*, $^{222}_{86}Rn$, has a *half-life* of $3 \cdot 825$ days. Naturally occurring *radioactive* gas, the immediate *disintegration* product of radium; chemically belongs to the *inert gases*.

RAINBOW. A colour effect produced by the *refraction* and internal *reflection* of sunlight in minute droplets of *water* in the air; the effect is visible only when the observer has his back to the *Sun*.

RAM JET. Atherodyde. A simple type of aerodynamic *reaction propulsion* system in which *thrust* is obtained by the *combustion* of *fuel* in air, compressed only by the forward *velocity* of the vehicle. A ram jet is also known as a 'flying drainpipe' as it consists essentially of a long duct into which fuel is fed at a controlled rate. However, the air intake and exhaust gas outlet need to be correctly designed in order to achieve maximum efficiency of the combustion process in that part of the duct which serves as a combustion chamber. The shape of the duct will depend upon whether or not the velocity of the vehicle is intended to be *supersonic*.

RAMAN EFFECT. When *monochromatic light* passes through a *transparent* medium, some of the light is scattered. If the *spectrum* of this scattered light is examined, it is found to contain, apart from light of the original *wave-length*, weaker lines differing from this by constant amounts. Such lines are called Raman lines, and they are due to the loss or gain of *energy* experienced by the *photons* of light as a result of interaction with the vibrating *molecules* of the medium through which they pass. The Raman effect is therefore useful in the study of molecular *energy levels*.

RAMSDEN EYE-PIECE. *Eye-piece* consisting of two plano-*convex lenses* (curved surfaces inwards) of equal *focal length f*, and separated by a distance of $2/3 f$. The eye-piece has low spherical *aberration*, is fairly *achromatic* and is very useful when cross-wires or a scale are desired in the eye-piece.

RANKINE SCALE OF TEMPERATURE. °R. The absolute *Fahrenheit scale*. Zero degrees Rankine is $-459 \cdot 69°$ F. and therefore $°F + 459 \cdot 69 = °R$.

RAOULT'S LAW. When a *solute* which does not dissociate (see *ionic hypothesis*) in *solution* is dissolved in a *solvent* to form a *dilute* solution, then (1) the ratio of the decrease in *vapour pressure* to the original vapour pressure is equal to N_1/N_2, N_1 and N_2 being the total numbers of *molecules* present of solute and solvent respectively; or, alternatively (2) the *elevation of the boiling point* of the solution above that of the pure solvent is proportional to N_1/N_2; or (3) the *depression of the freezing point* of the solution below that of the pure solvent is proportional to N_1/N_2.

RARE EARTH ELEMENTS. See *lanthanides*.

RARE GASES. See *inert gases*.

RAREFACTION. A reduction in *pressure*. The opposite of compression.

RASTER. The pattern of lines which scan the fluorescent screen of a *cathode ray tube* in a *television* receiver.

RATIO. The numerical relation one quantity bears to another of the same kind. E.g. 6 tons and 4 tons, and 30 and 20, are both in the ratio of 3 : 2.

RAY. Term to denote the *rectilinear* path along which any *radiation*, e.g. *light*, travels in any direction from a point in the source of the radiation. Loosely used to denote radiation of any kind.

RAYON. Formerly 'artificial silk', the term has been used to describe all types of man-made textile fibres, as distinct from those produced directly by plants (e.g. cotton) or animals (wool, silk). The use of the term 'rayon' to include fibres not made from *cellulose* and its derivatives has not, however, been universally accepted. The two most important types of rayon from cellulose are (1) *viscose* rayon, made by forcing a solution of viscose through fine holes into a *solution* which decomposes the viscose to give threads of cellulose, and (2) *cellulose acetate* rayon, made by forcing a solution of cellulose acetate through fine holes into warm air and allowing the *solvent* to *evaporate*, thus leaving threads of cellulose acetate.

R.D.X.* See *cyclonite*.

REACTANCE. X. A property of *alternating current* circuits which together with the *resistance*, R, makes up the *impedance* Z, according to the relation, $Z = (R^2 + X^2)^{\frac{1}{2}}$. If the circuit comprises the resistance, an *inductance* L and *capacitance* C all in series, the reactance is given by:

$$X = \omega L - 1/\omega C$$

where ω is the angular frequency ($\omega = 2\pi n$, n being the *frequency* of the alternating current).

REACTION, CHEMICAL. See *chemical reaction*.

REACTION PROPULSION. Jet propulsion. A form of aerodynamic propulsion in which a high *velocity* stream of *gas* (usually produced by *combustion*) reacts upon the vehicle in which it was produced, in accordance with *Newton's* (third) *law of motion*, so that the vehicle is propelled through the medium in which it is travelling. The lower the density of the medium, the higher the *efficiency* of the propulsion. Reaction propulsion is the only known method of propulsion through *space* where there is no supporting medium, and it is upon this principal that *rockets* are propelled.

REACTIVE (chem.). Readily entering into *chemical reactions*; chemically active.

REACTOR. 1. A device for introducing *reactance* into an electrical circuit (e.g. a *capacitor*). 2. See *nuclear reactor*.

REAGENT. Chemical substance used to produce a *chemical reaction*.

REALGAR. Natural red arsenic disulphide, As_2S_2.

RÉAUMUR SCALE. *Temperature* scale in which the *melting point* of *ice* is taken as 0° R. and the *boiling point* of *water* as 80° R.

RECIPROCAL OF A QUANTITY. 1 divided by the quantity; e.g. the reciprocal of 5 is $\frac{1}{5}$.

RECIPROCAL PROPORTIONS, law of. See *chemical combination, laws of.*

RECOIL ELECTRON. See *Compton effect.*

RECTIFICATION (chem.). Purification of a *liquid* by *distillation.*

RECTIFICATION (math.). The process of determining the length of a curve.

RECTIFICATION (phys.). Conversion of an *alternating* into a *direct current.* See *rectifier, rectifying valve.*

RECTIFIER (phys.). Device for transforming an *alternating current* into a *direct current*; consists of an arrangement which presents a much higher *resistance* to an *electric current* flowing in one direction than in the other. See *rectifying valve; crystal rectifier; barrier-layer rectifier; junction rectifier; semiconductor.*

RECTIFYING VALVE. The *thermionic valve* commonly used for rectification is the *diode.* The valve will pass current only when the *anode* is at a positive *potential* with respect to the *cathode.* Hence if an alternating potential is applied to a circuit containing such a valve, a *direct current* will flow through the circuit.

RECTILINEAR. In a straight line; consisting of straight lines.

RECTILINEAR PROPAGATION OF LIGHT. To a first approximation *light* travels in straight lines, as is evident from the formation of *shadows* and other everyday experience; see, however, *diffraction.*

RED GIANT. A type of *star*; see *stellar evolution.*

RED LEAD, minium. Pb_3O_4. Bright scarlet powder, used as a *pigment*, in *glass* manufacture, and as an *oxidizing agent.*

RED SHIFT. See *Doppler effect.*

REDUCED TEMPERATURE, PRESSURE, AND VOLUME. Ratios of the *temperature*, the *pressure*, and the *volume* to the *critical temperature, critical pressure*, and *critical volume* respectively.

REDUCING AGENT. A substance which removes oxygen from, or adds hydrogen to, another substance: in the more general sense, one which donates *electrons.* See *reduction.*

REDUCTION. The removal of oxygen from a substance, or the addition of hydrogen to it. The term is also used more generally to include any reaction in which an *atom* gains *electrons.*

REDUNDANCY. A term used in *information theory* to indicate that the information rate from a source is less than a hypothetical maximum value. Defined as the amount by which the ratio of the information rate to its hypothetical maximum value falls below unity; usually expressed as a percentage.

REFLECTION, ANGLE OF. The angle between a *ray* of *light* reflected from a surface, and the *normal* to the surface at that point.

REFLECTION OF LIGHT. Certain surfaces have the property of reflecting or returning *rays* of *light* which fall upon them, according to definite laws (see *reflection of light, laws of*).

REFLECTION OF LIGHT, LAWS OF. 1. The incident *ray*, the reflected ray, and the *normal* to the reflecting surface at the point of incidence lie in the same *plane*. 2. The *angle* between the incident ray and the normal (i.e. the angle of *incidence*) is equal to the angle between the reflected ray and the normal (i.e. the angle of *reflection*).

REFLECTION, TOTAL INTERNAL. See *total internal reflection*.

REFLECTOR. 1. Any surface which reflects *radiation*, particularly *electromagnetic radiation*. (See also *parabolic reflector*.) 2. A layer of material (which may contain *moderator*) surrounding the core of a *nuclear reactor* which reflects back into the core some of the *neutrons* which would otherwise escape.

REFLEX ANGLE. *Angle* greater than 180° and less than 360°.

REFLUX. Flow back; e.g. a reflux condenser is a *condenser* used so that the *vapour* over a *boiling liquid* is condensed to a liquid which flows back into the vessel, so preventing its contents from boiling dry.

REFRACTION, ANGLE OF. The angle between the refracted *ray* and the *normal* to the surface at the point of *refraction*. See Fig. 13.

REFRACTION, LAWS OF. 1. The incident *ray*, the refracted ray, and the *normal* to the surface of separation of the two media at the point of incidence lie in the same *plane*. 2. Snell's law. The ratio of the sine of the *angle* of *incidence* to the sine of the angle of *refraction* is a constant for any pair of media. See *refractive index*.

REFRACTION CORRECTION. The small correction which has to be made to the observed *altitude* of a heavenly body due to the *refraction* of the *light*, which it emits or reflects, by the Earth's *atmosphere*. All bodies appear to be slightly higher than they actually are.

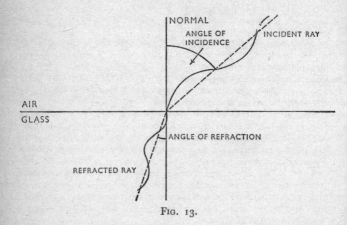

FIG. 13.

REFRACTION OF LIGHT. When a *ray* of *light* travels obliquely from one medium to another, it is bent or refracted at the surface separating the two media. The refraction occurs because light travels at slightly different *velocities* in different media; thus at the interface between media there is a slight change of *wave-length*. See Fig. 13. The ray before refraction is termed the incident ray; on being refracted it becomes the refracted ray. A line perpendicular to the refracting medium at the point where the incident ray enters it is the *normal*. *Glass*, *water*, etc., cause the incident ray to be turned towards the normal when the ray enters from a medium less optically dense, such as air. Similar considerations apply to *wave-motions* other than light.

REFRACTIVE INDEX of a medium, n or μ. The ratio of the sine (see *trigonometrical ratios*) of the angle of *incidence* to the sine of the angle of *refraction* when *light* is refracted from a *vacuum* (or, to a very close approximation, from air) into the medium. This is equivalent to the fundamental definition: the ratio of the *velocity* of *light* in free space to that in the medium. See *refraction of light*.

REFRACTIVITY. If the *refractive index* of a medium is n, its refractivity is defined as $n-1$. The 'specific refractivity' is given by $\dfrac{n-1}{d}$ where d is the *density* of the medium; the 'molecular refractivity' is defined as the specific refractivity multiplied by the *molecular weight*.

REFRACTOMETER. Apparatus for the measurement of the *refractive index* of a substance.

REFRACTORY (chem.). A material not damaged by heating to high *temperatures*.

REGELATION OF ICE. The *melting point* of *ice* is lowered by increased *pressure*; therefore ice near its melting point is melted by sufficient pressure, and solidification or regelation takes place again when the pressure is removed.

RELATIVE DENSITY. See *specific gravity*.

RELATIVE HUMIDITY, hygrometric state of the atmosphere. Can be defined either as: (1) the ratio of the *pressure* of the *water vapour* actually present in the atmosphere to the pressure of the vapour which would be present if the vapour were *saturated* at the same *temperature*; or (2) the ratio of the *mass* of water vapour per unit *volume* of the air to the mass of water vapour per unit volume of saturated air at the same temperature. The numerical difference between the two is very small and can normally be neglected. The relative humidity is usually expressed as a percentage. Its value may be determined from a knowledge of the *dew-point*, since the *saturated vapour pressure* at the dew-point is equal to the aqueous vapour pressure at the temperature of the experiment. The result is then obtained by reference to tables which give the saturated vapour pressure at different temperatures.

RELATIVISTIC MASS. The *mass* of a body which is travelling at a speed comparable to the *velocity* of *light*. The relativistic mass, m, of a body travelling at a velocity, v, is given by:

$$m = m_0 \, (1 - v^2/c^2)^{-\frac{1}{2}}$$

where m_0 is the *rest mass* and c is the velocity of light.

RELATIVISTIC PARTICLE. A particle which has a speed comparable to the *velocity* of *light*; i.e. a particle with a *relativistic mass* substantially in excess of its *rest mass*.

RELATIVITY, THEORY OF. A theory, formulated by Einstein, which recognizes the impossibility of determining absolute motion and leads to the concept of a four-dimensional *space-time* continuum. The special theory, which is limited to the description of events as they appear to observers in a state of uniform motion relative to one another, is developed from two axioms: (1) the laws of natural phenomena are the same for all observers, and (2) the velocity of *light* is the same for all observers irrespective of their own *velocity*. The more important consequences of this theory are (a) the *mass* of a body is a function of its velocity (see *relativistic mass*); (b) the *mass-energy equation* for the interconversion of mass and *energy*; (c) the *Fitzgerald-Lorentz contraction* appears as a natural consequence of the theory. The general theory, applicable to observers not in uniform relative motion, leads to a novel concept of the theory of *gravitation*. In this theory the presence of *matter* in *space* causes space to 'curve' in such a manner that the *gravitational field* is set up. Thus gravitation becomes a property of space itself. The validity of the theory of relativity has been amply confirmed in modern *physics*.

RELAY, ELECTRICAL. A device by which the *electric current* flowing in one circuit can open or close a second circuit and thus control the switching on and off of a current in the second circuit. Electrical relays may be mechanical switches operated by an *electromagnet*, or they may be *electronic* switches based upon mercury or gas-filled *thermionic valves*.

RELUCTANCE. The ratio of the *magnetomotive force* acting in a magnetic circuit to the *magnetic flux*.

RELUCTIVITY. The *reciprocal* of *magnetic permeability*.

REM. Roentgen equivalent man. The unit dose of *ionizing radiation* which gives the same biological effect as that due to one *roentgen* of *X-rays*.

REMANENCE. The residual magnetization of a *ferromagnetic substance* subjected to a *hysteresis cycle* when the magnetizing field is reduced to zero.

RENNET. An extract of the fourth stomach of the calf, containing *rennin*.

RENNIN. *Enzyme* having the power of coagulating the *protein* in milk.

RESINS. Natural resins are *amorphous organic compounds* which are secreted by certain plants and insects; usually *insoluble* in *water* but *soluble* in various *organic solvents*. Typical natural resins are *rosin* and *shellac*.

Synthetic resins were originally described as a group of synthetic substances whose properties resembled natural resins. The term is now applied more generally to any synthetic *plastic* material produced by *polymerization*, although chemically modified natural *polymers*, such as those based on *cellulose* or *casein*, are not usually classed as synthetic resins.

RESISTANCE, ELECTRICAL, of a *conductor* is the ratio of the *potential difference* between the ends of a conductor to the *electric current* flowing in the conductor. See *Ohm's law*. All materials except *superconductors* resist the flow of an electric current, converting a proportion of the *electrical energy* into *heat*. The extent to which a conductor resists the flow of a given current depends upon its physical dimensions, the nature of the material of which it is made, its *temperature*, and in some cases the extent to which it is illuminated. See *photo-conductive effect*. The practical unit of resistance is the *ohm*.

RESISTANCE THERMOMETER. The electrical *resistance* of a *conductor* varies with *temperature*, normally increasing with rise in temperature. This forms the basis of a convenient and accurate *thermometer*, in which the temperature is deduced from the measurement of the resistance of a spiral of a metal (usually platinum) in the form of a wire.

RESISTIVITY. Specific resistance. A constant for any material equal to the *reciprocal* of its *conductivity*. The resistivity is defined as the *resistance* offered by a centimetre cube of the material at $0°$ C. Thus the resistivity, ρ equals $\dfrac{R\,A}{L}$ where R is the resistance of a uniform *conductor* of length L and cross-sectional area A. Usually expressed in *ohm*-centimetres.

RESISTOR. A device used in *electronic* circuits primarily for its *resistance*. The most common types are either 'wire-wound', or made of finely ground carbon particles mixed with a *ceramic* binder.

RESOLUTION OF FORCES. The division of *forces* into components which act in specified directions.

RESOLVING POWER. The ability of an optical system (e.g. *microscope*, *telescope*, the eye, etc.) to produce separate images of objects very close together.

RESONANCE (chem.). The oscillation of *electrons* between *atoms* within an *ion* or *molecule*, as a consequence of which no single description can be given of the *valency bonds* between the atoms (see *valency, electronic theory of*). For example, if a *molecule* AB consists of *atoms* A and B joined by a covalent bond, at any instant the two electrons forming the bond may be; (1) both under the influence of *nucleus* A, i.e. $A^- B^+$, (2) both under the influence of nucleus B, i.e. $A^+ B^-$, or (3) equally under the influence of both nuclei, i.e. $A - B$. In practice the 'average' structure of the molecule will be somewhere between these 'pure' structures, and is called a 'resonance hybrid'.

RESONANCE (phys.). If, to a system capable of oscillation, a small periodic *force* is applied, the system is in general set into forced oscillations of small *amplitude*. As the *frequency* f of the exciting force approaches the *natural frequency* of the system, f_0, the amplitude of the oscillations builds up, becoming a maximum when $f = f_0$. The system is then said to be in resonance with the exciting force, or simply in resonance.

RESONANCE NEUTRON. See *resonance, nuclear*.

RESONANCE, NUCLEAR. Resonance is said to occur in *nuclear reactions* if the *energy* of an incident particle or *photon* is equal, or near to, the value of an appropriate *energy level* of the compound *nucleus*. Thus a resonance *neutron* is one whose energy corresponds to a particular energy level of a nucleus which will readily absorb it.

RESONANT CAVITY. A space enclosed by electrically conducting surfaces, in which electromagnetic *energy* may be stored or excited. The *frequency* of the oscillations within a resonant cavity will depend upon its physical dimensions.

RESONANT CIRCUIT. An *electronic* circuit containing both an *inductance* and a *capacitance* which is capable of *resonance*. When the *capacitor* discharges through the inductor an induced *E.M.F.* is produced which charges the capacitor again in the opposite sense, this again discharges through the inductor and the circuit will continue to oscillate in this way provided that it is supplied with *energy* from an external source. The *frequency* of the oscillation will depend upon the values of the capacitance and the inductance, and the circuit can therefore be tuned to resonate at any desired frequency by suitable alteration of the value of its components. Coupled with a *thermionic valve* or *transistor* to supply energy, a resonant circuit is used in *radio* transmitters to generate *radio frequency* oscillations, and in receivers for their selective detection.

RESORCINOL. *Meta*-dihydroxy*benzene*. $C_6H_4(OH)_2$. *Aromatic organic compound* obtained from *phenol*, m.p. 110° C. Used in the manufacture of synthetic *resins* and *drugs*.

RESPIRATION. *Aerobic* respiration is the process by which living *organisms*, or their components, take oxygen from the *atmosphere* and give off *carbon dioxide*. *Anaerobic* respiration is the process by which organisms, or their components, obtain *energy* from chemically combined oxygen when they do not have access to free oxygen. Many organisms can respire anaerobically for a short time only, but certain *bacteria* depend entirely on anaerobic respiration.

RESPIRATORY PIGMENT. A substance formed in *blood cells* or *blood plasma* which is capable of combining loosely and reversibly with oxygen, e.g. *haemoglobin*.

RESPIRATORY QUOTIENT. RQ. The ratio of the *volume* of *carbon dioxide* expired by an *organism* or tissue to the volume of oxygen consumed by it over the same period.

REST MASS. The *mass* of a body when at rest relative to the observer.

The mass of a body varies with its *velocity* (see *relativity, theory of*), a result of great importance when velocities approaching those of *light* are considered, e.g. in *nuclear physics*. See *relativistic mass*.

RESTITUTION, COEFFICIENT OF, *e*. A measure of the *elasticity* of bodies upon impact. For two smooth spheres of a given material colliding, *e* is equal to the ratio of the relative *velocity* of the spheres along their line of centres immediately after impact to their relative velocity before impact.

RESULTANT (phys.) of two or more *forces* or *velocities* is a single force or velocity which produces the same effect as the two or more forces or velocities acting together.

RETARDATION (phys.). Deceleration. Negative *acceleration*; rate of decrease of *velocity*.

RETORT (chem.). A *glass* vessel consisting of a large bulb with a long neck narrowing somewhat towards the end. In industrial processes, any vessel from which *distillation* takes place; in the canning industry, a large *autoclave* for heating sealed cans by *superheated steam* under pressure.

RETORT CARBON. See *gas carbon*.

RETRO-ROCKET. A small *rocket*, forming part of a larger one, which produces *thrust* in the opposite direction to that of the main rocket with the object of decelerating it; e.g. to enable a lunar-probe to make a 'soft' landing on the *Moon*.

REVERBERATORY FURNACE. Furnace designed for operations in which it is not desirable to mix the material with the *fuel*; the roof is heated by *flames*, and the *heat* is radiated down on to the material off the roof.

REVERSIBLE PROCESS (in *thermodynamics*). A process which can be performed in the reverse direction, the whole series of changes constituting the process being exactly reversed. A reversible process can take place only in infinitesimal steps about equilibrium states of the system.

REVERSIBLE REACTION. A *chemical reaction* which may be made, under suitable conditions, to proceed in either direction. See *chemical equilibrium*.

REYNOLDS NUMBER, *R*. A dimensionless quantity applied to a *liquid* flowing through a cylindrical tube, given by $R = \dfrac{V\rho a}{\eta}$, where $V = $ *velocity* of flow, $\rho = density$ of the liquid, and η the coefficient of *viscosity* of the liquid. At low velocities, the flow of the liquid is *streamline*. At a certain value of R, corresponding to a critical velocity V_c, the flow becomes *turbulent*.

r$_H$ SCALE. A scale of hydrogen pressures which gives a measure of the strength of a *reducing agent*. The r$_H$ value is defined as $\log_{10}$ $1 / $ [H], where [H] is the hydrogen pressure which would produce the same electrode potential as that of a given *oxidation-reduction* system at the same P_H value.

RHE. The unit of *fluidity*. The *reciprocal* of the *poise*.

RHENIUM. Re. Element. A.W. 186·20. At. No. 75. Hard, heavy grey *metal*, S.G. 20·53, m.p. 3167° C. Used in *thermocouples* and as a *catalyst*.

RHEOLOGY. Study of the deformation and flow of *matter*.

RHEOSTAN. *Alloy* of 52% copper, 25% nickel, 18% zinc, and 5% iron; used for electrical resistance wire.

RHEOSTAT. Variable electrical *resistor*.

RHODIUM. Rh. Element. A.W. 102·905. At. No. 45. Silvery-white hard *metal*, S.G. 12·5, m.p. 1966° C. Occurs with and resembles platinum. Used in *alloys*, *catalysts*, and *thermocouples*.

RHODOPSIN, visual purple. Complex *organic compound* formed in the retina of the eye. Makes the eye more sensitive in very dim light; lack of it causes night blindness. Formed with the aid of *vitamin A*.

RHOMBUS. *Quadrilateral* having all its sides equal.

RIBOFLAVIN. Lactoflavin. Vitamin B_2. $C_{17}H_{20}N_4O_6$. *Water soluble* substance which is a member of the *vitamin B* complex. Forms part of various *enzymes* concerned with cellular *respiration* and appears to be required by most living *organisms*.

RIBONUCLEIC ACID. RNA. Long thread-like *molecules* consisting of single *polynucleotide* chains. The *sugar* of the *nucleotides* is *ribose*, and the four nitrogenous bases which occur in them are the same as those found in *deoxyribonucleic* acid, except that *uracil* replaces *thymine*. RNA is the chief constituent, together with *protein*, of many types of *virus*, and it appears to be responsible for the self-replication of the virus. 'Messenger' RNA transmits the coded information contained by the *chromosomes* of the *nucleus* of a *cell* to the *protein*-making *ribosomes* of the *cytoplasm*. 'Transfer', soluble or s-RNA transfers the activated *amino acids* on to the messenger RNA.

RIBOSE. $C_5H_{10}O_5$. A *pentose monosaccharide sugar*, m.p. 95° C.; the *dextrorotary* form is of great biological importance as it occurs in the *nucleotides* of *ribonucleic acid*.

RIBOSOMES. Small granules (about 100 *Ångström units* in diameter) which occur in the *cytoplasms* of *cells* and which appear to be the sites of *protein* synthesis.

RIGIDITY MODULUS. *Elastic modulus* applied to a body under a shearing *strain*.

RING COMPOUND (chem.). Chemical *compound* in the *molecule* of which some or all of the *atoms* are linked in a closed ring. See *carbocyclic, heterocyclic compounds*.

RINGER'S FLUID. *Physiological saline* containing sodium, potassium, and calcium *chlorides*; widely used for sustaining *cells* or tissues during *in vitro* biochemical experiments.

RNA. See *ribonucleic acid*.

ROCHELLE SALT. COOK. $(CH.OH)_2.COONa.4H_2O$. Sodium potassium tartrate. White, crystalline, *soluble salt*, used in the preparation of *baking-powder*, Seidlitz powders, etc.

ROCHON PRISM. *Prism* used for obtaining plane-polarized light (see *polarization of light*) and in other related problems. Such a prism, made of *quartz*, may be used for work with *ultra-violet radiation*.

ROCK CRYSTAL. Pure natural crystalline form of *silica*, SiO_2.

ROCK SALT. Natural crystalline *sodium chloride*, NaCl.

ROCKET. A projectile driven by *reaction propulsion* which contains its own *propellants*. A rocket is therefore independent of the Earth's *atmosphere* both with respect to *thrust* and *oxidant* and provides the only known practicable means of propulsion in *space*. 'Chemical' rockets may be powered by either *solid* or *liquid fuels* which burn in oxygen, while 'nuclear' rockets would be powered by a propulsion reactor (see *nuclear reactor*). 'Multistage' or 'step' rockets are rockets built up of several separate sections; each stage being jettisoned when it has burnt out. The 'booster', or first stage, of a space rocket accelerates the projectile up to the thinner regions of the atmosphere, when subsequent stages take over the propulsion. Thus the necessarily high *escape velocity* is not achieved in denser parts of the atmosphere (which would introduce *friction* heating problems), moreover as each stage is jettisoned the projectile becomes substantially lighter and higher velocities can be achieved with less thrust (see *specific impulse*). Deceleration of rockets is obtained by the use of *retro-rockets*. 'Rocket motors' are also used on certain types of aircraft for take-off, or when a high thrust is required for a short period.

RODINAL*. Photographic *developer* consisting of an *alkaline solution* of para-aminophenol, $NH_2C_6H_4OH$, with sodium bisulphite, $NaHSO_3$.

ROENTGEN, THE. *r.* The amount of *X*- or *gamma-radiation* which will produce *ions* carrying 1 *electrostatic unit* of electricity of either sign in 1 c.c. of dry air.

ROENTGEN RAYS. See *X-rays*.

RONGALITE. *Compound* of sodium sulphoxylate and *formaldehyde*, $NaHSO_2.HCHO$. Used as a *reducing agent* in dyeing.

ROOT (math.). One of the equal *factors* of a number or quantity. The square root, $\sqrt[2]{}$ or $\sqrt{}$, is one of two equal factors; e.g. $9 = 3 \times 3$ or -3×-3; hence $\sqrt[2]{9} = \pm 3$. Similarly the *cube* or third *root* is denoted by $\sqrt[3]{}$, etc. May also be denoted by a fractional *index*; thus $\sqrt[2]{x} = x^{\frac{1}{2}}$; $\sqrt[5]{x} = x^{\frac{1}{5}}$. The root of an *equation* is a value of the unknown quantity which satisfies the equation.

ROOT MEAN SQUARE VALUE OF ALTERNATING QUANTITY. If y is a periodic *function* of t, of *period* T, the root mean square (R.M.S.) value of y is the square *root* of the mean of the square of y taken over a period. The R.M.S. value I of an *alternating current* is important since it determines the *heat* generated (RI^2) in a *resistance* R (see *electric current, heating effect of*). All ordinary A.C. measuring instruments give R.M.S. values of current, etc. If the alternating quantity can be represented by a pure *sine wave*, the R.M.S. value of the quantity A is related to the maximum value a of the quantity (i.e. *amplitude*) by the expression $A = a/\sqrt{2}$.

ROOT MEAN SQUARE VALUE OF VARIABLE. R.M.S. Given by the expression

$$\text{R.M.S.} = \sqrt{\frac{\text{(Sum of squares of the individual values of the variable)}}{\text{(total number of values)}}}$$

ROSE'S METAL. *Alloy* of 50% bismuth, 25% lead, and 25% tin; m.p. 94° C.

ROSIN. Colophony. A yellowish *amorphous resin* obtained as a residue from the *distillation* of *turpentine*. S.G. 1·08, m.p. 120°–150° C. Used in varnishes, *soaps*, and *soldering* fluxes. See also *ester gum*.

ROTAMETER*. A device for measuring the rate of flow of *fluids*; consists of a small float which is suspended by the fluid in a vertical calibrated tube. The height of the float gives a measure of the rate of flow.

ROTARY CONVERTER. An *alternating current electric motor* mechanically coupled to a *direct current generator*. Used for converting an AC supply into DC.

ROTARY DISPERSION. See *optical activity*.

ROTATION, OPTICAL. See *optical rotation*.

ROTOR. The rotating part of a *turbine, electric motor*, or *generator*.

RUBBER. Elastic *solid* obtained from the *latex* of the Hevea brasiliensis tree. Raw natural rubber consists mainly of the *cis*-form of poly*isoprene*, $(CH_2.CH:C(CH_3):CH_2)_n$, a *hydrocarbon polymer*, with *molecular weight* of about 300,000. Nearly all rubber articles are made by 'compounding' raw rubber, i.e. mixing it with other ingredients and then vulcanizing it in moulds by heating with sulphur and *accelerators*.

RUBBER, SYNTHETIC. A class of synthetic *elastomers* made from *polymers* or co-polymers (see *polymerization*) of simple *molecules*. See *butyl rubber, neoprene, nitrile rubber, styrene-butadiene rubber* (SBR), *silicone rubber*, and *stereo-regular rubbers*.

RUBIDIUM. Rb. Element. A.W. 85·47. At. No. 37. Soft, extremely *reactive* white *metal* resembling sodium. S.G. 1·53, m.p. 38·4° C. Occurs in a few rare *minerals*.

RUBY. Red form of *corundum*, Al_2O_3, which owes its colour to traces of chromium. Used in *lasers* and as a gem stone.

RULES OF FAJANS. Rules which describe the conditions determining whether an electrovalent or a covalent bond (see *valency, electronic theory of*) will be formed between *atoms*. Fajans' rules state that an electrovalent bond will be replaced by a covalent bond if: (1) the charge on either of the *ions* resulting from an electrovalent donation of *electrons* is large (i.e. if more than 1 or 2 electrons are donated); or (2) the volume of the *cation* is small or that of the *anion* is large.

RUST. *Hydrated oxide* of iron, mainly $Fe_2O_3.H_2O$, formed on the surface of iron when it is exposed to moisture and air.

RUTHENIUM. Ru. Element. A.W. 101·07. At. No. 44. Hard, brittle *metal*, S.G. 12·2, m.p. 2450° C. Occurs together with platinum.

RUTILE. Crystalline form of natural titanium dioxide, TiO_2.

RYDBERG CONSTANT. Constant relating to those atomic *spectra* which are similar to the hydrogen *atom* spectrum. The Rydberg constant for hydrogen is 109,737 cm.$^{-1}$.

S

SACCHARIMETER. Apparatus for determining the *concentration* of a *sugar solution* by measuring the *angle* of rotation of the plane of vibration of polarized light passing through a tube containing the solution. See *optical activity*; *polarization of light*.

SACCHARIN. $C_6H_4SO_2CONH$. White, crystalline, sparingly *soluble solid*; m.p. 227° C. When pure, has about 550 times the sweetening power of *sugar*, but has no food value, and may have harmful effects if used to excess. Manufactured from *toluene*, $C_6H_5CH_3$.

SACCHAROMETER. Type of *hydrometer* used for finding the *concentration* of *sugar solutions* by determining their *density*; usually graduated to read the percentage of sugar direct.

SACCHAROSE. See *sucrose*.

SAFETY LAMP. Davy lamp. An oil-lamp which will not ignite inflammable *gases*, e.g. *methane* (fire-damp). Has a cylinder of wire gauze acting as a chimney; the *heat* of the *flame* is conducted away by the gauze, and while fire-damp will burn inside the gauze, the *temperature* of the gauze does not rise sufficiently high to ignite the gas outside.

SALICYLIC ACID. $OH.C_6H_4COOH$. White crystalline solid, m.p. 159° C. Used as an antiseptic and in the form of a derivative as *aspirin*.

SAL VOLATILE. Commercial 'ammonium carbonate', actually consisting of a mixture of ammonium bicarbonate, NH_4HCO_3, ammonium carbamate, $NH_4O.CO.NH_2$, and ammonium carbonate, $(NH_4)_2CO_3$.

SAL-AMMONIAC. See *ammonium chloride*, NH_4Cl.

SALINOMETER. Type of *hydrometer* used for the determination of *concentration* of *salt solutions* by measuring their *density*.

SALT (chem.). Chemical *compound* formed when the hydrogen of an *acid* has been replaced by a *metal*. A salt is produced, together with *water*, when an acid reacts with a *base*. Salts are named according to the acid and the metal from which the salt is derived; thus *copper sulphate* is a salt derived from copper and *sulphuric acid*.

SALT, COMMON. See *sodium chloride*, NaCl.

SALTCAKE. See *sodium sulphate*, $Na_2SO_4.10H_2O$.

SALTPETRE, nitre. See *potassium nitrate*.

SALTS OF LEMON. Potassium quadroxalate, $KH_3C_4O_8.2H_2O$. White, *soluble*, poisonous, crystalline *salt*. Used for removing ink-stains.

SAMARIUM. Sm. Element. A.W. 150·35. At. No. 62. S.G. 7·8. See *lanthanides*.

SAND. Hard, granular powder, generally composed of granules of impure *silica*, SiO_2.

SAPONIFICATION. *Hydrolysis* of an *ester*; term often confined to the hydrolysis of an ester using an *aklali*, thus forming a *salt* (a *soap* in the case of some of the higher *fatty acids*) and the free *alcohol*.

SAPONIFICATION NUMBER. One of the characteristics of a *fat or oil*; the number of *milligrams* of *potassium hydroxide* required for the complete *saponification* of one gram of the fat or oil.

SAPPHIRE. Natural crystalline form of blue, *transparent corundum* (alumina, Al_2O_3); the colour being due to traces of cobalt or other *metals*.

SATELLITES. Bodies which rotate in *orbits* round other bodies of greater *mass* under the influence of their mutual *gravitational field*. Particularly bodies, or moons, which rotate around *planets*. E.g. the *Moon* is a satellite of the *Earth*. See also *satellites, artificial*.

SATELLITES, ARTIFICIAL. In 1957 the first man-made artificial *satellite* was launched by Russia into *orbit* around the *Earth*. This, and subsequent Russian and American artificial satellites have been used to obtain, and *radio* back to Earth, information concerning conditions prevailing in the *upper atmosphere* and the *ionosphere*. Valuable information has also been obtained relating to *cosmic rays*, the *density* of *matter* and the frequency of *meteors* in *space*, the shape and *magnetic fields* of the Earth, and the nature of solar *radiations*. As a result of the earlier American satellites the *Van Allen radiation belts* were discovered.

'Communication' satellites are artificial Earth satellites used for relaying radio (and *television*) signals, around the curved surface of the Earth. 'Passive' satellites merely reflect the transmissions from their surfaces, while 'active' satellites are equipped to receive and retransmit signals. See also *synchronous orbit*.

SATURATED COMPOUND (chem.). A *compound* which does not form *addition compounds*; a compound the *molecule* of which contains no double or multiple *valency bonds* between the *atoms*.

SATURATED SOLUTION. A *solution* which can exist in *equilibrium* with excess of *solute*. The saturation *concentration* is a function of the *temperature*.

SATURATED VAPOUR. A *vapour* which can exist in *equilibrium* with its liquid.

SATURATED VAPOUR PRESSURE. The *pressure* exerted by a *saturated vapour*. This pressure is a function of the *temperature*.

SATURN (astr.). *Planet*, with nine small *satellites*, and surrounded by characteristic rings (see *Saturn's rings*). *Orbit* lies between those of *Jupiter* and *Uranus*. Mean distance from the *Sun*, 886·7 million miles. *Sidereal period* ('year'), 29·46 years. Mass, approximately 95·14 times that of the *Earth*, diameter 74,130 miles. Surface temperature, about $-150°$ C.

SATURN'S RINGS. Three concentric rings, probably composed of the remains of a broken-up *satellite*, which are seen round the *planet Saturn*.

SBR. See *styrene-butadiene rubber*.

SCALAR QUANTITY. Any quantity which is sufficiently defined when the magnitude is given in appropriate units. Compare *vector*.

SCALER. Scaling circuit. An *electronic* device or circuit which produces an output *pulse* when a prescribed number of input pulses have been received. If the prescribed number is two (or ten) the circuit is referred to as a binary (or decade) scaling circuit or scaler.

SCANDIUM. Sc. Element. A.W. 44·956. At. No. 21. The *metal* has not been isolated, but the element occurs in small quantities as the oxide Sc_2O_3.

SCANNING. The repeated and controlled traversing of: (1) a *mosaic* in a television *camera*, or a screen in a *cathode-ray tube*, with an *electron* beam; (2) an airspace with a *radar aerial*; or more generally (3) any area or volume with a moving detector in order to measure some quantity or detect some object.

SCATTERING. The deflection of any *radiation* as a result of its interaction with *matter*. E.g. the change in direction of a particle or *photon* on interacting with a *nucleus* or *electron*. If the scattered particle or photon loses *energy* by causing *excitation* of the struck nucleus the scattering is said to be 'inelastic'; if energy is not lost in this way the scattering is 'elastic'. See also *scattering of light*.

SCATTERING OF LIGHT. When a *beam* of *light* traverses a material medium, scattering of the beam takes place. Two types of scattering occur: (1) by random *reflection*; i.e. small particles suspended in the medium act as tiny *mirrors* and, being randomly orientated with respect to the beam, produce random reflections. This type occurs when the size of the particles is large in comparison with the *wave-length* of the light: (2) by *diffraction*; this occurs when particles which are small compared with the wave-length of the light are present in the medium. Owing to diffraction phenomena, the particles act as centres of radiation and each particle scatters the light in all directions. In this type, the degree of scattering is proportional to the inverse fourth *power* of the wave-length of the light. Thus, blue light is scattered to a greater extent than red. The blue colour of the sky is due to scattering by the actual *molecules* of the *atmosphere*.

SCHEELE'S GREEN. Bright green *precipitate*, probably consisting of cupric arsenite, $Cu_3(AsO_3)_2.2H_2O$. Used as a *pigment* and *insecticide*.

SCHOTTKY DEFECT. See *vacancy*.

SCHWEITZER'S REAGENT. Deep blue *solution* formed by the action of *ammonia* solution on cupric hydroxide, $Cu(OH)_2$. Dissolves *cellulose*, which is re-precipitated by the action of dilute *acids*; this is the basis of the cuprammonium process of *rayon* manufacture.

SCINTILLATION COUNTER. A device in which *light* flashes, produced by a scintillator (see *phosphor*) when exposed to *ionizing radiation*, are converted into electrical *pulses* by a *photomultiplier*, thus enabling the number of ionizing events to be counted.

SCINTILLATION SPECTROMETER. A device for determining the *energy* distribution of a given *radiation*. Consists of a *scintillation counter* which incorporates a *pulse height analyser*.

SCINTILLATOR. See *phosphor*.

SCLEROPROTEIN. Class of complex, *insoluble*, fibrous *proteins*, (e.g. *keratin*, *collagen*, *elastin*) which occur in the surface coatings of animals and which form the framework binding *cells* together in animal tissues.

-SCOPE. Suffix applied to names of instruments for observing or watching, usually as distinct for measuring. E.g. *telescope*.

SCRUPLE. 1/24 ounce Troy. See *troy weight*.

SEA-WATER. The approximate composition (not including inland seas such as the Dead Sea) is water, 96·4%; common *salt*, NaCl, 2·8%; magnesium chloride, $MgCl_2$, 0·4%; magnesium sulphate, $MgSO_4$, 0·2%; calcium sulphate, $CaSO_4$, and potassium chloride, KCl, 0·1% each.

SECANT. A straight line cutting a *circle* or other curve.

SECANT (trig.). See *trigonometrical ratios*.

SECOND. 1. Fundamental unit of time redefined in 1960 as the fraction 1/31,556,925·9747 of the tropical year for 1900 January 0 at 12 hours ephemeris time. 2. Measure of *angle*: 1/60 of a minute, 1/3600 of a degree.

SECONDARY CELL. See *accumulator*.

SECONDARY EMISSION of *electrons*. When a primary *beam* of rapidly-moving electrons strikes a *metal* surface, secondary electrons are emitted from the surface. The effect is of importance in the *thermionic valve*, the *photomultiplier*, etc. In the thermionic valve, the emission occurs when the electrons strike the *anode*, and may be suppressed or controlled in multi-electrode tubes (*tetrode*, *pentode*) by various grids called the suppressor and screen grids.

SECTOR. See *circle*.

SECULAR VARIATION OF MAGNETIC DECLINATION. If the *Earth*'s magnetic North Pole is considered to rotate round the geographical North Pole, completing a cycle in about 960 years, a representation of a steady variation of *magnetic declination*, known as the secular variation, will be seen. Thus, the magnetic declination in London is at present westerly, and decreasing until it is due to become zero at the beginning of the twenty-second century.

SEEBECK EFFECT. If two wires of different *metals* are joined at their ends to form a circuit and the two junctions are maintained at different *temperatures*, an *electric current* flows round the circuit.

SEGER CONES. Device for estimating the approximate *temperature* of a furnace. Cones made of material softening at a definite temperature.

SEGMENT. See *circle* and *sphere*.

SEISMOGRAPH. Instrument for recording earthquake shocks.

SELENIUM. Se. Element. A.W. 78·96. At. No. 34. Non-metal resembling sulphur in its chemical properties. S.G. 4·81, m.p. 217° C. Exists in several *allotropic forms*. The so-called 'metallic' selenium, a silvery-grey crystalline *solid*, varies in electrical *resistance* on exposure to *light* and is used in *photo-electric cells*. Occurs as selenides of metals, together with their *sulphides*; used in the manufacture of *rubber* and of ruby *glass*.

SELENIUM CELL. *Photo-electric cell* depending for its action on the *photo-conductive effect*, or the *photo-voltaic effect*.

SELENIUM RECTIFIER. A *rectifier* which consists of alternate layers of iron and selenium in contact.

SELF-ABSORPTION. The decrease in the *radiation* from a *radioactive* material caused by the absorption of a part of the radiation by the material itself.

SELF-INDUCTANCE. Coefficient of *self-induction*.

SELF-INDUCTION. The *magnetic field* associated with an *electric current* cuts the *conductor* carrying the current. When the current changes, so does the magnetic field, resulting in an induced *E.M.F.* (See *induction, electromagnetic.*) This phenomenon is called self-induction. The induced E.M.F. is proportional to the rate of change of the current, the constant of proportionality being called the coefficient of self-induction, or the self-inductance. The magnitude of the self-inductance is a function only of the geometry of the electrical circuit and can be calculated in a few simple cases. The unit of self-inductance is the *henry*.

SEMICONDUCTOR. An electrical *conductor* whose *resistance* decreases with rising *temperature* and the presence of impurities, in contrast to normal metallic conductors for which the reverse is true. Semiconductors, which may be *elements* or *compounds*, include germanium, silicon, selenium, and lead telluride. In general, semiconductors consist of *covalent crystals*, 'ideal' examples of which at the *absolute zero* of temperature would pass no *electric current* as all the *valency electrons* would be held by the covalent bonds. At normal temperatures, however, some of the electrons have sufficient thermal *energy* to break free from the bonds leaving *holes*. Electrons liberated in this way will have random thermal motions, but in an imposed *electric field* there will be a net drift against the field resulting in so called *N-type conductivity*. The behaviour of the holes is more complex, but they may be regarded as positive charges free to move about the crystal giving rise to *P-type conductivity*. The total current passed by such an *intrinsic semiconductor* is therefore the sum of the electron current and the hole current in the direction of the field. A rise in temperature will create more *carriers*, due to more bonds being broken by thermal energy, and thus lower resistance. The foregoing refers to 'ideal' crystals, but real crystals will have inherent *defects*, *dislocations*, and impurities which will produce additional carriers (see *extrinsic semiconductor*). In practical semiconductors impurities are added in controlled quantities during crystal growth, the number of *valency electrons* of the impurity *atoms* determining whether the *majority* *carriers* will be P- or N-type. A P-N *semiconductor junction* is formed when there is a change along the length of a crystal from one type of impurity to the other. At a P-N junction an internal electric field is created between the charged impurity *ions* of the two types. This field is sufficient to prevent the drift of electrons from the N-side to the P-side of the junction, and the drift of holes in the opposite direction. If an external positive *voltage* is applied to the P-side and a negative voltage to the N-side, the internal field can be overcome and a substantial current will flow as a result of the tendency of the majority carriers on each side to migrate to the other side: the magnitude of the current will depend upon the applied voltage. Reversing the voltage increases the effect of the internal field and the only current to flow will be the small number of *minority carrier* electrons on the P-side carried over to the N-side, similarly minority carrier holes will be carried from the N- to P-regions. The reverse current is therefore small and does not depend upon the applied voltage. The P-N junction is thus a very efficient *rectifier* and is widely used for this purpose; it is also the basis of the *transistor*.

SEMICONDUCTOR DIODE. See *crystal rectifier*.

SEMICONDUCTOR JUNCTION. A plane which separates two layers of a *semiconductor* each of which have different electrical characteristics. For example, a P-N junction separates the P- region (in which *holes* are the *majority carriers*) from the N- region (in which *electrons* are the majority carriers).

SEMI-PERMEABLE MEMBRANE. A membrane allowing the passage of some substances and not of others; a partition which permits the passage of pure *solvent molecules* more readily than those of the dissolved substance. E.g. copper ferrocyanide, $Cu_2Fe(CN)_6$, is permeable to *water*, but only very slightly permeable to dissolved substances. Used as a partition between *solution* and solvent in osmotic measurements (see *osmotic pressure*) and in *dialysis*.

SEMI-POLAR BOND. A *valency bond* in which two *electrons* are donated by one *atom* (usually nitrogen or oxygen) to another atom which requires both of them to complete its *octet*. This is equivalent to one electrovalent bond and one covalent bond (see *valency, electronic theory of*) and is therefore called a semi-polar bond.

SEPARATION ENERGY. The *energy* required to remove a particle (a *proton* or a *neutron*) from a particular atomic *nucleus*.

SERIES (math.). A sequence of numbers or mathematical expressions such that the nth term may be written down in general form, and any particular term (say, the rth) may be obtained by substituting r for n; e.g. x^n is the general term of the series $1, x, x^2, x^3 \ldots x^n$.

SERIES, RESISTANCES IN. If a number of *conductors* of electricity are connected in series, i.e. one after the other, so that the current flows through each in turn, the total *resistance* is the sum of the separate resistances of the conductors. See Fig. 14 on page 271.

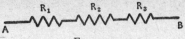

FIG. 14.

SERPEK PROCESS. Process for the *fixation of atmospheric nitrogen*. Aluminium is made to react with nitrogen to form aluminium nitride, which is then decomposed by *steam* to give *ammonia*.

SERUM. The *liquid* which remains after the clotting and removal of *blood cells* and *fibrin* from the *blood*; any similar body liquid.

SERVOMECHANISM. A mechanism which converts a small low-powered mechanical motion into a mechanical motion requiring considerably greater power. The output power is always proportional to the input power, and the system may include a negative *feedback* device (usually *electronic*).

SEXTANT. Instrument for determining the *angle* between two objects (e.g. horizon and *star*). Commonly employed for determining the radius of a *position circle*.

SHADOW. A dark patch formed by a body which obstructs *rays of light*. A shadow cast by an object in front of a *point source* of light is a sharply defined area; a source of light of appreciable size produces two distinct regions, the *umbra* or full shadow, and the *penumbra* or half-shadow. See Fig. 15.

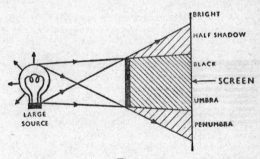

FIG. 15.

SHEAR. A *stress* applied to a body in the *plane* of one of its faces.

SHELLAC. A yellowish natural *resin* secreted by the lac insect (Laccifer lacca) which is parasitic on certain trees native to India and Thailand. Consists of several *polyhydroxy organic acids* (predominantly aleuritic acid, $C_{16}H_{32}O_5$, and shellolic acid, $C_{15}H_{20}O_6$) together with 3%–5% of *wax*. Shellac produces smooth, durable *films* from alcoholic *solutions* and *alkaline* dispersions, which adhere to a variety of surfaces: used in varnishes, polishes, leather dressings, and sealing wax. Owing to its electrical insulation properties it is used in insulating varnishes and in micanite*.

SHELLS, ELECTRON. According to the interpretation of *quantum mechanics*, the *electrons* contained within an *atom* circle round the *nucleus* in *orbits* at various distances from the nucleus. These orbital electrons may be visualized as forming a series of concentric shells: electrons in the same shell having the same principal *quantum number*, n. The shells are designated by the letters K-P (equivalent to values of n from 1-6) in order of increasing distance from the nucleus. The number of electrons in each shell is restricted (see *Pauli's exclusion principle*), but each shell is capable of containing $2n^2$ electrons. Within each shell, electrons are further classified into sub-shells (or *energy* sub-levels) according to their orbital *angular momentum*, which is represented by their azimuthal quantum number, l. The separate sub-shells are distinguished by the letters s, p, d, and f (corresponding to values of l of 0, 1, 2, and 3). E.g. an electron designated 4f, has a principal quantum number of 4 (N shell) and an azimuthal quantum number of 3 (f sub-shell).

SHERARDIZING. A method of plating iron or *steel* with zinc, to form a *corrosion* resistant coating. The iron or steel is heated in contact with zinc powder to a *temperature* slightly below the *melting point* of zinc. At this temperature the two metals amalgamate forming internal layers of zinc-iron *alloys* and an external layer of pure zinc.

SHOCK WAVE. A very narrow region of high *pressure* and *temperature* in which air flow changes from *subsonic* to *supersonic*. See also *sonic boom*.

SHOOTING STAR. See *meteor*.

SHORT CIRCUIT. If a *potential difference* exists between two points A and B (e.g. the terminals of an electrical supply), a system of *conductors* connecting A and B constitutes a *circuit*. If now A and B are placed in contact, or joined by a conductor of much lower *resistance* than the rest of the circuit, most of the current will flow direct between A and B, which are then said to be short-circuited or 'shorted'.

SHORT SIGHT. See *myopia*.

SHOWER. The production by one high *energy* particle, originating from *cosmic rays* or *accelerators*, of several fast particles. 'Cascade' showers (or soft showers) consist of *electrons*, *positrons*, or *photons* formed by successive *pair productions* or *radiative collisions*. 'Penetrating' showers contain *nucleons* and *muons* capable of penetrating up to about 20 cm. of lead. 'Auger' showers (or extensive showers) extend over areas of up to 1000 square metres.

SHUNT, ELECTRICAL. A device for altering the amount of *electric current* flowing through a piece of apparatus, such as a *galvanometer*. Consists of a *conductor* connected in *parallel* with the apparatus.

SIDEBAND. The band of *frequencies* lying on either side of a *modulated* *carrier wave*; the width of each sideband is equal to the highest modulating frequency.

SIDE-CHAIN (chem.). An *aliphatic radical* or group attached to a *benzene* or other cyclic group in the *molecule* of an *organic compound*. E.g. in *toluene*, $C_6H_5.CH_3$, the *methyl group*, CH_3, is a side-chain attached to a benzene ring.

SIDEREAL DAY. The period of a complete rotation of the *Earth* upon its *axis*, with respect to the *fixed stars*.

SIDEREAL PERIOD OF A PLANET. The 'year' of a *planet*. The actual period of its revolution round the *Sun*.

SIDEREAL YEAR. The time interval in which the *Sun* appears to perform a complete revolution with reference to the fixed *stars*. 365·2564 mean *solar days*.

SIDERITE. Natural ferrous carbonate, $FeCO_3$. Important ore of iron.

SIEMENS-MARTIN PROCESS. See *open-hearth process*.

SIGMA PILE. An assembly consisting of a *neutron* source and a *moderator*, without any *fissile* material, which is used to study the properties of moderators.

SIGN, ALGEBRAICAL. The plus or minus sign, $+$ or $-$, indicating opposite senses or directions; thus $+5$ is numerically equal, but opposite in sign, to -5.

SILAGE. Stored form of cattle-fodder produced by a limited *fermentation* of green fodder pressed down and stored in a pit. *Lactic acid* is formed during the process.

SILANES. Class of silicon *hydrides* of the general formula Si_nH_{2n+2}, forming a *homologous series* analogous to the *hydrocarbons*.

SILICA. Silicon dioxide SiO_2. Hard, *insoluble*, white or colourless *solid* with a high *melting point*. Very abundant in nature in the forms of *quartz*, *rock-crystal*, *flint*, and as *silicates* in rocks.

SILICA GEL. A form of silicon dioxide, SiO_2, with a highly porous structure capable of adsorbing (see *adsorption*) 40% of its *weight* of *water* from a *saturated vapour*. Used in *gas* drying and as a *catalyst* support.

SILICATE. *Salt* of silicic acid, H_2SiO_3. A very large number of rocks, earths, and other *minerals* consist of silicates of calcium, aluminium, magnesium, and other *metals*. Such silicates are conveniently considered as being *compounds* of *silica* and the *oxide* of the metal in question.

SILICOL PROCESS. Manufacture of hydrogen by the action of *sodium hydroxide* (caustic soda, NaOH) *solution* on silicon.

SILICON. Si. Element. A.W. 28·086. At. No. 14. Non-metal similar to carbon in its chemical properties. Occurs in two *allotropic forms*; a brown *amorphous* powder and dark grey *crystals*; S.G. 2·42, m.p. 1420° C. Occurs in nature as *silica* and as various *silicates*. Used in *alloys* and in the form of *silicates* in *glass*. *Silicones* are also widely used.

SILICONE RUBBERS. Dimethyl siloxane *polymers*. A group of synthetic *rubbers* with high and low *temperature* resistance superior to that of natural rubbers.

SILICONES. Term originally applied to *compounds* of the general formula R_2SiO, where R stands for *hydrocarbon radicals*. Now defined as polymeric (see *polymerization*) organosiloxanes of the general type $(R_2SiO)_n$. Used as lubricants, for water-repellent finishes, high-*temperature* resisting *resins* and lacquers.

SILK. A thread-like substance produced by the silkworm. Consists mainly of the *proteins* sericin and fibroin.

SILVER. Ag. Element. A.W. 107·87. At. No. 47. White, rather soft *metal*; S.G. 10·5, m.p. 960·5° C. Extremely malleable and ductile; the best known *conductor* of electricity. Occurs as the metal, and as *argentite* or silver glance, Ag_2S; *horn silver*, AgCl; and other *compounds*. Extracted by alloying with lead, and then separating the lead by *cupellation* and other methods. Used in coinage and jewellery; *compounds* used in *photography*.

SILVER BROMIDE. AgBr. Pale yellow, *insoluble salt* m.p. 434° C., used in *photography*.

SILVER GLANCE. See *argentite*.

SILVER NITRATE, lunar caustic. $AgNO_3$. White, *soluble* crystalline *salt* m.p. 209° C. Used in marking-inks, medicine, and chemical analysis.

SILVER PLATING. Depositing a layer of metallic silver, generally by *electrolysis*. See *electroplating*.

SIMPLE HARMONIC MOTION. S.H.M. A point is said to move in simple harmonic motion when it oscillates along a line about a central point

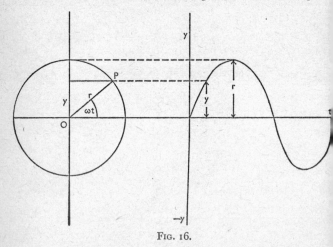

FIG. 16.

O, so that its *acceleration* towards O is always proportional to its distance from O. Thus, if a point P moves in a *circle*, centre O and radius r, with a constant *angular velocity* ω, the projection of P on any diameter will move in S.H.M. If the distance from O of the projection of P on a vertical diameter is y, at time t, then a *graph* of y against t will give a 'sine wave' of *amplitude* r and *equation* y=rsinωt. (See Fig. 16.) This equation may be rewritten in the more general from:

$$y = r\sin 2\pi \left(\frac{t}{T} - \frac{x}{\lambda} \right)$$

where T is the *period* of the wave, λ its *wave-length* and x the distance it has travelled from O in time t.

SINE. See *trigonometrical ratios*.

SINE WAVE. Sinusoidal wave. See *simple harmonic motion*.

SINTERING. Compressing *metal* particles into a coherent *solid* body. The process is carried out under *heat*, but at a *temperature* below the *melting point* of the metal. Certain non-metals such as *ceramics* and *glass* may also be sintered.

SINUSOIDAL. Having the characteristics of a sine wave. See *simple harmonic motion*.

SIPHON. Bent tube used for transferring *liquid* from one level to a lower level via a third level higher than either. If the shorter arm of an inverted U-tube filled with liquid is immersed below the liquid surface in *A* (see Fig. 17), liquid will flow from *A* to *C* through the tube. The siphon depends for its action on the fact that the *pressure* at *A* tending to force the liquid up the tube is $P - P_{ab}$ and the pressure acting upwards on the liquid at *C* is $P - P_{bc}$, where P=external atmospheric pressure, and P_{ab} and P_{ac} are the pressures due to the *weights* of the liquid columns *AB* and *AC* respectively. Hence flow from *A* to *B* will occur provided *BC* is greater than *AB*.

FIG. 17.

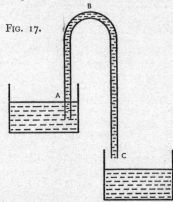

SI UNITS. See *Système International d'Unites*.

SKIP DISTANCE. There is a minimum angle of *incidence* at the *ionosphere* below which a *sky wave* of a given *frequency* cannot be reflected, but is transmitted through to outer *space*. Consequently there is a region surrounding a *radio* transmitter within which no sky wave can be received. The minimum distance at which reception of the sky wave is possible is called the skip distance.

SKY WAVE. Ionospheric wave. A *radio* wave may travel from transmitting *aerial* to receiving aerial by one of two paths: either directly along the ground (see *ground wave*), or by reflection from the *ionosphere*. In the latter case it is called a sky wave or ionospheric wave.

SLAG. Non-metallic material obtained during the *smelting* of metallic ores; generally formed as a molten mass floating on the molten m*e*tal.

SLAKED LIME. Calcium hydroxide, $Ca(OH)_2$, formed by the action of water on *quicklime*, CaO.

SLAKING. The addition of *water*.

SLATE. Natural form of aluminium silicate formed from *clay* hardened by *pressure*.

SLIDE RULE. Mathematical instrument used for rapid calculations; in principle consists of a grooved ruler with a scale, with another similarly marked ruler sliding inside the groove. Multiplication and division are carried out by adding or subtracting lengths on the two rulers, the divisions on which are in a logarithmic scale, by a process analogous to addition and subtraction which could be carried out on two rulers by adding or subtracting lengths.

SLOW NEUTRON. A *neutron* whose *kinetic energy* does not exceed about 10 *electron-volts*.

SMELTING. Extraction of a *metal* from its ores by a process involving *heat*. Generally the process is one of chemical *reduction* of the *oxide* of the metal with carbon in a suitable furnace.

SMOG. A dark, thick, dust- and soot-laden, sulphurous *fog* which, under certain meteorological conditions, pollutes the atmosphere of some industrial cities and the lungs of their inhabitants.

SMOKE. A suspension of fine particles of a *solid* in a *gas*; smoke from *coal* consists mainly of fine particles of carbon.

SNELL'S LAW. See *refraction, laws of*.

SOAP. A mixture of the sodium *salts* of *stearic acid*, $C_{17}H_{35}COOH$, *palmitic acid*, $C_{15}H_{31}COOH$, and *oleic acid*, $C_{17}H_{33}COOH$; or of the potassium salts of these acids ('soft soap'). Made by the action of *caustic soda* or *caustic potash* on *fats*, the process of *hydrolysis* or *saponification* giving the soap, with *glycerin* as a by-product. The term soap is also applied to *fatty acid* salts of *metals* other than sodium or potassium although such compounds are unlike the ordinary soaps.

SODA. Term applied to various sodium *compounds*; washing soda, sodium carbonate, $Na_2CO_3,10H_2O$; baking soda, sodium bicarbonate, $NaHCO_3$; caustic soda, $NaOH$.

SODA-LIME. A *solid mixture* of *sodium hydroxide*, NaOH, and *calcium hydroxide*, Ca(OH)$_2$, made by slaking quicklime (see *slaked lime*) with a *solution* of *sodium hydroxide* and drying by *heat*.

SODA NITRE. *Caliche.* Impure natural *sodium nitrate*.

SODA WATER. *Water* containing *carbon dioxide*, CO$_2$, under *pressure*; releasing the pressure lowers the *solubility* of the gas, and thus causes *effervescence.*

SODIUM. Na. (Natrium.) Element. A.W. 22·9898. At. No. 11. Soft, silvery-white *metal*, S.G. 0·971, m.p. 97·5° C. Very *reactive*, tarnishes rapidly in air; reacts violently with *water* to form *sodium hydroxide*, NaOH, and hydrogen *gas*. *Compounds* are very abundant and widely distributed; the commonest is *sodium chloride*, NaCl (common salt). Essential to life. The metal is used in the preparation of *organic compounds.*

SODIUM BICARBONATE, NaHCO$_3$. White, *soluble salt*, used in *baking-powder.*

SODIUM CARBONATE, washing soda. Na$_2$CO$_3$.10H$_2$O. White, crystalline, *soluble salt*, m.p. 850° C. Used in the household.

SODIUM CHLORIDE, common salt, salt. NaCl. White, crystalline, *soluble salt*, m.p. 801° C. Occurs extensively in *sea water* and as halite.

SODIUM HYDROXIDE, caustic soda, NaOH. White *deliquescent solid*, m.p. 318·4° C. Dissolves in *water* to give an *alkaline solution*.

SODIUM NITRATE, NaNO$_3$. White, *soluble*, crystalline *salt*, m.p. 306·8° C.; occurs naturally as *Chile saltpetre*; used as a *fertilizer* and in the manufacture of *nitric acid.*

SODIUM PEROXIDE, Na$_2$O$_2$. Yellow powder, formed when sodium *metal* burns in air. Reacts with *water* to give *sodium hydroxide* and oxygen *gas.*

SODIUM SILICATE, Na$_2$SiO$_3$. White, *soluble*, crystalline *salt*, used in the household as 'water-glass'.

SODIUM SULPHATE, Glauber's salt. Saltcake, Na$_2$SO$_4$.10H$_2$O. White, *soluble*, crystalline *salt.*

SODIUM THIOSULPHATE, sodium hyposulphite, *hypo*. Na$_2$S$_2$O$_3$.5H$_2$O. White, crystalline, very *soluble salt*, used in *photography.*

SOFT IRON. Iron containing little carbon, as distinct from *steel*; iron which does not retain *magnetism* permanently, but loses most of it when the magnetizing field is removed.

SOFT RADIATION. *Ionizing radiation* of relatively long *wave-length* and low penetrating power, as opposed to 'hard' radiation which is of shorter wave-length and high penetrating power.

SOFT SOAP. Potassium *soap*.

SOFT WATER. *Water* which forms an immediate lather with *soap*. See *hard water.*

SOIL. Soils vary enormously in their chemical composition. The *inorganic* portion of a soil is composed of *silicates* of various *metals*, mainly of aluminium, but also of iron, calcium, magnesium, etc.; free *silica* (sand) and other *inorganic* matter, depending on the source. *Organic* matter in the soil is mainly derived from decomposed plants; much of it is in the form of a class of black, sticky substances known collectively as *humus*.

SOL. See *colloidal solution*.

SOLAR CELL (BATTERY). Electric *cell* which converts *energy* from the *Sun* into *electrical energy*. Usually a *semiconductor* device sensitive to the *photo-voltaic effect*; e.g. a P-N *semiconductor junction* in a *crystal* of silicon. Used in artificial *satellites* and *space probes* to power *electronic* equipment.

SOLAR CONSTANT. The *energy* which would (in the absence of the *atmosphere*) be received per minute by an area of 1 sq. cm. placed at the mean distance of the *Earth* from the *Sun* and at right angles to the incident *radiation*; approximately 2 *calories* per minute per square centimetre.

SOLAR CORPUSCULAR STREAMS. Streams of electrically charged particles (*protons* and *electrons*) emitted by the *Sun*, predominantly during *solar flares* and *sunspot* activity. Some of these particles become trapped in the Earth's magnetic field (see *magnetism, terrestrial*) forming the outer *Van Allen radiation belt*, but some penetrate to the *upper atmosphere* where they congregate in narrow zones in the region of the Earth's *magnetic poles* producing auroral displays (see *aurora borealis*).

SOLAR DAY. The variable interval between two successive returns of the *Sun* to the *meridian*. The mean solar day is the average value of this. See *time measurement*.

SOLAR FLARES. Short high *temperature* outbursts seen as bright areas in the *chromosphere* of the Sun. Jets of particles (known as *solar corpuscular streams*) and strong *radio frequency electromagnetic radiations* (see *radio astronomy*) are emitted during solar flares. Solar flares are associated with *sunspots* and usually cause magnetic and *radio* disturbances on *Earth*.

SOLAR PARALLAX. The *angle* subtended by the mean equatorial radius of the *Earth* at a distance of one *astronomical unit*.

SOLAR SYSTEM, THE. The system of nine *planets* – *Mercury, Venus*, the *Earth, Mars, Jupiter, Saturn, Uranus, Neptune*, and *Pluto* – and of the belt of *asteroids* revolving in elliptical *orbits* round the *Sun*. The orbits are nearly circular, and lie very nearly in the same *plane*. See Table 2, page 332.

SOLDER. An *alloy* for joining *metals*. Soft solders are alloys of tin and lead in varying proportions; brazing solders are usually composed of copper and zinc.

SOLENOID. A coil of wire wound uniformly on a cylindrical former, having a length which is large compared with its radius. When a current of i *electromagnetic units* is passed through the solenoid, a uniform *magnetic field* H is produced inside the coil parallel to its *axis*. The magnitude of H in *oersteds* is given by $H = 4\pi n i$, where n is the number of turns per unit length of the solenoid.

SOLID (math.). A three-dimensional figure, having length, breadth, and thickness; a figure occupying *space* or having a measurable *volume*.

SOLID ANGLE. The ratio of the area of the surface of the portion of a *sphere* enclosed by the conical surface forming the angle, to the square of the radius of the sphere. See *steradian*.

SOLID SOLUTION. A solid *homogeneous mixture* of two or more substances. E.g. some *alloys* are solid solutions of the *metals* in each other, the process of *solution* having taken place in the molten state.

SOLID STATE. The *physical state of matter* in which the constituent *molecules*, *atoms*, or *ions* have no *translatory motion* although they vibrate about the fixed positions which they occupy in a *crystal lattice*. A solid is said to possess *cohesion*, remaining the same shape unless changed by external *forces*. Certain solids are not crystalline, they are then said to be *amorphous*. A crystalline solid has a definite *melting point* at which it becomes a *liquid*; amorphous solids have no precise melting point, but when heated become increasingly pliable until they assume the properties usually associated with liquids, they may therefore be thought of as 'supercooled' liquids.

SOLID STATE PHYSICS. The branch of *physics* which deals with the nature and properties of *matter* in the *solid state*. The term is often used to refer especially to the study of the properties of *semiconductors*.

SOLIDIFYING POINT. The constant *temperature* at which a *liquid* solidifies under a given *pressure*, usually the standard *atmosphere*.

SOLSTICE. The time (or, more accurately, the point) at which the *Sun* reaches its greatest *declination* North or South. The points are situated upon the *ecliptic* half-way between the *equinoxes*; the times are approximately 21 June and 21 December.

SOLUBILITY. The extent to which a *solute* will dissolve in a *solvent*. Usually expressed in grams per 100 gm. of solvent at a specified *temperature*.

SOLUBILITY PRODUCT. The product of the *concentrations* of the *ions* of a dissolved *electrolyte* when in *equilibrium* with undissolved substance. For sparingly *soluble* electrolytes, the solubility product is a constant for a given substance at a given *temperature*. When the solubility product for a given compound is exceeded in a *solution*, some of it is precipitated until the product of the ionic concentrations falls to the constant value.

SOLUBLE. Capable of being dissolved (usually in *water*).

SOLUTE. A substance which is dissolved in a *solvent* to form a *solution*.

SOLUTION. A *homogeneous* molecular *mixture* of two or more substances of dissimilar molecular structure; term commonly applied to solutions of *solids* in *liquids*. Other types of solutions include *gases* in liquids, the *solubility* of gases decreasing with rise in *temperature*; gases in solids; liquids in liquids; and solids in solids (e.g. some *alloys*), see *solid solutions*.

SOLVATION. The combination of *solvent molecules* with *molecules* or *ions* of the *solute*.

SOLVAY PROCESS, ammonia-soda process. Industrial preparation of *washing-soda*, $Na_2CO_3.10H_2O$, from common *salt*, NaCl, and *calcium carbonate*, $CaCO_3$. By the action of *ammonia*, NH_3, and *carbon dioxide* (obtained by heating $CaCO_3$) on salt *solution*, the less soluble *sodium bicarbonate*, $NaHCO_3$, is precipitated. The action of *heat* on this gives the required sodium carbonate, while the ammonia is recovered from solution by the action of the *lime* which remains when the calcium carbonate is heated.

SOLVENT. Substance (usually *liquid*) having the power of dissolving other substances in it; that component of a *solution* which has the same *physical state* as the solution itself. E.g. in a solution of *sugar* in *water*, water is the solvent, while sugar is the *solute*.

SOLVENT EXTRACTION. See *extraction*.

SOMATIC. Pertaining to the body. Somatic *cells* are the cells of which the body of an *organism* is constructed, as opposed to the reproductive or germ cells. See also *mutation*. In another sense the word 'somatic' refers to the body as opposed to the mind: e.g. psychosomatic medicine is the study of the influence of psychological factors upon physiological illness.

SONIC BOOM. The loud noise created by the *shock wave* set up by an aircraft or missile travelling at *supersonic speeds*. A subsonic aircraft produces pressure waves ahead of itself, which travel at the speed of *sound*, and 'clear a path' for the oncoming aircraft. In supersonic flight the aircraft overtakes the pressure waves so that a shock wave *cone* is created with the nose of the aircraft at its vertex. In level flight the intersection of the shock wave cone with the ground produces a *hyperbola*, at all points along which the sonic boom is simultaneously experienced: subsequently the boom will be experienced at all points within the hyperbola's path over the ground.

SOUND. A physiological sensation received by the ear. It is caused by a vibrating source and transmitted as a longitudinal pressure *wave motion* (see *longitudinal waves*) through a material medium such as air.

SOUND, VELOCITY OF. The *velocity* of propagation of *sound* waves (see *wave motion*). This velocity is a function of the *temperature* and of the nature of the propagating medium. In *gases* it is independent of the *pressure*. In air at $0°$ C. it is 1120 feet or 332 metres per second, approximately 760 miles per hour.

SOXHLET EXTRACTION APPARATUS. Device for extracting the *soluble* portion of any substance by a continuous circulation of the boiling *solvent* through it.

SPACE. That part of the boundless four dimensional *continuum* in which *matter* can be physically (rather than temporally) extended. (See *space-time*.) More colloquially, space (or 'outer' space) is that part of the Universe which lies beyond the Earth's *atmosphere* and in which the density of matter is very low.

SPACE PROBE. A *rocket*-propelled missile which has sufficient *velocity* to escape from the Earth's *atmosphere*. Space probes are used for making measurements of conditions within the *solar system* which cannot be made by terrestrial observation. The measurements are made by miniaturized *electronic* equipment within the probe, the results of which are signalled back to earth by *radio*. A Moon-probe, or Lunar-probe, is one intended to study the *Moon* and its environment.

SPACE-REFLECTION SYMMETRY. See *parity*.

SPACE-TIME. The development of the theory of *relativity* has led to the disappearance of a clear-cut distinction between a three-dimensional *space* and an independent *time*; in the modern view, space and time are considered as being welded together in a four-dimensional *space-time continuum*.

SPALLATION. A *nuclear reaction* in which a high *energy* incident particle, or *photon*, causes several particles or fragments to be emitted by the target *nucleus*. The *mass number* and *atomic number* of the target nucleus may thus be reduced by several units.

SPARK. See *electric spark*.

SPARK COIL. See *induction coil*.

SPARKING-PLUG. Device for providing an *electric spark* for exploding the *mixture* of air and *petrol vapour* in the cylinder of the *internal-combustion engine*.

SPARKING POTENTIAL, sparking voltage. The difference in *potential* (i.e. the *voltage*) required for an *electric spark* to pass across a given gap. See *Paschen's law*.

SPECIFIC ACTIVITY. The *activity* per unit *mass* of a pure *radioactive isotope*; or the activity of a radioactive isotope in a material per unit mass of that material. Usually expressed in *curies* per gram.

SPECIFIC CHARGE. The *electric charge* to *mass* ratio of an *elementary particle*.

SPECIFIC GRAVITY, S.G. The ratio of the *density* of a substance at the *temperature* under consideration to the density of *water* at the temperature of its maximum density (4° C.). Numerically equal to the density in grams per cubic centimetre, but is stated as a pure number, while the density is stated as *mass* per unit *volume*.

SPECIFIC HEAT. See *heat, specific*.

SPECIFIC IMPULSE. A term used in connexion with *rockets*. The ratio of the *thrust* produced (in lbs) to the rate of *fuel* consumption (lbs per sec.). The specific impulse therefore has the dimension of 'seconds', and may be thought of as the length of time one pound of *propellant* would last if expended at a rate which would continuously produce one pound of thrust.

SPECIFIC INDUCTIVE CAPACITY. Obsolete term for *dielectric constant*.

SPECIFIC RESISTANCE. See *resistivity*.

SPECIFIC VOLUME. The *volume*, at a specified *temperature* and *pressure*, occupied by 1 gm. of the substance. The *reciprocal* of the *density*.

SPECTRAL LINES. See *line spectrum*.

SPECTRAL SERIES. The emission *spectrum* of any substance may be analysed into one or more groups of *frequencies* (or *wave-lengths*), the frequencies in each group forming a series. For example, the spectrum of the hydrogen *atom* possesses series given by the expression

$$\nu = \text{constant}\left(\frac{1}{n_0^2} - \frac{1}{n^2}\right),$$

where $\bar{\nu}$ is the frequency of the spectral *lines*. For the different series, n_0 takes the values 1, 2, 3, 4, etc. For any one value of n_0, n may have all *integral* values from $n_0 + 1$ upwards, the expression then giving the frequencies of all the lines in that particular series.

SPECTROGRAPH. Instrument by which *spectra* may be photographed; a photograph taken by means of such an instrument. See *spectrographic analysis*.

SPECTROGRAPHIC ANALYSIS. Investigation of the chemical nature of a substance by the examination of its *spectrum*, using the fact that the position of emission and absorption *lines* and *bands* in the spectrum of a substance is characteristic of it.

SPECTROMETER. 1. A type of *spectroscope* so calibrated that it is suitable for the precise measurements of *refractive indices*. 2. An instrument for measuring the *energy* distribution of a particular type of *radiation*, e.g. a *scintillation spectrometer*.

SPECTROPHOTOMETER. A *photometer* for comparing two *light* radiations *wave-length* by wave-length.

SPECTROSCOPE. Instrument for *spectrographic analysis* or the observation of *spectra*.

SPECTRUM. The result obtained when *electromagnetic radiations* are resolved into their constituent *wave-lengths* or *frequencies*. In the visible region (i.e. *light* waves) a well-known example is provided by the coloured bands produced when white light is passed through a *prism* or *diffraction grating*. The *colours* of this spectrum, in order of decreasing wave-lengths, are: red, orange, yellow, green, blue, indigo, violet. Spectra formed from bodies emitting radiations are termed *emission spectra*. When white light is passed through a semi-transparent medium, selective absorption of radiations of certain wave-lengths or bands of wave-lengths takes place; the spectrum of the transmitted light is called an *absorption spectrum*. A continuous spectrum is one in which all wave-lengths, between certain limits, are present. A *line spectrum* is one in which only certain wave-lengths or 'lines' appear. The emission and absorption spectra of a substance are fundamental characteristics of it and are often used as a means of identification. Such spectra arise as a result of transitions between different *stationary states* of the *atoms* or *molecules* of the substance, electromagnetic waves being emitted or absorbed simultaneously with the transition. The frequency ν of the emitted or absorbed radiation is given by $E_1 - E_2 = h\nu$, where E_1 and E_2 are the *energies* of the first and second states respectively between which the transition takes place, and h is *Planck's constant*. When E_1 is greater than E_2, electromagnetic waves are emitted; in the converse case, they are absorbed.

SPECTRUM COLOURS. The *colours* visible in the continuous *spectrum* of *white light*. Red, orange, yellow, green, blue, indigo, and violet.

SPECULAR REFLECTION. Perfect or regular reflection of *electromagnetic radiation*, e.g. *light*. Occurs whenever the reflecting surface is flat to approximately $1/8$ of a *wave-length* of the radiation incident upon it.

SPECULUM METAL. *Alloy* of $2/3$ copper and $1/3$ tin; used for *mirrors* and *reflectors*.

SPEED. Ratio of the distance covered to the time taken by a moving body. Speed in a specified direction is *velocity*.

SPELTER. Commercial zinc, about 97% pure, containing lead and other impurities.

SPERMACETI. White, waxy *solid* consisting mainly of cetyl palmitate, $C_{15}H_{31}COOC_{16}H_{33}$. M.p. $40°-50°$ C. Obtained from the head of the sperm whale. Used in the manufacture of *soaps* and cosmetics.

SPERMATOCYTE. A male *gametocyte* which undergoes *meiosis* to form spermatids which change into *spermatozoa*.

SPERMATOZOON. Sperm. Male *gamete*, four of which are derived by *meiosis* from a single *spermatocyte*.

SPHERE (math.). *Solid* figure generated by the revolution of a semi-circle about a diameter as *axis*. The flat surface of a section cut by a *plane* passing through the centre is a *great circle*; surface of a section cut off by any other plane is a small circle. The solid cut off by a plane of a great circle is a hemisphere; that cut off by a small circle is a segment. The *volume* of a sphere having radius $r = \frac{4}{3}\pi r^3$; surface area $= 4\pi r^2$.

SPHERICAL ABERRATION. See *aberration, spherical*.

SPHERICAL TRIANGLE. A *triangle* drawn on a spherical surface, bounded by the arcs of three *great circles*. The properties of such triangles differ from those of *plane* triangles; calculations relating to them form the purpose of spherical trigonometry.

SPHERICAL TRIGONOMETRY. *Trigonometry* which deals with *spherical triangles*.

SPHEROID. *Solid* figure generated by an *ellipse* rotating about its minor axis (oblate spheroid, a 'flattened sphere') or about its major axis (prolate spheroid, an 'elongated sphere').

SPHEROMETER. Instrument for the accurate measurement of small thicknesses, or curvature of spherical surfaces.

SPIEGEL, spiegeleisen. *Alloy* of iron, manganese, and carbon, used in the manufacture of *steel* by the *Bessemer process*.

SPIN. Term of special significance in *nuclear physics*. Sub-atomic particles (*electrons, neutrons, nuclei, mesons*, etc.) may possess, in addition to other forms of *energy* such as energy of translation, energy due to the spinning of the particle about an *axis* within itself. This gives rise to a spin energy term in the quantum analysis (see *quantum mechanics*) of permissible *energy levels*. Quantum considerations limit the magnitude of the spin *angular momentum* of *orbital electrons* to two values, given by m_s. $\dfrac{h}{2\pi}$ or

$m_s.\hbar$ (see *Planck's constant*) where m_s is the spin *quantum number* which can have the values $\pm\frac{1}{2}$. The plus and minus signs indicate that the spin can be clockwise or anti-clockwise.

SPINELS. Group of *minerals* having the general composition $MO.R_2O_3$, M being a *bivalent metal* (magnesium, ferrous iron, manganese, zinc) and R a *tervalent* metal (aluminium, chromium, ferric iron). See *ferrites*.

SPIRAL GALAXIES. Spiral nebulae. *Galaxies* in which the *stars*, dust, and *gas* clouds are concentrated in the arms of a spiral. Spiral galaxies are believed to have evolved from 'elliptical' galaxies. The *Galaxy* to which the *solar system* belongs is also spiral in form.

SPIRILLUM. A spiral-shaped *bacterium*.

SPIRITS OF SALT. *Solution* of *hydrochloric acid*.

SPIRITS OF WINE. See *ethyl alcohol*.

SPONTANEOUS COMBUSTION. The *combustion* of a substance of low *ignition point*, which results from the *heat* produced within the substance by slow *oxidation*.

SPUTTERING. Process for depositing a thin uniform film of a *metal* on to a surface. A disc of the metal to be 'sputtered' is made the *cathode* of a low-pressure discharge system (see *discharge in gases*). The material to be coated is placed between cathode and *anode*, the whole arrangement being enclosed and evacuated to a *pressure* of between 1 and 0·01 mm. A discharge is set up by applying a *voltage* (1000–20,000 volts) between anode and cathode. Metallic *atoms* are ejected from the cathode and are deposited on the surface to be coated.

SQUARE. 1. *Quadrilateral* having all its sides equal and all its *angles* right angles. 2. The square of a quantity is that quantity raised to the second *power*, i.e. multiplied by itself.

SQUARE ROOT. See *root*.

SQUARE WAVE. A *wave motion* which alternates between two fixed values for equal lengths of time, the time of transition between the two values being negligible compared to the duration of each fixed value.

SQUARING THE CIRCLE. The problem of constructing a *square* exactly equal in area to a given *circle*. The exact area of a circle cannot be determined, except in terms of π, which cannot be expressed as an exact fraction or decimal, although any required degree of approximation can be obtained. The problem, therefore, appears to be impossible of solution.

STABILIZATION (chem.). Prevention of chemical *decomposition* of a substance by the addition of a 'stabilizer' or 'negative *catalyst*'.

STABLE (chem.). Not readily decomposed.

STABLE EQUILIBRIUM (phys.). A body at rest is in stable *equilibrium* if, when slightly displaced, it tends to return to its original position of equilibrium. If the displacement tends to increase, the body is said to be in unstable equilibrium. Positions of stable equilibrium are positions of minimum *potential energy*; those of unstable equilibrium are of maximum potential energy.

STAINLESS STEEL. A class of chromium *steels* containing 70%–90% iron, 12%–20% chromium, 0·1%–0·7% carbon.

STALACTITE. Downward growth of *calcium carbonate*, $CaCO_3$, formed on the roof of a cave by the trickling of *water* containing calcium *compounds*.

STALAGMITE. Upward growth from the floor of a cave; of the same nature and origin as a *stalactite*.

STALAGMOMETRY. The measurement of *surface tension* by determining the *weight* (or *volume*) of a drop of the *liquid* hanging from the end of a tube.

STALLOY*. *Steel* containing 3·5% silicon, having low *energy* losses due to *hysteresis*. Used in portions of electrical apparatus which are subjected to alternating *magnetic fields*.

STAND OIL. A *drying oil* which has been thickened by heating in an inert atmosphere (without the addition of driers). The thickening is due to *polymerization* of some of the constituents.

STANDARD ATMOSPHERE. See *atmosphere, the normal or standard*.

STANDARD CELL. A specially prepared *primary cell*, e.g. the *Weston cell*, characterized by a high constancy of *E.M.F.* over long periods of time. The E.M.F. is a function of the *temperature*, and in the Weston cell it decreases by about 1 part in 10^5 per 1° rise.

STANDARD DEVIATION. A measure, used in *statistics*, of the scatter of a series of numbers or measurements about their *mean* value. Defined as the *square root* of the average value of the *squares* of the deviations from their mean value.

STANDARD TEMPERATURE AND PRESSURE. S.T.P. See *N.T.P.*

STANDING WAVE. Stationary wave. A wave produced by the simultaneous transmission of two similar *wave motions* in opposite directions.

STANNIC. *Compound* of quadrivalent tin.

STANNOUS. *Compound* of bivalent tin.

STANNUM. See *tin*.

STARCH. Amylum. *Polysaccharide carbohydrates* consisting of chains of *glucose* units arranged in one of two forms: *amylose* and *amylopectin*. Most *natural* starches are mixtures of these two forms (e.g. potato and cereal starches are 20%–30% amylose and 70%–80% amylopectin). Starch is a white, tasteless *insoluble* powder which on *hydrolysis* (by boiling with *dilute acids*, or by reacting with *amylases*) gives first *dextrin* and finally glucose. Starch is stored by plants in the form of granules and occurs in most seeds.

STARCH GUM. See *dextrin*.

STARS. Heavenly bodies of a similar nature to the *Sun*, i.e. intensely hot, glowing masses which produce their *energy* by *thermonuclear reactions*. The nearest star to the Sun is over 4 *light-years* away; the other *fixed stars* visible to the naked eye are all members of the *Galaxy* and many of them are members of *binary star* systems. The stars are not uniformly distributed throughout the Universe, being grouped into enormous clusters called *galaxies*. The nearest galaxy to ours is some 16×10^5 *light-years* away. See also *stellar evolution*.

STASSFURT DEPOSITS. Natural deposits of several *inorganic salts*. The deposit consists of several strata, of a total estimated thickness of 2500 feet. Source of potassium and sodium *compounds* in the form of *carnallite*; also of magnesium bromide, $MgBr_2.6H_2O$, and *rock-salt*.

STATCOULOMB. The unit of *electric charge* in the *metric system*. 3×10^9 statcoulombs $= 1$ *coulomb*.

STATES OF MATTER. See *physical states of matter*.

STATIC ELECTRICITY. See *electricity, static*.

STATICS. Branch of *mechanics*; the mathematical and physical study of the behaviour of *matter* under the action of *forces*, dealing with cases where no motion is produced.

STATIONARY ORBIT. See *synchronous orbit*.

STATIONARY STATES. Term used in *quantum mechanics*. If only certain energy values or *energy levels* for the total energy of a system are permissible, the energy is said to be *quantized*. These levels are characteristic of the state of the system; such states are called stationary states. A transition from one stationary state to another can occur only with the emission or absorption of energy in the form of *photons*; i.e. *electromagnetic radiation* is emitted or absorbed.

STATISTICS. Collection and study of numerical facts or data.

STATOR. The fixed part of any *electric motor* or *generator* which contains the stationary magnetic circuits.

STEADY STATE THEORY. A theory in *cosmology* which postulates that the Universe has always existed in a steady state, that the *expansion of the Universe* is compensated by the continuous creation of *matter* which is viewed as a property of *space*, and that despite local evolutionary processes, the Universe as a whole is not evolving. The rate at which matter would have to be spontaneously created to compensate for the Universe's expansion (about 10^{-46} grams per c.c. per second) is far too low to be measurable and therefore evidence to support this theory has to be sought in other directions. If it could be established that the *density* of matter throughout the Universe does not vary with distance or time, this would support the steady state theory rather than its main competitor the *super-dense theory*. *Radio astronomy* is being used to assess the density of matter at the most distant parts of the observable Universe in order to decide between these two theories.

STEAM. *Water*, H_2O, in the gaseous state; water above its *boiling point*. Invisible *gas*; the white clouds which are frequently termed 'steam' consist of droplets of *liquid* water formed by the *condensation* of steam.

STEAM ENGINE. Machine utilizing *steam* power; either a steam turbine (see *turbine*) or a reciprocating steam engine, consisting essentially of a cylinder in which a piston is moved backwards and forwards by the expansion of steam under pressure.

STEAM POINT. The *temperature* at which the maximum *vapour pressure* of *water* is equal to standard atmospheric pressure (see *atmosphere*), i.e. the normal *boiling point*. In the *Centigrade scale* of temperature the steam point is given the value of 100° C.

STEARATES. *Salts* or *esters* of *stearic acid*.

STEARIC ACID. $C_{17}H_{35}COOH$. *Organic compound* belonging to the group of *fatty acids*. White *solid*, m.p. 69° C. Occurs in the form of *tristearin*, a *glyceride*, in many *fats*.

STEARIN. *Tristearin;* term also sometimes applied to a mixture of *palmitic* and *stearic acids* (see *stearine*).

STEARINE. Hard, white waxy *solid* consisting mainly of *stearic* and *palmitic acids*. Made by the *saponification* of natural *fats*.

STEEL. Iron containing from 0·1% to 1·5% carbon in the form of *cementite* (iron carbide, Fe_3C). The properties of different steels vary according to the percentage of carbon and of *metals* other than iron present, and also according to the method of preparation. Prepared by the *open-hearth* and *Bessemer processes*.

STEELYARD. Weighing-machine for heavy loads. In principle consists of a long, rigid bar, with a pan or hook at one end for taking the load to be weighed. The rod is pivoted about a fixed point or fulcrum near the *centre of gravity*, which is fairly near the end with the pan or hook. The other portion of the bar is graduated, and a movable weight slides along this, the weight balanced by it being proportional to its distance from the centre of gravity. See Fig. 18.

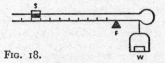

FIG. 18.

STEFAN'S LAW. The total *energy* emitted in the form of *heat radiation* per unit time from unit area of a black body is proportional to the fourth power of its *absolute temperature* (see *black body radiation*). The constant of proportionality, Stefan's constant, $= 5·6697 \times 10^{-5}$ *erg.* cm.$^{-2}$ sec.$^{-1}$ deg.$^{-4}$. Also known as the Stefan-Boltzmann Law and constant.

STELLAR EVOLUTION. According to current views *stars* evolve during the course of their history. It is thought that they are born from *condensations* of *gas* (mostly hydrogen) which is compressed as a result of the *gravitational field* between the constituents. The compression is so great in the interior of the gas that *thermonuclear reactions* occur during which hydrogen is converted into helium (and possibly heavier *elements*) with the evolution of *energy*. On a *Hertzsprung-Russell diagram* the stars remain on the 'main sequence' until they have consumed some 10%

of their hydrogen. They then become *red giants* and consume their hydrogen at increased rates so that eventually they contract and become *white dwarfs*. See also *novae* and *supernovae*.

STELLITE*. *Alloy* of cobalt (35%–80%), chromium (15%–40%), tungsten (10%–25%), molybdenum (0%–40%), and iron (0%–5%). Hard and non-corroding; used for surgical instruments.

STEP-ROCKET. See *rocket*.

STERADIAN. Unit of *solid angle*. That solid angle which encloses a surface on the *sphere* equal to the *square* of the radius.

STERE. Metric unit of *volume*; 1 cubic metre.

STEREOCHEMISTRY. *Chemistry* involving consideration of the arrangement in *space* of the *atoms* in a *molecule*. If a molecule is considered as a three-dimensional entity in space, possibilities of *stereoisomerism* or space *isomerism* arise; thus, a molecule consisting of four different *radicals* or *atoms* attached to a central carbon atom can exist in two distinct space arrangements, one being a *mirror image* of the other. Such isomerism is associated with *optical activity*.

STEREOISOMERISM. *Isomerism* caused by possibilities of different arrangement in three-dimensional space of the *atoms* within a *molecule*, resulting in two isomers which are mirror images of each other. See also *cis-trans isomerism*.

STEREO-REGULAR RUBBERS. A group of synthetic *rubbers* manufactured by a solution *polymerization* process using special *catalysts* which control the stereoisomeric (see *stereoisomerism*) regularity of the products. These materials can therefore be made to resemble closely the structure of natural rubber. In *cis* – 1, 4 poly*isoprene*, the structure of natural rubber is substantially duplicated, and this *elastomer* can be used for many of the purposes which were the exclusive preserve of natural rubber. A similar product is *cis* – 1, 4 poly*butadiene* which is also used in place of natural rubber. See also *ethylene* – *propylene rubber*.

STEREOSCOPE. Optical device by which two-dimensional pictures are given the appearance of depth and solidity.

STEROIDS. Derived *lipids* which include *sterols*, the bile acids, certain *hormones* and *glucosides*, and *vitamin* D.

STEROLS. Derived *lipids* of the *steroid* group. *Cholesterol* and *ergosterol* are typical examples; present in many living *organisms* in which they play an essential part.

STIBINE, antimony hydride. SbH_3. Poisonous *gas*.

STIBNITE. Natural antimony sulphide, Sb_2S_3. Principal ore of antimony.

STILBOESTROL. $(HO.C_6H_4.C\cdot C_2H_5:)_2$. Crystalline *organic compound*, m.p. 171° C; used in medicine as an *oestrogen*.

STILL. A *metal* or *glass* apparatus used for the *distillation* of *liquids*.

STIMULATED EMISSION. See *maser* and *laser*.

STOCHASTIC PROCESS. A process which has some element of *probability* in its structure.

STOICHIOMETRIC. A *compound* is said to be stoichiometric when it is pure, i.e. when its component *elements* are present in the exact proportions represented by its chemical *formula*. A stoichiometric *mixture* is one which will yield on reaction a stoichiometric compound (e.g. two *molecules* of hydrogen and one molecule of oxygen constitute a stoichiometric mixture because they yield exactly two molecules of *water* on *combustion*).

STOICHIOMETRY. Part of *chemistry* dealing with the composition of substances; more particularly with the determination of combining proportions or *chemical equivalents*.

STOKES' LAW. A small *sphere* falling under the action of gravity through a *viscous* medium ultimately reaches a constant *velocity* equal to $v = \dfrac{2gr^2(d_1 - d_2)}{9\eta}$ where r = radius of the sphere, d_1 = *density* of the sphere, d_2 = density of the medium, and η = the coefficient of *viscosity* of the medium.

STOPPING POWER. A measure of the ability of a substance to reduce the *kinetic energy* of a charged particle passing through it. The 'linear' stopping power is the energy lost per unit distance; the 'mass' stopping power is the linear stopping power divided by the *density* of the substance. Stopping power is often expressed relative to such standard substances as air or aluminium.

STORAGE BATTERY. See *accumulator*.

STRAIN (phys.). When a body is deformed by an applied *stress* the strain is the ratio of the dimensional change to the original or unstrained dimension. The strain may be a ratio of lengths, areas, or volumes.

STRAIN GAUGE, ELECTRICAL. Consists essentially of a grid of fine resistance wire supported on a paper base. This is attached by a suitable adhesive to the surface under test, so that any strains set up in the latter are accurately transferred to the gauge wire. The electrical *resistance* of the gauge is proportional to the *strain*, so that methods of measuring resistance may be used for measuring strain. The gauge is suitable for measuring strains of the order of 10^{-4} to 10^{-2}.

STRANGENESS. Certain *elementary particles* (K-mesons and *hyperons*) *decay* about 10^{12} times more slowly than would be expected from the large amounts of *energy* released in the processes. These particles, which are called strange particles, have been arbitrarily assigned a *quantum number*, s, to account for this strangeness. For ordinary particles (*nucleons, pions, muons*, etc.) s = 0; each strange particle has a specific, *integral* value of s which is not equal to 0.

STRATOSPHERE. Layer of the *atmosphere* beginning approximately 7 miles above the surface of the *Earth*.

STRATUM. Layer.

STREAMLINE. A *streamline* is a line in a *fluid* such that the *tangent* to it at every point is in the direction of the *velocity* of the fluid particle at that point, at the instant under consideration. When the motion of the fluid is such that, at any instant, continuous streamlines can be drawn through the whole length of its course, the fluid is said to be in streamline flow.

STREPTOMYCIN. *Antibiotic* substance produced by the Actinomyces mould. Effective against several types of disease *bacteria*, including some against which *penicillin* is inactive.

STRESS (phys.). A *force* per unit area. When a stress is applied to a body (within its *elastic limit*) a corresponding *strain* is produced, and the ratio of stress to strain is a characteristic constant of the body. See *elastic modulus*.

STROBOSCOPE. An instrument with the aid of which it is possible to view objects which are moving rapidly with a periodic motion (see *period*) and to see them as if they were at rest. For example, if a disc, rotating at n revolutions per second, is illuminated by a source which is flashing at the same *frequency*, then at any particular flash the eye will see the disc in exactly the same position as it was for the previous flash. The disc will therefore appear stationary. If the frequency of the motion is not quite equal to that of the flashing, the disc will appear to rotate slowly.

STRONG NUCLEAR INTERACTIONS. The interactions which give rise to the *exchange forces* between *nucleons*, *hyperons*, and some *mesons*. These are the strongest forces known in nature being 100 times more powerful than electromagnetic interactions and 10^{12} times more powerful than *weak nuclear interactions*.

STRONTIUM. Sr. Element. A.W. 87·62. At. No. 38. *Reactive metal* resembling calcium. S.G. 2·6; m.p. 757° C. Occurs as celestine, $SrSO_4$, and strontianite, $SrCO_3$. *Compounds* colour a *flame* crimson; used in fireworks. Strontium oxide, SrO, combines with *cane-sugar* to form an *insoluble* 'saccharate'; this is used in *sugar* refining.

STRONTIUM UNIT. SU. A measure of the *concentration* of strontium – 90 in an *organic* medium (e.g. milk, bone, *soil*, etc.) relative to the concentration of calcium in the same medium. 1 $SU = 10^{-12}$ *curies* of strontium – 90 per gram of calcium.

STRYCHNINE. $C_{21}H_{22}N_2O_2$. *Alkaloid* which occurs in the seeds of nux vomica. White, crystalline substance, slightly *soluble* in *water*; m.p. 284° C. Has an intensely bitter taste and a powerful and very dangerous action on the nervous system. Used in medicine in minute doses.

STYRENE. Phenylethylene. $C_6H_5.CH:CH_2$. Colourless *aromatic liquid*, b.p. 146° C. Polymerizes to a *thermoplastic* material (see *polystyrene*) and used in the manufacture of synthetic *rubber*. See *styrene-butadiene rubber*.

STYRENE-BUTADIENE RUBBER. SBR. Widely used, general purpose synthetic *rubber*. Copolymer (see *polymerization*) of *butadiene* and about 35% of *styrene*, which is *vulcanized* in a similar manner to natural rubber. Properties are in general inferior to natural rubber, except for abrasion resistance, but passenger car tyres are made very largely from SBR.

This *elastomer* is not suitable, however, for incorporation into heavy duty tyres.

SUB-. Prefix denoting under, below.

SUB-ATOMIC. Term applied to particles smaller than, or forming a part of, the *atom*. See *atom, structure of*.

SUB-CRITICAL. Said of a *nuclear reactor* in which the effective *multiplication constant* is less than unity, and in which the nuclear *chain reaction* is therefore not self-sustaining.

SUBLIMATE. *Solid* obtained by the direct *condensation* of a vaporized solid without passing through the *liquid* state.

SUBLIMATION (chem.). The conversion of a *solid* direct into *vapour*, and subsequent *condensation*, without melting.

SUBSONIC. Adjective used to describe a *speed* which is less than Mach 1. See *Mach number*.

SUBSTANTIVE DYES. See *direct dyes*.

SUBSTITUTION PRODUCT. A *compound* obtained by replacing an *atom* or group by another atom or group in a *molecule*.

SUBSTRATE. A substance whose reactivity is increased by a specific *enzyme*.

SUBTEND (math.). Two points, A and B, are said to subtend the *angle* ACB at the point C.

SUCCINIC ACID. $(CH_2COOH)_2$. White crystalline *organic dibasic acid*, m.p. 185° C. Used in the manufacture of *dyes*, lacquers, and other products.

SUCCINITE. See *amber*.

SUCRASE. See *invertase*.

SUCROCLASTIC. *Sugar*-splitting; applied to *enzymes* which have the power of hydrolyzing complex *carbohydrates*. E.g. *invertase*.

SUCROSE. Cane-sugar, beet sugar, saccharose. Common 'sugar' of the household. $C_{12}H_{22}O_{11}$. White, sweet, *disaccharide*, crystalline *solid*, m.p. 160°–186° C. Found in numerous plants, particularly the sugar cane, sugar beet and maple tree sap.

SUCTION. This is not a positive *force* which 'draws' a *liquid* up; a liquid raised by so-called suction is actually pushed up by atmospheric *pressure*, which is greater than the pressure of the partial *vacuum* caused by the suction.

SUGAR. In general, any sweet, *soluble, monosaccharide, or disaccharide carbohydrate*; term commonly applied to *sucrose*.

SUGAR OF LEAD. See *lead acetate*.

SULPHATE. *Salt* of sulphuric acid.

SULPHATE OF AMMONIA. See *ammonium sulphate*.

SULPHIDE. A *binary compound* of an *element* or group with sulphur; a *salt* of *hydrogen sulphide*, H_2S.

SULPHITE. *Salt* of sulphurous acid, H_2SO_3.

SULPHONAMIDE DRUGS. Sulpha drugs. A group of *organic compounds*, containing the sulphonamide group $SO_2.NH_2$ or its *derivatives*; includes *prontosil*, sulphanilamide, sulphapyridine, sulphathiazole, sulpha-diazine, and many others. Of great value in the treatment of many diseases caused by *bacteria*.

SULPHONIC ACIDS. *Acid organic compounds* which contain the sulphonic acid group, $-SO_2.OH$.

SULPHUR. S. Element. A.W. 32·064. At. No. 16. Non-metallic *element* occurring in several *allotropic forms*. The stable form under ordinary conditions is rhombic or alpha-sulphur, a pale-yellow brittle crystal-line *solid*, S.G. 2·07, m.p. 112·8° C., b.p. 444·6 C. Burns with a blue *flame* to give *sulphur dioxide*; combines with many *metals* to form *sulphides*. Occurs as the element in many volcanic regions and as sulphides of many *metals*. Extracted in vast quantities in Texas by the *Frasch process* Used in the manufacture of *sulphuric acid, carbon disulphide*, for *vulcaniz-ing rubber*, in the manufacture of *dyes* and various chemicals, for killing moulds and pests, and in medicine. Essential to life.

SULPHUR DIOXIDE. SO_2. Colourless *gas* with a choking, penetrating smell; *liquid* SO_2 is used in refrigerators.

SULPHUR POINT. The *temperature* of equilibrium between *liquid* sulphur and its *vapour* at a *pressure* of one standard atmosphere; 444·6° C

SULPHUR TRIOXIDE. SO_3. White crystalline *solid*, m.p. 16·8° C. Com-bines with *water* to form *sulphuric acid*.

SULPHURETTED HYDROGEN. See *hydrogen sulphide*.

SULPHURIC ACID. Vitriol, oil of vitriol. Colourless, oily *liquid*. S.G. 1·84. Extremely corrosive, reacts violently with *water* with evolution of *heat*, chars *organic* matter. *Dibasic acid*. Prepared by the *lead chamber* and the *contact processes*. Used extensively in many processes in chemical industry, and in the lead *accumulator*.

SULPHURIC ACID, FUMING. See *oleum*.

SULPHURIC ETHER. Diethyl ether. See *ethers*.

SUN, THE. Incandescent, approximately spherical heavenly body around which the *planets* rotate in elliptical *orbits* (see *solar system*). The Sun is a 'main sequence' *star* (see *Hertzprung-Russell diagram*), being one of some 10^{11} stars which constitute our *Galaxy*. Mean distance from the *Earth* approximately $92·96 \times 10^6$ miles, distance to nearest star approximately 25×10^{12} miles. The diameter of the Sun is about 864,100 miles, its *mass* 2×10^{27} tons, its average *density* 1·4 grams per c.c. The visible surface of the Sun, called the *photosphere*, is at a *tempera-ture* of about 6000° C.; its interior temperature is some 13,000,000° C. At this internal temperature *thermonuclear reactions* occur in which hydrogen is converted into helium, these reactions providing the Sun with its vast supply of *energy*. The Sun is composed of about 90% hydrogen, 8% helium, and only 2% of the heavier *elements*.

SUNSPOTS. Large patches, which appear black by contrast with their sur-roundings, visible upon the surface of the *Sun*. Owing to the rotation of the Sun, they appear to move across its surface. Their appear-ance is spasmodic, but their number reaches a maximum approximately every eleven years. (See *eleven year period*.) Connected with such phenomena as magnetic storms and the *Aurora Borealis*. See *solar flares* and *solar corpuscular streams*.

SUPER-. Prefix denoting over, above.

SUPER-CONDUCTIVITY. The electrical *resistance* of a *metal* or *alloy* is a function of *temperature*, decreasing as the temperature falls and tending to zero at the *absolute zero*. It is found that for certain metals and alloys (e.g. lead, vanadium, tin) the resistance changes abruptly, becoming vanishingly small at a temperature in the neighbourhood of a few degrees above absolute zero. This phenomenon is termed super-conductivity, and the temperature at which it sets in is the transition temperature. A current induced by a *magnetic field* in a ring of super-conducting material will continue to circulate after the magnetic field has been removed. (See also *cryotron*.) This effect has been used to produce large magnetic fields without the expenditure of appreciable quantities of *electrical energy*.

SUPERCOOLING, undercooling. The *metastable* state of a *liquid* cooled below its *freezing point*. A supercooled liquid will usually freeze on the addition of a small particle of the *solid* substance, and often on the addition of any solid particle or even on shaking; the *temperature* then rises to the freezing point.

SUPER-CRITICAL. Said of a *nuclear reactor* in which the effective *multiplication factor* exceeds unity, and in which the nuclear *chain reaction* is therefore self-sustaining.

SUPERDENSE THEORY. The theory in *cosmology* that the Universe has evolved from one 'superdense' agglomeration of *matter* which suffered a cataclysmic explosion. The observed *expansion of the Universe* is regarded as a result of this explosion, the *galaxies* flying apart like fragments from an exploding bomb. This hypothesis, which presupposes a finite beginning and probably a finite end to the history of the Universe, is in opposition to the *steady state theory*.

SUPERHEATED STEAM. *Steam* above a *temperature* of 100° C. ; obtained by heating *water* under a *pressure* greater than atmospheric.

SUPERHEATING. Heating a *liquid* above its *boiling point*, when the liquid is in a *metastable* state. See *supercooling*.

SUPERHETERODYNE. Superhet. Abbreviation of 'supersonic heterodyne'. A method of *radio* reception in which the *frequency* of the *carrier wave* is changed in the receiver to a 'supersonic' *intermediate frequency* (i.e. a frequency above the audible limit for *sound*) by a *heterodyne* process.

SUPERNOVAE. *Stars* which suffer an explosion becoming some 10^8 times brighter than the *Sun* during the process. Relatively rare events, only two having been recorded within our *Galaxy*, although they have been observed fairly regularly in other *galaxies*. Believed to be caused when a star runs out of hydrogen and contracts under its own *gravitational field*. The contraction causes a sufficiently high *temperature* in the interior for *thermonuclear reactions* to occur which produce heavy *elements*. The formation of heavy elements, with *atomic numbers* in excess of about 40, absorbs *energy* and the star collapses inwards, increasing its speed of rotation and ultimately flinging a large portion of its *matter* into *space*. It is believed that the *planets* of the *solar system* consist of matter thrown into space by a supernova, which was subsequently collected by the Sun's gravitational field. The residue of a supernova explosion is a *white dwarf* star.

SUPERPHOSPHATE. Artificial *fertilizer* consisting mainly of calcium dihydrogen phosphate, $Ca(H_2PO_4)_2$.

SUPERSATURATION. The *metastable* state of a *solution* holding more dissolved *solute* than is required to *saturate* the solution.

SUPERSONIC. Adjective used to describe a *speed* in excess of Mach 1. See *Mach number*.

SUPERSONICS. See *ultrasonics*.

SUPPLEMENTARY ANGLES. *Angles* together totalling 180°, or two right angles.

SURD. Irrational quantity; a *root* which cannot be expressed as an exact number or fraction; e.g. $\sqrt{2}$.

SURFACE ACTIVE AGENT. Surfactant. Substance introduced into a *liquid* in order to affect (usually to increase) its spreading, wetting, and similar properties (i.e. properties which depend upon its *surface tension*). Many *detergents* fall into this class.

SURFACE COLOUR. Certain reflecting surfaces, e.g. *metal* surfaces exhibit selective reflection of *light* waves; i.e. they reflect some *wavelengths* (*colours*) more readily than others. When illuminated by *white light*, such surfaces reflect light deficient in certain wave-lengths, and the body appears coloured. The body is then said to show surface colour, as opposed to *pigment colour*. Bodies showing surface colour when viewed by transmitted light appear to be of the *complementary colour* to that observed when viewed by reflected light. Substances which show pigment colour appear the same colour whether viewed by reflected or transmitted light.

SURFACE TENSION. An open surface of a *liquid* is under a state of tension, causing a tendency for the portions of the surface to separate from each other; the surface thus shows properties similar to those of a stretched elastic film over the liquid. The tension is an effect of the *forces* of attraction existing between the *molecules* of a liquid. Measured by the force per unit length acting in the surface at right angles to an element of any line drawn in the surface. A surface tension exists in any boundary surface of a liquid.

SURFACTANT. See *surface active agent*.

SUSCEPTIBILITY, MAGNETIC. See *magnetic susceptibility*.

SUSPENSION (chem.). A two-phase system (see *phase*) consisting of very small *solid* particles distributed in a *liquid dispersion medium*.

SUSPENSOID SOL. See *colloidal solutions*.

SYLVINE. Natural potassium chloride, KCl, usually containing *sodium chloride* as an impurity. Important source of potassium *compounds*.

SYMBIOSIS. A relationship between two different types of *organism* which live together for their mutual benefit. E.g. the relationship between *cellulose*-digesting *bacteria* and the herbivores whose alimentary tract they inhabit.

SYMBOL (chem.). A letter or letters representing an *atom* of an *element*; e.g. S = one atom of sulphur. Often loosely taken to mean the element in general, e.g. Fe = iron. See *formula*. The symbols of all the elements are given in Table 1, on pages 330–2.

SYMMETRY. The correspondence of parts of a figure with reference to a *plane*, line, or point of symmetry. Thus, a *circle* is symmetrical about any diameter; a *sphere* is symmetrical about a plane of any great circle.

SYNAPSE. A junction between *neurons* by which nerve impulses are transferred within the nervous systems of animals. A synapse is usually formed between the *axon* of one neuron and the cell body or *dendrite* of another.

SYNCHRO-CYCLOTRON. A type of *cyclotron* which enables relativistic energies (see *relativistic particle*) to be achieved by modulating the *frequency* of the accelerating *electric field*.

SYNCHRONOUS MOTOR. An *alternating current electric motor* whose speed of rotation is proportional to the *frequency* of its power supply.

SYNCHRONOUS ORBIT. Stationary orbit. The *orbit* of an artificial Earth *satellite* which has a *period* of 24 hours. The altitude corresponding to such an orbit is about 22,300 miles; a satellite in a circular orbit parallel to the *equator* at this altitude would appear to be stationary in the sky. Communication satellites in synchronous orbits are ideal for relaying *radio* signals between widely separated points on the Earth's surface.

SYNCHROTRON. An *accelerator* of the *cyclotron* type in which the *magnetic field* is modulated but the *electric field* is maintained at a constant *frequency*.

SYNCHROTRON RADIATION. High *energy electrons* within a *synchrotron* emit *light* as a consequence of their *acceleration* in a strong *magnetic field*: this emission is known as synchrotron radiation. The term is also used to describe the emission of *radio frequency electromagnetic radiations* from interstellar gas clouds in *radio galaxies* (see *radio astronomy*) as this emission is believed to be an analogous phenomenon.

SYNERESIS. Separation of *liquid* from a *gel*.

SYNODIC PERIOD OF A PLANET. The period between two successive *conjunctions* with the *Sun*, as observed from the *Earth*.

SYNTHESIS (chem.). 'Putting together'; the formation of a *compound* from its *elements* or simpler compounds.

SYNTHETIC (chem.). Artificially prepared from the component *elements* or simpler materials; not obtained directly from natural sources.

SYSTÈME INTERNATIONAL D'UNITES. An international system of units derived from the *M.K.S. System* in which the basic units are the *metre, kilogram, second, ampere,* degree *Kelvin* and *candela.* Derived units include the *joule, newton* and *watt.*

T

TACHOMETER. An instrument for measuring the rate of revolution of a revolving shaft.

TALC. *Hydrated* magnesium silicate, $3MgO.4SiO_2.H_2O$.

TALLOW. The rendered fat of animals, particularly cattle and sheep. Consists of various *glycerides*.

TANDEM GENERATOR. An *accelerator* of the *electrostatic generator* type. The name is derived from the fact that it consists essentially of two *Van der Graaff generators* in series, thus enabling twice as much *energy* to be obtained for a given accelerating *potential* as could be obtained from a single machine. Negative *ions* are accelerated from ground potential, the *electrons* are then 'stripped' off and the positive particles accelerated back to ground potential.

TANGENT GALVANOMETER. *Galvanometer* consisting of a coil of wire (n turns of radius r) held in a vertical plane parallel to the Earth's *magnetic field*, H, with a small magnetic needle pivoted at the centre of the coil which is free to rotate in a horizontal plane. A direct *electric current*, i, flowing through the coil produces a magnetic field at right angles to that of the Earth. The needle takes up the direction of the *resultant* of these two fields: if θ is the *angle* of deflection of the needle from its equilibrium position parallel to the Earth's field, then the current will be given by: $i = Hr \tan \theta / 2\pi n$

TANGENT OF AN ANGLE. See *trigonometrical ratios*.

TANGENT TO A CURVE. A straight line touching the curve at a point. The tangent to a *circle* at any point is at right angles to the radius of the circle at that point.

TANNIC ACID. White, *amorphous, soluble solid* extracted from gallnuts; a class of similar substances widely distributed in plants. Ester-like (see *esters*) in chemical constitution, of high *molecular weight*. Used in *tanning* and in the manufacture of *ink*.

TANNING. The conversion of raw animal hide into leather by the action of substances containing *tannin, tannic acid,* or other agents.

TANNINS. Class of complex *organic compounds* of vegetable origin. Consists of *mixtures* of *derivatives* of poly-hydroxy *benzoic acids*; e.g. *tannic acid*.

TANTALUM. Ta. Element. A.W. 180·948. At. No. 73. Greyish-white *metal*, very ductile and malleable. S.G. 16·6, m.p. 2996° C. Occurs together with niobium in a few rare *minerals*; extracted by *reduction* of the *oxide* with carbon in an electric furnace. Used for electric lamp *filaments,* in *alloys*, in cemented *carbides* for very hard tools, and in electrolytic *rectifiers*.

TAR. Name given to various dark, viscous *organic* materials; e.g. *coal-tar*.

TARTAR. See *argol*.

TARTAR EMETIC. Potassium antimonyl tartrate,
$$2K(SbO)C_4H_4O_6.H_2O.$$
Used in medicine and as a *mordant* in dyeing.

TARTARIC ACID. COOH.(CH.OH)$_2$.COOH. *Organic acid* existing in four stereoisomeric forms (see *stereoisomerism*). The common form, *d*-tartaric acid, obtained from *argol*, is a white, *soluble*, crystalline *solid*, m.p. 170° C. Used in dyeing, calico-printing, and in making *baking-powder* and effervescent 'health salts'.

TARTRATE. *Salt* of *tartaric acid*.

TAUTOMERISM, dynamic isomerism. The existence of a *compound* as a mixture of two *isomers* in equilibrium. The two forms are convertible one into another, and removal of one of the forms from the *mixture* results in the conversion of part of the other to restore the equilibrium; but each of the two forms may give rise to a stable series of *derivatives*. See also *keto-enol tautomerism*.

TEAR GASS, lachrymators. Substances which can be distributed in the form of a *vapour* or *smoke*, producing an irritating effect on the eyes.

TECHNETIUM, masurium. Tc. Element. At. No. 43. The most stable *isotope*, $^{99}_{43}$Tc., has a *half-life* of 5×10^5 years. Very rare.

TEKTITES. Small glass-like bodies whose chemical composition is unrelated to the geological formations in which they are found: believed to be associated with *meteorites* of extra-terrestrial origin. 'Carbonaceous' tektites contain traces of carbon *compounds*.

TELECOMMUNICATIONS. The telegraphic or telephonic communication of signals, images, or sounds by line or *radio* transmission.

TELEGRAPH. A method of transmitting messages over a distance by means of electrical impulses sent through wires. By depressing a key at the transmitting end, a circuit is closed and an *electric current* flows through the conducting wire or cable to the receiver; the dots and dashes of the Morse code being obtained by varying the length of time for which the current flows. At the receiving end, the feeble electrical impulses are made to operate a *relay*, which then closes a local circuit, carrying a larger current. This current either sounds a *buzzer*, a *telephone*-receiver, or causes the dots and dashes to be automatically recorded.

TELEMETER. Apparatus for recording a physical event at a distance.

TELEPHONE. The circuit, which is closed when the line is connected, consists essentially of a transmitter and a receiver connected by an electrical *conductor*. The transmitter is usually a carbon *microphone*, by means of which variable electrical impulses, depending on the nature of the *sounds* made into the microphone, are caused to flow through the circuit. In the telephone-receiver these impulses flow through a pair of coils of wire wound upon soft iron pole-pieces attached to the poles of a *magnet*; an iron diaphragm near these coils experiences variable pulls, and thus vibrates so as to produce sounds corresponding to those made into the microphone.

TELEPHOTO LENS. Combination of a *convex* and a *concave lens*, used to replace the ordinary lens of a *camera* in order to magnify the normal image. The size of the image obtained on the photographic *film* varies as the *focal length* of the lens. The telephoto lens system increases the effective focal length without the necessity of increasing the distance between the film and the lens.

TELESCOPE. Device for viewing magnified images of distant objects. In the refracting telescope the *objective* is a large *convex lens* which produces a small, bright, real *image*; this is viewed through the *eyepiece*, which is another convex lens, serving to magnify the image. In the reflecting telescope a large *concave* mirror is used instead of the objective lens to produce the real image, which is then magnified by the eyepiece. For terrestrial needs, these types of telescope are unsuitable, since the images formed are inverted; for terrestrial purposes telescopes are equipped with a further lens or *prism* which causes the image to be seen erect. See also *radio telescope*.

TELEVISION. The transmission of visible, moving images by electrical means. In 'closed circuit' television the transmission is by line; in 'broadcast' television it is by *radio* waves. In either case *light* waves are converted into electrical impulses by a television *camera* and reconverted into a picture on the screen of a *cathode ray tube* in the receiver. In broadcast television the transmitter consists of equipment for broadcasting modulated *radio frequency electromagnetic radiations* representing a complete television signal, which includes *sound*, vision, and synchronizing signals. The receiver is based on the *superheterodyne* principle, the sound and vision signals being fed to separate *intermediate frequency* amplifiers, *detectors*, and output stages.

TELLURIC. 1. Pertaining to the *Earth* (as a *planet*), or the earth or *soil*. 2. Derived from or containing tellurium.

TELLURIUM. Te. Element. A.W. 127·6. At. No. 52. Silvery-white, brittle non-metal, resembling sulphur in its chemical properties. S.G. 6·24, m.p. 452° C. Exists in several *allotropic forms*.

TEMPERATURE. The temperature of a body is a measure of its 'hotness', which can be defined as a property determining the rate at which *heat* will be transferred to or from it. Temperature is thus a measure of the *kinetic energy* of the *molecules*, *atoms*, or *ions* of which *matter* is composed. Measured in degrees, *Centigrade*, *Fahrenheit*, *Réaumur*, or *Kelvin*.

TEMPERATURE SCALE, INTERNATIONAL. A practical scale of *temperature* defined to conform as closely as possible to the thermodynamic *Centigrade scale*. The *ice* and *steam points* are first assigned the values 0° and 100° C. respectively. Other reproducible equilibrium temperatures are assigned numerical values from measurements using the *gas thermo-*

meter. Any temperature is then determined on this scale by using the stated interpolation instrument for the temperature range under investigation; e.g. for the range 0°–660° C. the interpolation instrument to be used is the platinum *resistance thermometer*. The instrument is calibrated at the fixed equilibrium temperatures according to a specified procedure.

TEMPERING OF STEEL. Imparting a definite degree of hardness to *steel* by heating to a definite *temperature* (which is sometimes determined by the *colour* which the steel assumes) and then *quenching*, i.e. cooling, in *oil* or *water*.

TEMPORARY HARDNESS OF WATER. Hardness of *water*, which is destroyed by *boiling*. See *hard water*.

TEMPORARY MAGNETISM, induced magnetism. *Magnetism* which a body (e.g. soft iron) possesses only by virtue of being in a *magnetic field* and which largely disappears on removing the body from the field.

TENSILE STRENGTH. Tenacity. The tensile (pulling) *stress* which has to be applied to a material to break it. Measured as a *force* per unit area; e.g. *dynes* per square centimetre; pounds or tons per square inch.

TENSOR. Quantity expressing the ratio in which the length of a *vector* is increased.

TERA-. Prefix denoting one million million (10^{12}).

TERBIUM. Tb. Element. A.W. 158·924. At. No. 65. See *lanthanides*.

TERMINAL VELOCITY. If a body free to move in a resisting medium is acted upon by a constant *force* (e.g. a body falling under the force of gravity through the atmosphere), the body accelerates until a certain terminal velocity is reached, after which the *velocity* remains constant.

TERNARY FISSION. A very rare form of *nuclear fission* as a result of which a heavy *nucleus* breaks up into three fragments of comparable *mass*. The term is also used for the more frequent case in which one of the three fragments (e.g. an *alpha-particle*) is much lighter than the others.

TERPENES. Class of *hydrocarbons* occurring in many fragrant *essential oils* of plants. Colourless *liquids*, generally with a pleasant smell; include pinene, $C_{10}H_{16}$, the chief ingredient of *turpentine*; and limonene, $C_{10}H_{16}$, found in the essential oils of oranges and lemons.

TERRESTRIAL MAGNETISM. See *magnetism, terrestrial*.

TERVALENT, trivalent. Having a *valency* of three.

TETRA-. Prefix denoting four, fourfold.

TETRAD. *Element* having a *valency* of four.

TETRAFLUOROETHYLENE. $CF_2 \cdot CF_2$. A fluorinated *olefine* which polymerizes (see *polymerization*) into a *thermoplastic* material with good electrical insulation properties (trade names 'Teflon', and 'Fluon').

TETRAHEDRON. Four-faced, *solid* figure, contained by four *triangles*; a *pyramid* with a triangular base.

TETRODE. *Thermionic valve* containing four *electrodes*; a *cathode*, an *anode* or plate, a *control grid*, and (between the two latter) a screen grid. The screen grid serves to prevent interaction between the control grid and the anode.

THALLIUM. Tl. Element. A.W. 204·37. At. No. 81. White malleable *metal* resembling lead. S.G. 11·85, m.p. 303·5° C.

THEINE. See *caffeine*.

THEODOLITE. Instrument for the measurement of *angles*, used in surveying. Consists essentially of a *telescope* moving along a circular scale graduated in degrees.

THEOREM. A statement or proposition which is proved by logical reasoning from given facts and justifiable assumptions.

THERAPEUTICS. Healing; remedial treatment of diseases.

THERM. Practical unit of quantity of *heat*; 100,000 *British thermal units*, 25,200,000 *calories*.

THERMAL CAPACITY. See *capacity, thermal*.

THERMAL CROSS-SECTION. A nuclear *cross-section* as measured with *thermal neutrons*.

THERMAL DIFFUSION. If a *temperature* gradient is maintained over a *volume* of *gas* containing *molecules* of different *masses*, the heavier molecules tend to diffuse down the temperature gradient, and the lighter molecules in the opposite direction. This forms the basis of a method of separating the different *isotopes* of an *element* in certain cases.

THERMAL DISSOCIATION. See *dissociation*.

THERMAL NEUTRONS. *Neutrons* of very slow speed and consequently of low *energy*. Their energy is of the same order as the thermal energy of the *atoms* or *molecules* of the substance through which they are passing; i.e. about 0·025 *electron-volts* which is equivalent to an average *velocity* of about 2200 metres per second. Thermal neutrons are responsible for numerous types of *nuclear reactions*, including *nuclear fission*.

THERMAL REACTOR. A *nuclear reactor* in which most of the *nuclear fissions* are caused by *thermal neutrons*.

THERMAL SPIKE. The zone of high *temperature* briefly produced in a substance along the path of a high *energy* particle or *nuclear fission* fragment.

THERMAL VALUE OF A CHEMICAL REACTION. Heat of reaction. The quantity of *heat* given out or absorbed in a *chemical reaction*, usually per *gram-equivalent* of reacting substances. See *Hess's law*.

THERMALIZE. To bring *neutrons* into thermal equilibrium with their surroundings: to reduce the *energy* of neutrons with a *moderator*: to produce *thermal neutrons*.

THERMION. *Ion* emitted by a hot body.

THERMIONIC VALVE, tube. A system of *electrodes* arranged in an evacuated *glass* or *metal* envelope. For special purposes a *gas* at low *pressure* may be introduced into the valve. The electrodes are: (1) a *cathode* which emits *electrons* when heated; (2) an *anode* or plate maintained at a positive *potential* with respect to the cathode; the electrons emitted by the latter are attracted to it. Most valves also contain a number of perforated electrodes or grids (see *control grid*) interposed between the cathode and anode, designed to control the flow of current through the valve. The cathode can be in the form of a *filament* heated by an *electric current* passing through it, or an electrode heated indirectly by a separate filament. See *diode, triode, tetrode, pentode*.

THERMIONICS. Branch of science dealing with the emission of *electrons* from substances under the action of *heat*, particularly the study and design of *thermionic valves*.

THERMISTOR. A *semiconductor*, the electrical *resistance* of which decreases rapidly with increase of *temperature*; e.g. the resistance may be of the order of 10^5 ohms at 20° C. and only 10 ohms at 100° C. Used as a sensitive *temperature*-measuring device and to compensate for temperature variations of other components in a circuit.

THERMIT, thermite. A mixture of aluminium powder and the *oxide* of a *metal*, e.g. iron oxide. When ignited by magnesium ribbon, a *chemical reaction* begins in which the aluminium combines with the oxygen of the oxide, forming aluminium oxide and the metal. A great quantity of *heat* is given out during the reaction, the reduced metal (see *reduction*) appearing in the molten state. The mixture is used for *welding* iron and *steel*, and in incendiary bombs; the principle is applied in the *extraction* of certain metals from their oxides (see *Goldschmidt process*).

THERMOCHEMISTRY. Branch of *physical chemistry* dealing with the quantities of *heat* absorbed or evolved during *chemical reactions*. See *Hess's law*.

THERMOCOUPLE. Instrument for the measurement of *temperature*. Consists of two wires of different *metals* joined at each end. One junction is at the point where the temperature is to be measured and the other is kept at a lower fixed temperature. Owing to this difference of temperature of the junctions, a thermo-electric *E.M.F.* is generated, causing an *electric current* to flow in the circuit (see *Seebeck effect*). This current can be measured by means of a *galvanometer* in the circuit, or the thermo-electric E.M.F. can be measured using a *potentiometer*.

THERMODYNAMIC TEMPERATURE SCALE. See *Kelvin scale of temperature*.

THERMODYNAMICS. The study of the general laws governing processes which involve *heat* changes and the conservation of *energy*.

THERMODYNAMICS, LAWS OF. 1. The law of the conservation of *energy*. In a system of constant *mass*, energy can be neither created nor destroyed. A special case of this general law is the principle of the *mechanical equivalent of heat*. 2. Heat cannot be transferred by any continuous, self-sustaining process from a colder to a hotter body. Or stated in terms of *entropy*; the entropy of a closed system increases with time. 3. See the *Nernst heat theorem*. The consequence of this law is that the *absolute zero* of temperature can never be attained.

THERMO-ELECTRIC POWER. The rate of change of the thermo-electric *E.M.F.* of a *thermocouple* circuit with the *temperature* of the hot junction.

THERMO-ELECTRICITY. *Electricity* produced by the direct conversion of *heat* energy into *electrical energy*. See *thermocouple*; *Thomson effect*.

THERMOGRAPH. Self-registering *thermometer*; apparatus which records *temperature* variations during a period of time on a *graph*.

THERMOMETER. Instrument for the measurement of *temperature*. Any physical property of a substance which varies with temperature can be used to measure the latter; e.g. the *volume* of a *liquid* or *gas* maintained under a fixed *pressure*; the pressure of a gas at constant volume; the electrical *resistance* of a *conductor*; the *E.M.F.* produced at a *thermocouple* junction, etc. The property chosen depends on the temperature range, the accuracy required, and the ease with which the instrument can be made and used. The common mercury thermometer depends upon the expansion of mercury with rise in temperature. The mercury is contained in a bulb attached to a narrow graduated sealed tube; the expansion of the mercury in the bulb causes a thin thread of it to rise in the tube. See also *gas thermometer*; *pyrometers*; *resistance thermometer*; *thermocouple*; *Beckmann thermometer*; *thermometer, clinical*; *thermometer, maximum and minimum*.

THERMOMETER, CLINICAL. Mercury *thermometer* designed to measure the *temperature* of the human body, and graduated to cover a range of a few degrees on either side of the normal body temperature. A constriction in the tube near the bulb causes the mercury thread to break when the thermometer is taken away from the warm body, and the mercury in the bulb starts to contract. The thread thus remains in the tube to indicate the maximum temperature reached, until it is shaken down.

THERMOMETER, MAXIMUM AND MINIMUM. Thermometer which records the highest and lowest *temperatures* reached during a period of time. Consists of a bulb filled with *alcohol*, which, by expansion, pushes a mercury thread along a fine tube, graduated in degrees. At each end of the mercury thread is a small *steel* 'index' which is pushed by the mercury; one is thus left at the farthest point reached by the mercury thread, corresponding to the maximum temperature, and the other at the lowest point.

THERMO-MILLIAMMETER. Instrument for measuring small alternating *electric currents*. The current passes through a wire made of *constantan* or platinum, which is in contact with or very close to a *thermocouple*. The thermocouple is connected to a sensitive *milliammeter*, the heat of the constantan wire producing a thermo-electric current in the thermocouple; this current is recorded by the milliammeter. In a more sensitive instrument, the heater wire and thermocouple are arranged in an evacuated *quartz* envelope.

THERMONUCLEAR BOMB. See *nuclear weapons*.

THERMONUCLEAR REACTION. A *nuclear fusion* reaction in which the interacting particles or *nuclei* possess sufficient *kinetic energy*, as a result of their thermal agitation, to initiate and sustain the process. The hydrogen bomb (see *nuclear weapons*) makes use of thermonuclear reactions by employing a fission bomb to attain the required *temperature*, which is in excess of 20×10^6 °C. Controlled thermonuclear reactions attempt to make use of fusion reactions in *deuterium* and *tritium* gas, at a temperature in the range 50×10^7 to 5×10^9 °C., for the purpose of generating *electrical energy*. The central problem in achieving this end is that of *containment*, i.e. separating the *plasma* (or high temperature ionized gas) from the walls of the containing vessel. In general, the plasma may be contained either by the use of externally applied *magnetic fields*, or by the magnetic fields produced by currents flowing in the plasma itself (see *pinch effect*). The nature and instabilities of these magnetic fields is the subject of contemporary research. The machines in which these experiments are carried out may be classified according to whether the *magnetic lines of force* of the containing field are closed- or open-ended. The closed field group include *torus*-shaped machines such as *ZETA*, while the open-ended machines include those using *magnetic mirrors* or rotating plasmas.

THERMOPILE. Instrument for detecting and measuring *heat* radiations. Consists of a number of rods of antimony and bismuth, connected alternately in series. When the junctions are exposed to heat, the thermo-electric current produced (see *thermocouple*) may be detected or measured by a sensitive *galvanometer*.

THERMOPLASTIC. Substance which becomes plastic on being heated; a *plastic* material which can be repeatedly melted or softened by heat without change of properties.

THERMOSETTING PLASTICS. *Plastics* which, having once been subjected to *heat* (and *pressure*), lose their plasticity.

THERMOSTAT. Instrument for maintaining a constant *temperature*, by the use of a device which cuts off the supply of *heat* when the required temperature is exceeded, and automatically restores the supply when the temperature falls below that required. Usually consists of a *bimetallic strip* so arranged that when it is heated (or cooled) the power supply contacts are opened (or closed).

THIAMIN(E). Aneurin. Vitamin B₁. $C_{12}H_{17}ON_4SCl$. Member of *vitamin* B complex, white crystalline powder, *soluble* in *water* and *alcohol*. Widely required by many living *organisms* for the *metabolism* of *carbohydrates*. Occurs in liver, milk, eggs, and fruit.

THIAZOLE. $S.CH:N.CH:CH$. Colourless, *volatile liquid*, b.p. 116·8° C., whose *molecule* consists of a five-membered ring. *Derivatives* used in dyestuffs and in medicine.

THIO-. Prefix denoting sulphur, in the naming of chemical *compounds*.

THIOKOLS*. *Rubber*-like *polymer* materials of the general formula $(RS_x)_n$, where R is an *organic bivalent radical*, and x is usually between 2 and 4. Very resistant to the swelling action of *oils*. Undergo a form of *vulcanization* on being heated with certain metallic *oxides*.

THIOUREA. Thiocarbamide. $NH_2CS.NH_2$. Colourless *organic compound*, m.p. 180° C. Used in the manufacture of thiourea-aldehyde *plastics*.

THIXOTROPY. Defined as the rate of change of *viscosity* with time. Certain *liquids*, e.g. some *paints*, possess the property of increasing in viscosity with the passage of time when the liquid is left undisturbed. On shaking, the viscosity returns to its original value.

THOMSON EFFECT, Kelvin effect. A *temperature* gradient along a conducting wire gives rose to an *electric potential* gradient along the wire.

THOMSON SCATTERING. The scattering of *photons* of *electromagnetic radiations* by *electrons* according to J. J. Thomson's formula.

THORIDES. Natural *radioactive isotopes* which occur in the *radioactive series* containing thorium.

THORIUM. Th. Element. A.W. 232·038. At. No. 90. Dark grey *radioactive metal*, S.G. 11·2, m.p. 1845° C. *Compounds* occur in *monazite*.

THRESHOLD. The lowest value of any stimulus, signal, or agency which will produce a specified effect. E.g. *threshold frequency*.

THRESHOLD FREQUENCY. *Light* incident on a *metal* surface will give rise to the emission of *electrons* (see *photo-electric effect*) only if the *frequency* of the light is greater than a certain *threshold* value which is characteristic of the metal used.

THROMBIN. An *enzyme* formed in the *blood* of vertebrates which acts upon *fibrogen* to form *fibrin*, therefore essential to the process of blood clotting. Thrombin is formed from a blood *protein*, prothrombin.

THROMBOCYTES. See *blood platelets*.

THRUST. The propulsive *force* produced by a *reaction propulsion* motor. Usually measured in *pounds*. See also *specific impulse*.

THULIUM. Tm. Element. A.W. 168·934. At. No. 69. See *lanthanides*.

THYMINE. 5-methyluracil. $C_5H_6N_2O_2$. One of the two *pyrimidine* bases occurring in the *nucleotides* of *deoxyribonucleic acid*, which plays a part in the formulation of the *genetic code*.

THYMOL, 3-hydroxy-*p*-cymene. $C_{10}H_{14}O$. *Organic compound* belonging to the *phenols*. White *crystals*, m.p. 51·5° C., b.p. 233·5° C. Smells of thyme. Occurs in many *essential oils*; used as a mild *antiseptic*.

THYRATRON. A gas-filled *thermionic valve* (usually a *triode*) in which a *voltage* applied to the *control grid* initiates, but does not limit, the *anode* current. Used as an *electronic* switch.

THYROXIN(E). $C_{15}H_{11}I_4NO_4$. Iodine containing *amino acid* produced by the thyroid gland.

TIDES are caused by the attraction exerted upon the seas by the *Moon*, and to a lesser extent by the *Sun*. At full and new moon the tidal force of the Sun is added to that of the Moon, caushing high spring tides; while at half-moons the forces are opposed, causing low neap tides.

TIMBRE. See *quality of sound*.

TIME MEASUREMENT. The unit of time is the *second* to which all time-measuring devices are ultimately referred. Such devices include the *pendulum* and the *quartz clock*. See also *year*.

TIME REFLECTION SYMMETRY. The proposition that any physical situation should be reversible in time. Known to hold for *strong nuclear interactions* and electromagnetic interactions, but some doubt remains as to its validity with respect to *weak nuclear interactions*. According to this principle, if time could be reversed (i.e. run backwards) the time reflection of a particular physical situation would correspond to what one would normally see by reflecting the situation in a space mirror, except that all the particles would be replaced by their *anti-particles*. Thus, if left-polarized (see *parity*) neutrinos exist, right-polarized anti-particles must also exist: experimental evidence appears to confirm this.

TIN. Sn. (Stannum.) Element. A.W. 118·69. At. No. 50. Silvery-white *metal*, S.G. 7·31, m.p. 231·85° C. Soft, malleable, and ductile. Un-affected by air or *water* at ordinary *temperatures*. Occurs in three *allotropic forms*, below 18° C. passes into 'grey tin', causing *tin plague*. Occurs as tin oxide, SnO_2, *cassiterite* or tinstone. Metal is extracted by heating the *oxide* with powdered carbon in a *reverberatory furnace*. Used for tin-plating and in many *alloys*.

TIN PLAGUE. Allotropic change (see *allotropy*) in which white tin changes into a grey, powdery form at low *temperatures*.

TIN PLATE. Iron coated with a thin layer of tin, by dipping into the molten *metal*.

TINCAL. Impure form of *borax*.

TINCTURE. An alcoholic extract or a *solution* in *alcohol*.

TINSTONE. See *cassiterite*.

TISSUE CULTURE. The preparation of fragments of the tissues or *cells of organisms* for biochemical examination *in vitro*. Tissue cultures are usually maintained in correctly balanced *physiological saline*.

TITANIUM. Ti. Element. A.W. 47·90, At. No. 22. Malleable and ductile *metal* resembling iron. S.G. 4·5, m.p. 1850° C. *Compounds* are fairly widely distributed in Nature, but the metal is difficult to extract. Used in *alloys*. The oxide, TiO_2, is used as a white *pigment*.

TITRATION. Operation forming the basis of *volumetric analysis*. The addition of measured amounts of a *solution* of one *reagent* from a *burette* to a definite amount of another reagent until the action between them is complete, i.e. till the second reagent is completely used up.

T.N.T. See *trinitrotoluene*.

TOBACCO MOSAIC VIRUS. TMV. A simple *virus* widely used in bio-chemical and biological studies, particularly concerning the trans-ference of the *genetic code*. The virus particle consists of a single helix of *ribonucleic acid* containing some 6400 *nucleotides*, coated with about 2200 *molecules* of a single *protein*, each molecule of which comprises a *polypeptide* chain of 158 *amino acids* in a known sequence.

TOCOPHEROL. Vitamin E. $C_{29}H_{50}O_2$. A *vitamin* which has been shown to prevent sterility in rats; its effect in human *metabolism* is not established.

TOLUENE, toluol. $C_6H_5CH_3$. *Hydrocarbon* of the *benzene* series. Colourless, inflammable *liquid* with a peculiar smell. B.p. 110° C. Occurs in *coal-tar*. Used as a starting-point in the preparation of *dyes*, drugs, *saccharin*, and *T.N.T.*

TOLUIDINE. $CH_3.C_6H_4.NH_2$. *Amine* derived from *toluene*. Exists in three isomeric (see *isomerism*) forms. Used for making *dyes*.

TOLUOL. See *toluene*.

TONE OF SOUND. See *quality of sound*.

TONNE. Metric ton; 1000 *kilograms*; 2204·62 lb., 0·9842 ton.

TOPAZ. Crystalline aluminium silicate and fluoride.

TOPOLOGY. A branch of *geometry* concerned with the way in which figures are 'connected', rather than with their shape or size. Topology is thus concerned with the geometrical factors which remain unchanged when an object undergoes a continuous deformation (e.g. by bending, stretching, or twisting) without tearing or breaking.

TOROIDAL. Having the shape of a toroid or *torus*.

TORQUE. See *couple*.

TORR. A unit of *pressure* used in the field of high vacuum: equivalent to 1mm. of mercury.

TORRICELLIAN VACUUM. Space, containing mercury *vapour*, which is produced at the top of a column of mercury when a long tube sealed at one end is filled with mercury and inverted in a trough of the metal. The mercury sinks in the tube until it is balanced by the atmospheric pressure (see *barometer*), the Torricellian vacuum being the space above it. See Fig. 1, page 30.

TORSION. 'Twisting' about an *axis*, produced by the action of two opposing *couples* acting in parallel *planes*.

TORSION BALANCE. If a wire is acted upon by a *couple* the *axis* of which coincides with the wire, the wire twists through an angle determined by the applied couple and the *rigidity modulus* of the wire. The amount of twist produced can thus be used to measure an applied *force*. In the torsion balance, the force to be measured is applied at right angles to, and at the end of, an arm attached to the wire.

TORUS (phys.). A 'doughnut' or anchor-ring shaped *solid* of circular or elliptical cross-section.

TOTAL INTERNAL REFLECTION. When *light* passes from one medium to another which is optically less dense, e.g. from *glass* to air (see *refraction* and *density, optical*), the *ray* is bent away from the *normal*. If the incident ray meets the surface at such an angle that the refracted ray must be bent away at an angle of more than 90°, the light cannot emerge at all, and is totally internally reflected.

TOURMALINE. Class of natural crystalline *minerals*, consisting of *silicates* of various *metals* and containing boron. The *crystals* show some interesting pyroelectric (see *pyroelectricity*), *piezo-electric* and optical *effects*.

TOXIC. Poisonous.

TOXICOLOGY. The study of poisons.

TOXIN. Poison; the name is generally confined to intensely poisonous substances produced by certain *bacteria*, which cause dangerous effects when they attack food or the human body.

TRACE ELEMENT. An *element* required in very small quantities by an *organism*. Such elements often form essential constituents of *enzymes*, *vitamins*, or *hormones*.

TRACER. See *radioactive tracing*.

TRAJECTORY. The path of a *projectile*.

TRANSDUCER. A device which receives waves (electrical, acoustical, or mechanical) from one or more media or transmission systems and supplies related waves (not necessarily of the same type as the input) to one or more other media or transmission systems. If the transducer derives *energy* from sources other than the input waves it is said to be 'active': if the input waves are the only source of energy it is said to be 'passive'.

TRANS-FORM. See *cis-trans isomerism*.

TRANSFORMATION CONSTANT. See *disintegration constant*.

TRANSFORMATION, NUCLEAR. The change of one *nuclide* into another.

TRANSFORMER. Device by which an *alternating current* of one *voltage* is changed to another voltage, without alteration in *frequency*. A step-up transformer, which increases the voltage and diminishes the current, consists in principle of an iron core on which is wound a *primary coil* of a small number of turns of thick, insulated wire; and, forming a separate circuit, a secondary coil of a larger number of turns of thin, insulated wire. When the low-voltage current is passed through the primary coil, it induces a current in the secondary (see *induction*) by producing an alternating *magnetic field* in the iron core. The ratio of the voltage in the primary to that in the secondary is very nearly equal to the ratio of the number of turns in the primary to that in the secondary. The step-down transformer works on the same principle, with the coils reversed.

TRANSISTOR. A *semiconductor* device capable of amplification in a similar manner to *thermionic valves*. Consists of two P-N *semiconductor junctions* back to back forming either a P-N-P or N-P-N structure. In a P-N-P transistor the thin central N-region is called the *base*, one P-region is called the *emitter*, the other the *collector*. In an N-P-N transistor the P-region is the base. In order to obtain amplification an N-P-N transistor is included in a circuit which supplies a positive *voltage* to the collector (N-region) and a negative voltage to the emitter (the other N-region). The collector in this type of transistor therefore corresponds to the *anode* of a thermionic valve while the emitter corresponds to the *cathode*. The base (P-region) is also positively biased and is analogous to the *control grid*. With this arrangement the large number of *electrons* in the emitter region are attracted to the P-layer, which, if it is sufficiently thin, will allow the electrons to pass through it and be attracted into the positive collector. The magnitude of the collector current will depend on the extent of the positive bias on the P-layer base. By suitable design the device can be made to give a collector current some 20–100 times the base current. The advantages of a transistor over a valve are that it is less bulky and fragile, that it requires no heater current, and that the voltage at the collector need only be a few volts. A P-N-P transistor works in an exactly analogous manner to an N-P-N device, but the collector current consists mainly of *holes* instead of electrons. The device described here is a *junction transistor*, as this type has almost entirely replaced the earlier 'point contact' transistor.

TRANSITION ELEMENTS. *Elements* which have chemical properties resembling those of their horizontal neighbours in the *periodic table*. These elements have incomplete inner electron *shells* and are characterized by their variable *valencies*: they occur in the middle of the long periods of the periodic table.

TRANSITION, NUCLEAR. A change in the configuration of an atomic *nucleus*. It may involve a *transformation* (e.g. by *alpha-* or *beta-particle* emission) or a change in *energy level* by the emission of a *gamma-ray*.

TRANSITION TEMPERATURE. 1. Transition point. The *temperature* at which one form of a polymorphous substance (see *polymorphism*) changes into another; the temperature at which both forms can co-exist. 2. See *super-conductivity*.

TRANSLATORY MOTION. Motion which involves a non-reciprocating movement of *matter* from one place to another.

TRANSLUCENT. Permitting the passage of *light* in such a way that an object cannot be seen clearly through the substance; e.g. frosted *glass*.

TRANSMISSION COEFFICIENT. Transmittance. When a *beam of light* (or other *electromagnetic radiation*) passes through a medium the radiation is absorbed to a greater or less extent (depending upon the medium and the *wave-length* of the radiation) and the intensity of the beam decreases. The ratio of the intensity after passing through unit distance of the medium to the original intensity is called the transmission coefficient.

TRANSMITTANCE. See *transmission coefficient*.

TRANSMUTATION OF ELEMENTS. Changing one chemical *element* into another. Once the aim of *alchemy*; subsequently held to be impossible; with the present knowledge of *radioactivity* and atomic structure it is seen that the process goes on continuously in *radioactive* elements. Artificial transmutation by suitable *nuclear reactions* forms the basis of experimental *nuclear physics*. See also *transition, nuclear*, and *transformation, nuclear*.

TRANSPARENT. Permitting the passage of *light* in such a way that objects can be seen clearly through the substance.

TRANSURANIC ELEMENTS. *Elements* beyond uranium in the *periodic table*; i.e. elements of *atomic number* greater than 92. Such elements do not occur in Nature, but may be obtained by suitable *nuclear reactions*; they are all *radioactive* and members of the *actinide* group. See Table 5, page 335.

TRANSVERSE. Cross-wise; in a direction at right angles to the length of the body under consideration.

TRANSVERSE WAVES. Waves in which the vibration or displacement takes place in a *plane* at right angles to the direction of propagation of the wave; e.g. *electromagnetic radiation*. See also *longitudinal waves*.

TRAPEZIUM. *Quadrilateral* having two of its sides parallel. The area of a trapezium having parallel sides *a* and *b* units in length, and vertical height *h* units is given by $\dfrac{h(a+b)}{2}$.

TRIAD. *Element* having a *valency* of three.

TRIANGLE. *Plane* figure bounded by three straight lines. The three *angles* total 180°. The area of any triangle is given by the following expressions: 1. Half the *product* of one of the sides and the perpendicular upon it from the opposite vertex ($\frac{1}{2} \times$ base $\times$ height). 2. Half the product of any two of the sides and the *sine* of the angle between them ($\frac{1}{2}$ *bc sin A*). 3. $\sqrt{s(s-a)\ (s-b)\ (s-c)}$, where *a*, *b*, and *c* are the lengths of the sides, and *s* is half the sum of *a*, *b*, and *c*.

TRIANGLE OF FORCES. If three *forces* acting at the same point can be represented in magnitude and direction by the sides of a *triangle* taken in order, they will be in *equilibrium*.

TRIANGLE OF VELOCITIES. If a body has three component *velocities* which can be represented in magnitude and direction by the sides of a *triangle* taken in order, the body will remain at rest.

TRIBASIC ACID. An *acid* having three *atoms* of *acidic hydrogen* in the *molecule*, thus giving rise to three possible series of *salts*; e.g. *phosphoric acid*, H_3PO_4, can give rise to trisodium phosphate, Na_3PO_4; disodium hydrogen phosphate, Na_2HPO_4, and sodium dihydrogen phosphate, NaH_2PO_4.

TRIBO-ELECTRICITY. See *electricity, frictional*.

TRIBOLUMINESCENCE. The emission of *light* when certain *crystals* (e.g. *cane-sugar*) are crushed.

TRICHLORETHYLENE. $CHCl:CCl_2$. Colourless *liquid*, b.p. 87° C.; widely used as industrial *solvent* and *anaesthetic*.

TRIGLYCERIDES. See *glycerides*.

TRIGONOMETRICAL RATIOS. If a perpendicular *AB* is drawn from any point on arm *OA* of an *angle AOB* to the other arm, the following ratios are constant for the particular angle: *AB/AO*, sine (sin *AOB*); *OB/AO*, cosine (cos *AOB*); *AB/OB*, tangent (tan *AOB*); *AO/AB*, cosecant (cosec *AOB*); *AO/OB*, secant (sec *AOB*); and *OB/AB*, cotangent (cot *AOB*). See Fig. 19, page 310.

TRIGONOMETRY. Branch of mathematics using the fact that numerous problems may be solved by the calculation of unknown parts (i.e. sides and *angles*) of a *triangle* when three parts are known. The solution of such problems is greatly assisted by the use of the *trigonometrical ratios*.

TRILLION. 10^{18}, a million million million (British); 10^{12}, a million million (American).

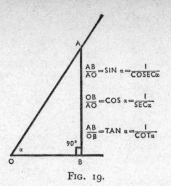

$$\frac{AB}{AO} = SIN\ \alpha = \frac{1}{COSEC\alpha}$$

$$\frac{OB}{AO} = COS\ \alpha = \frac{1}{SEC\alpha}$$

$$\frac{AB}{OB} = TAN\ \alpha = \frac{1}{COT\alpha}$$

Fig. 19.

TRIMER. A substance composed of *molecules* which are formed from three molecules of a *monomer*.

TRINITROTOLUENE, T.N.T. $C_7H_5(NO_2)_3$. Pale yellow, crystalline *solid*, made by the *nitration* of *toluene*. High explosive.

TRIODE. *Thermionic valve* containing three *electrodes*: an *anode* or plate, a *cathode*, and a *control grid*.

TRIOLEIN, olein. $(C_{17}H_{33}COO)_3.C_3H_5$. *Glyceride* of *oleic acid*; *liquid* oil which occurs in many natural *fats and oils*.

TRIPALMITIN, palmitin. $(C_{15}H_{31}COO)_3.C_3H_5$. *Glyceride* of *palmitic acid*; *solid*, fat-like substance which occurs in palm-oil and many other natural *fats and oils*.

TRIPLE POINT. The point at which the gaseous, *liquid*, and *solid phases* of a substance are in *equilibrium*. For a given substance, the triple point occurs at a unique set of values of the *temperature, pressure,* and *volume*.

TRISTEARIN, stearin. $(C_{17}H_{35}COO)_3.C_3H_5$. *Glyceride* of *stearic acid*; *solid*, fat-like substance which occurs in natural *fats*; formed by the hydrogenation of *triolein*. See *hydrogenation of oils*.

TRITIATED COMPOUND. A *compound* in which some hydrogen *atoms* have been replaced by *tritium*, so that it may be used in *radioactive tracing*.

TRITIUM. $T.^3_1H$. *Radioactive isotope* of hydrogen with *mass number* 3 and *atomic mass* 3·016. The *abundance* of tritium in natural hydrogen is only one *atom* in 10^{17}, and its half life is 12·5 years. It can, however, be made artificially in *nuclear reactors* and *tritiated compounds* are used in *radioactive tracing*.

TRITON. The *nucleus* of a *tritium atom*.

TRIVALENT, tervalent. Having a *valency* of three.

TROCHOTRON. A multi-*electrode thermionic valve* used as a *scaler*.

TRONA. Natural crystalline sodium sesquicarbonate,

$$Na_2CO_3.NaHCO_3.2H_2O.$$

TROPOPAUSE. The upper boundary of the *troposphere*, above which the *temperature* remains constant.

TROPOSPHERE. The lower part of the Earth's *atmosphere* in which *temperature* decreases with height, except for local areas of 'temperature inversion'.

TROTYL. See *trinitrotoluene*.

TROUTON'S RULE. The ratio of the latent heat of vaporization (see *heat, latent*) per *gram-molecule*, to the *boiling point* in degrees *Absolute* is a constant for all substances. The rule is only approximate.

TROY WEIGHT.

> 1 grain = 0·0648 gram.
> 20 grains = 1 scruple.
> 24 grains = 1 pennyweight.
> 3 scruples = 1 drachm.
> 8 drachms = 1 ounce troy = 1·1 ounce avoirdupois.

TRYPSIN. *Enzyme* produced by the pancreas. In the process of digestion, breaks up *proteins* into *amino-acids*.

TUBE OF FORCE. Theoretical concept. Tube formed by the *lines of force* drawn out into space through every point on a small closed curve upon the surface of a charged *conductor*.

TUNGSTEN. W. Wolfram. Element. A.W.183.85. At No. 74. Grey hard *metal*, ductile, malleable, and resistant to *corrosion*; S.G. 19·3, m.p. 3370° C. Occurs as *wolframite*, $FeWO_4$, and scheelite, $CaWO_4$. Obtained by converting the ore to the *oxide* and then reducing the latter. Used in *alloys*, in cemented *carbides* for hard tools, and for electric lamp *filaments*. The names *tungsten* and *wolfram* for this element were both officially recognized in 1951.

TUNING, RADIO. See *resonant circuit*.

TUNNEL DIODE. A *semiconductor* device which has negative *resistance* over a part of its operating range. Consists of a P-N *semiconductor junction* in which both the P- and N- regions contain very large numbers of impurity *atoms*, thus producing a high *potential* barrier at the junction. If a small *voltage* is applied to the device, positive at the P- region, an *electron* current will flow (despite the high potential barrier) as a result of the *tunnel effect*. After a certain voltage has been reached this effect is reduced and the current declines with increasing voltage, thus exhibiting the negative resistance characteristic. At higher voltages the normal *majority carrier* current flows and the current again increases with voltage. Used in switching circuits and where low noise amplification is required up to *frequencies* of about 1,000 *megacycles* per second.

TUNNEL EFFECT. The passage of an *electron* through a narrow *potential* barrier in a *semiconductor*, despite the fact that, according to classical *mechanics*, the electron does not possess sufficient *energy* to surmount the barrier. Explained by *quantum mechanics* on the assumption that electrons are not completely localized in *space*, a part of the energy of the wave associated with the electron being able to 'tunnel' through the barrier.

TURBINE. Any motor in which a shaft is steadily rotated by the impact of a current of *steam*, air, *water*, or other *fluid* directed from jets or nozzles upon blades of a wheel.

TURBO-GENERATOR. A steam *turbine* coupled to an electric *generator* for the production of *electric power*. Usual arrangement in a 'conventional' power station.

TURBULENT FLOW. The type of *fluid* flow in which the motion at any point varies rapidly in direction and magnitude.

TURPENTINE, oil of turpentine. *Liquid* extracted by *distillation* of the *resin* of pine trees. B.p. 155°–165° C. Composed chiefly of pinene (see *terpenes*). Used as a *solvent*.

TURQUOISE. Natural basic aluminium phosphate, coloured blue or green by traces of copper.

TWADDELL SCALE of *specific gravity* of *liquids*. Degrees Twaddell = 200 (S.G. − 1); S.G. = 1 + Degrees Twaddell/200.

TYNDALL EFFECT. The *scattering of light* by particles of *matter* in the path of the light, thus making a visible 'beam', such as is caused by a *ray* of light illuminating particles of dust floating in the air of a room.

TYPE METAL. *Alloy* of 60% lead, 30% antimony, and 10% tin. Owing to the presence of antimony, expands on solidifying and thus gives a sharp cast.

U

UDELL, aludel. Earthenware receiver for condensing iodine *vapour*; shaped like a short pipe with a constricted end.

ULTRA-CENTRIFUGE. High speed *centrifuge*. Used in the determination of the *molecular weights* of large *molecules* in high *polymers* and *proteins*.

ULTRA-HIGH FREQUENCIES. U.H.F. *Radio frequencies* in the range 300 to 3000 *megacycles* per second.

ULTRAMARINE. Artificial form of *lapis lazuli*, made by heating together *clay*, *sodium sulphate*, carbon, and sulphur.

ULTRAMICROSCOPE. Instrument, making use of the *Tyndall effect* for showing the presence of particles which are too small to be seen with the ordinary *microscope*. A powerful *beam* of *light* is brought to a focus in the *liquid* which is examined; suspended particles appear as bright specks by *scattering the light*.

ULTRASONIC FREQUENCY. A *frequency* in excess of about 20,000 cycles per second.

ULTRASONIC GENERATOR. A device for the production of pressure waves of *ultrasonic frequency*.

ULTRASONICS. Supersonics. The study of pressure waves which are of the same nature as *sound* waves, but the *frequency* of which are above the audible limit.

ULTRA-VIOLET MICROSCOPE. A *microscope* in which the object is illuminated by *ultra-violet radiation*. *Quartz* lenses are used and the image is recorded photographically. As ultra-violet radiation is of shorter *wave-length* than visible *light*, greater magnification can be obtained than with an optical microscope.

ULTRA-VIOLET RADIATION. *Electromagnetic radiation* in the *wave-length* range of approximately 4×10^{-5} cm. to 5×10^{-7} cm.; i.e. between visible *light* waves and *X-rays*. The longest ultra-violet waves have wave-lengths just shorter than those of violet light, the shortest perceptible by the human eye. Affect the photographic plate; their action on *ergosterol* in the human body produces *vitamin* D. Radiation from the *Sun* is rich in such rays; they may be produced artificially by the *mercury vapour lamp*.

UMBRA. Region of complete *shadow*.

UNCERTAINTY PRINCIPLE. Indeterminancy principle. It is impossible to determine with accuracy both the position and the *momentum* of a particle (e.g. an *electron*) simultaneously. The more accurately the position is known, the less accurately can the momentum be determined. The principle, which was first stated by Heisenberg, arises from the dual particle/wave nature of *matter*. See *De Broglie wave-length*.

UNFILLED APERTURE. A method of constructing a *radio telescope* in which two *aerials* of different shapes are combined into one *radio interferometer* in such a way that only two perpendicular arms of the aerial system are built, giving the effect of two large apertures. The two arms may be spaced at varying distances apart, or they may be superimposed one upon another as in the 'Mills Cross' radio telescope. Unfilled aperture telescopes are suitable for use at long *wave-lengths*.

UNIAXIAL CRYSTAL. Doubly refracting *crystal* possessing only one *optic axis*.

UNICELLULAR. Said of an *organism* which consists of only one *cell* (e.g. *bacteria*, protozoa, etc.)

UNIFIED FIELD THEORY. A theory which attempts to describe the electromagnetic and *gravitational fields* in one set of *equations*. No such satisfactory theory has yet been devised.

UNIT. A quantity or dimension adopted as a standard of measurement.

UNIT QUANTITY. E.g. unit length; a length of one, in whatever system of units is specified.

UNITY (math.). One.

UNIVALENT (chem.). Monovalent. Having a *valency* of one.

UNSATURATED COMPOUND (chem.). A *compound* having some of the *atoms* in its *molecule* linked by more than one *valency bond*; a compound which can form *addition compounds*.

UNSTABLE (chem.). Easily decomposed.

UNSTABLE EQUILIBRIUM. See *stable equilibrium*.

UPPER ATMOSPHERE. The upper *atmosphere* of the *Earth* is usually taken to include its gaseous envelope from 30 *kilometres* upwards (i.e. that part of the atmosphere which is inaccessible to direct observations by balloons). Information obtained from *space probes* and artificial Earth *satellites* has indicated the following *densities* and *temperatures*.

Height (Km)	Density gm/c.c.	Temperature °A
50	$1\cdot0 \times 10^{-6}$	270
100	$4\cdot8 \times 10^{-10}$	212
200	$3\cdot6 \times 10^{-15}$	1230
300	$3\cdot3 \times 10^{-14}$	1360
400	$5\cdot1 \times 10^{-15}$	1440
600	$3\cdot4 \times 10^{-15}$	1480
800	$4\cdot6 \times 10^{-16}$	1480

Up to about 100 km. the composition of the upper atmosphere is similar to that at ground level (see *atmosphere*). Above this height the *dissociation* of oxygen into *atoms* is almost complete, and at above 150 km. the nitrogen separates out owing to its greater *mass* so that monatomic oxygen predominates. There is considerable *ionization* in the upper atmosphere as a result of solar *ultra-violet radiation* and *X-rays* See *ionosphere*.

URACIL. Pyrimidinedione. $C_4H_4N_2O_2$. A *pyrimidine* base which occurs in the *nucleotides* of *ribonucleic acid*.

URANIUM. U. Naturally occurring *radioactive element*. A.W. 238·03, At. No. 92. Hard white *metal*, S.G. 18·68, m.p. 1150° C. The natural element consists of 99·28% $^{238}_{92}$U (*half-life* $4\cdot5 \times 10^9$ years) and 0·71% $^{235}_{92}$U (half-life $7\cdot1 \times 10^8$ years). The latter *isotope* is capable of sustaining a nuclear *chain reaction* and is of greater importance in *nuclear reactors* and *nuclear weapons*.

URANUS (Astr.). *Planet* possessing five *satellites*, with its *orbit* lying between those of *Saturn* and *Neptune*. Mean distance from the *Sun*, 1783·1 million miles. *Sidereal period* ('year') 84 years. *Mass* approximately 14·52 times that of the *Earth*, diameter 29,270 miles. Surface temperature, about − 180° C.

URAO. Natural crystalline sodium sesquicarbonate,
$$Na_2CO_3.NaHCO_3.2H_2O.$$

UREA, carbamide. $CO(NH_2)_2$. White, crystalline, *organic compound*, m.p. 132° C. Occurs in the urine. The first organic compound to be prepared artificially. Used as a *fertilizer* and in *urea-formaldehyde resins*.

UREA-FORMALDEHYDE RESINS. *Thermosetting resins* with good *oil* resistant properties, produced by the condensation *polymerization* of *urea* and *formaldehyde*.

UREASE. An *enzyme* capable of splitting *urea* into *ammonia* and *water*.

URETHANE RESINS. A group of synthetic *resins* based on urethane (ethyl carbamate), $NH_2COOC_2H_5$. Used in lacquers, varnishes and foams.

URIC ACID. $C_5H_4O_3N_4$. *Organic acid*, belonging to the *purine* group; colourless, crystalline *solid*, slightly *soluble* in *water*. Occurs in very small amounts in the urine of some animals as a breakdown product of *amino acids* and *nucleic acids*. Sodium and potassium *salts* of the acid are deposited in the joints in cases of gout.

UROTROPINE. See *hexamethylene tetramine*.

V

VACANCY. Schottky defect. An irregularity which occurs in a *crystal lattice* when a site normally occupied by an *atom* or *ion* is unoccupied. See *defect*.

VACCINE. A preparation containing *viruses* or other *micro-organisms* (either killed or of attenuated virulence) which is introduced into the human system to stimulate the formation of *antibodies*. In this way immunity (partial or complete) to subsequent infection by this type of micro-organism is conferred.

VACUUM. *Space* in which there are no *molecules* or *atoms*. A perfect vacuum is unobtainable, since every material which surrounds a space has a definite *vapour pressure*. The term is generally taken to mean a space containing air or other *gas* at very low *pressure*. 'Ultra-high' vacua (i.e. vacua in which the pressure does not exceed 10^{-9} *Torr*) occur naturally at heights of more than 800 Kilometres above the *Earth's* surface, and by special techniques pressures of 10^{-12} Torr can be achieved in the laboratory.

VACUUM DISTILLATION. The process of *distillation* carried out at a reduced *pressure*. The reduction in pressure is accompanied by a depression in the *boiling point* of the substance to be distilled, thus lower *temperatures* can be employed. This process therefore enables substances to be distilled which at normal pressures would decompose.

VACUUM TUBE. See *thermionic valve*; *discharge in gases*.

VALENCE BAND. The range of energies (see *energy bands*) in a *semi-conductor* corresponding to states which can be occupied by the *valency electrons* which bind the *crystal* together. Electrons missing from the valence band give rise to *holes*.

VALENCY. The combining power of an *atom*; the number of hydrogen atoms which an atom will combine with or replace. E.g. the valency of oxygen in water, H_2O, is 2.

VALENCY BOND. The link holding *atoms* together in a *molecule*. In the case of two *univalent* atoms joined together, a single valency bond holds them together; it is possible for an atom to satisfy two or three valency bonds of another atom, giving rise to a *double* or triple *bond*.

VALENCY ELECTRON. An outer *electron* of an *atom* which takes part in formation of a *valency bond*.

VALENCY, ELECTRONIC THEORY OF. An explanation of *valency* on the basis of modern views on atomic structure (see *atom*, *structure of*), and particularly on the assumption that certain arrangements of outer *electrons* in *atoms* (e.g. *octets* or outer *shells* of 8 electrons) are stable and tend to be formed by the transfer or sharing of electrons between atoms. The chief types of linkage are: (1) electrovalent bonds formed by the transfer of electrons from one atom to another; the atom which loses an electron becomes a positive *ion*, and the other a negative *ion*. This provides an explanation of the behaviour of *electrolytes*. (2) Covalent bonds. The sharing of a pair of electrons, one being provided by each atom. This applies to many non-ionizable bonds, e.g. those in *organic compounds*. If both electrons in a covalent bond are donated by the same atom, the bond is referred to as a co-ordinate or dative bond. Many bonds possess electronic configurations intermediate between the above forms. See *resonance* (chem.).

VALVE, WIRELESS. See *thermionic valve*.

VAN ALLEN RADIATION BELTS. Two belts of charged particles trapped within the Earth's *magnetic field* which were discovered by J. Van Allen in 1958 from the results of artificial *satellite* and *space probe* experiments. The inner belt, ranging from 1500 to 3500 miles above the Earth's surface, is believed to consist of secondary charged particles emitted by the Earth's *atmosphere* as a consequence of the impact of *cosmic rays*. The outer belt lies between 8000 and 12,000 miles above the Earth, and it is believed that the particles it contains originate from the *Sun*.

VAN DE GRAAFF GENERATOR. *Electrostatic generator* used for accelerating charged particles of atomic magnitudes, e.g. *protons*, to high *energies*.

VAN DER WAALS' EQUATION OF STATE. $\left(p + \dfrac{a}{v^2} \right)(v - b) = RT$ for a *gram-molecule* of a substance in the gaseous and *liquid phases* where $p = pressure$, $v = volume$, $T = absolute\ temperature$, $R =$ the *gas constant*; $\dfrac{a}{v^2}$ is a correction for the mutual attraction of the *molecules*, and b is a correction for the actual volume of the molecules themselves. The equation represents the behaviour of ordinary *gases* more correctly than the *perfect gas* equation $pv = RT$.

VAN DER WAALS' FORCE. Attractive *force* existing between *atoms* or *molecules* of all substances. The force arises as a result of *electrons* in neighbouring atoms or molecules (see *atom, structure of*) moving in sympathy with one another. This force is responsible for the term a/v^2 in *van der Waals' equation of state*. In many substances this force is small compared with the other inter-atomic attractive and repulsive forces present.

VANADIUM. V. Element. A.W. 50·942. At. No. 23. Very hard white *metal*, S.G. 5·966, m.p. 1715° C. Occurs in a few rather rare *minerals*. Used in *alloys*.

VAN'T HOFF'S LAW. The *osmotic pressure* of a dilute *solution* is equal to the *pressure* which the *solute* would exert in the gaseous state, if it occupied a *volume* equal to the volume of the solution, at the same *temperature*.

VAPOUR. Substance in the gaseous state, which may be liquefied by increasing the *pressure* without altering the *temperature*. A *gas* below its *critical temperature*.

VAPOUR DENSITY. A measure of the *density* of a gas or *vapour*; usually given relative to oxygen or hydrogen. The latter is the ratio of the *weight* of a certain *volume* of the gas to the weight of an equal volume of hydrogen, measured under the same conditions of *temperature* and *pressure*. Numerically this ratio is equal to half the *molecular weight* of the gas.

VAPOUR PRESSURE. All *liquids* and *solids* give off *vapour*, consisting of *molecules* of the substance. If the substance is in an enclosed space, the *pressure* of the vapour will reach a maximum which depends only upon the nature of the substance and the *temperature*; the vapour is then saturated and its pressure is the *saturated vapour pressure*.

VAREC, kelp. *Ash* of seaweed, from which iodine is extracted.

VARIABLE (math.). A symbol or term which assumes, or to which may be assigned, different numerical values.

VARIATION (math.). If a quantity y is some *function* of another quantity x, ($y=f(x)$), then, as x varies, y varies in a manner determined by the function. If $f(x) = x \times$ a constant, then y is said to vary directly as x, or to be directly proportional to x; $y \propto x$. If $f(x) = $ constant$/x$, y is said to vary inversely as x, or to be inversely proportional to x; $y \propto 1/x$.

VASELINE*. See *petrolatum*.

VAT DYES. Class of *insoluble dyes* which are applied by first reducing them to leuco-compounds which are *soluble* in *alkalis*. The *solution* is applied to the material, and the insoluble dye is regenerated in the fibres by *oxidation*. *Indigo* and many synthetic dyes belong to this class.

VECTOR. Any physical quantity which requires a direction to be stated in order to define it completely. E.g. *velocity*.

VECTORS, PARALLELOGRAM LAW OF. If a particle is under the action of two like *vector* quantities which are represented by the two sides of a *parallelogram* drawn from a point, the *resultant* of the two vectors is represented in magnitude and direction by the diagonal of the parallelogram drawn through the point.

VECTORS, TRIANGLE LAW OF. If a particle is acted upon by two *vector* quantities represented by two sides of a *triangle* taken in order, the *resultant* vector is represented by the third side of the triangle.

VELOCITIES, PARALLELOGRAM OF. A special case of the parallelogram of *vectors*. See *parallelogram of velocities*.

VELOCITIES, TRIANGLE OF. A special case of the triangle of *vectors*. See *triangle of velocities*.

VELOCITY. Rate of motion in a given direction; measured as length per unit time.

VELOCITY MODULATION. The *modulation* of the *velocity* of a stream of *electrons* by alternately accelerating and decelerating them. See also *klystron*.

VELOCITY RATIO OF A MACHINE. The ratio of the distance through which the point of application of the applied *force* moves, to the distance through which the point of application of the resistance moves in the same time. For an 'ideal' machine which requires no *energy* to move its component parts, the velocity ratio is equal to the *mechanical advantage*.

VELOCITY, RELATIVE. The *velocity* of one body relative to another is the rate at which the first body is changing its position with respect to the second. If the velocities of two bodies are represented by two sides of a *triangle* taken in order, their relative velocity is represented by the third side.

VENETIAN WHITE. A mixture of *white lead* and barium sulphate, $BaSO_4$, in equal parts. Used in *paints*

VENUS (Astr.). *Planet* with its *orbit* between those of *Mercury* and the *Earth*. Mean distance from the Sun, 67·24 million miles. *Sidereal period* ('year'), 224·701 days. *Mass*, approximately 0·815 that of the Earth, diameter 7640 miles. There is no evidence of oxygen in the *atmosphere* of the planet, but the Mariner *space probe* indicated that its surface temperature is about 800° F. and that it is covered by a dense cloud layer with freezing temperatures high up in the atmosphere.

VERDIGRIS. Green deposit formed upon copper; consists of *basic* copper carbonate or sulphate of variable composition.

VERMILION. Scarlet form of mercuric sulphide, HgS; used as a *pigment*.

VERNIER. Device for measuring subdivisons of a scale. For a scale graduated in (say) inches and tenths, a vernier consists of a scale which slides alongside of the main scale, and on which a length of nine-tenths of an inch is subdivided into ten equal parts. Each vernier division is thus 0·9 of an inch. If it is desired to measure a length *AB*, the main scale is placed with its zero mark at *A*, and the vernier scale is slid till its zero mark (the '*V*' of the vernier) is at *B*. By noting which division on the vernier scale is exactly in line with a division on the main scale, the second decimal place of the length *AB* is obtained. Thus, if *B* falls between 4·6 and 4·7 inches on the main scale, and the fourth division on the vernier scale is just in line with a main scale division line, the length *AB* is 4·64 inches. See Fig. 20.

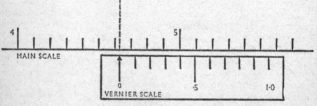

FIG. 20.

VERONAL. Diethylbarbituric acid; member of the *barbiturate* group of drugs, used as a *hypnotic*.

VERY HIGH FREQUENCIES. VHF. *Radio frequencies* in the range 30 to 300 *megacycles* per second.

VESICANT. Blister-producing.

VIBRATION, PLANE OF. See *polarization of light*.

VIDEO FREQUENCY SIGNAL. The signal which transmits the picture and synchronizing information in a *television* system.

VINASSE. Residual *liquid* obtained after *fermentation* and *distillation* of beetroot molasses. Used as a source of *potassium carbonate*.

VINEGAR. *Liquid* containing 3%–6% *acetic acid*, obtained by the *oxidation* of *ethyl alcohol* by the action of *bacteria* on wine, beer, or fermented wort.

VINYL GROUP. The *unsaturated univalent radical* $CH_2:CH$. Vinyl *compounds*, e.g. vinyl chloride, $CH_2:CHCl$, often readily undergo *polymerization* forming products from which important *plastics* and artificial textile fibres are made. See *polyvinyl chloride* and *polyvinyl acetate*.

VIRGIN NEUTRONS. *Neutrons*, produced by any means, before they have experienced a collision.

VIROLOGY. The study of *viruses*.

VIRTUAL IMAGE. See *image, virtual*.

VIRTUAL STATE. In *classical physics* a *force* between bodies not in contact (e.g. electrostatic repulsion) is represented by a *field*. In *quantum mechanics* this force may be represented by an exchange of particles between the interacting bodies. The exchanged particle is not in a 'real' state, however, although its properties can be calculated; such a particle is described as existing in the virtual state. E.g. electrically charged particles may be visualized as interacting as the result of the exchange of virtual *photons*. A virtual particle which is responsible for a force can, by the addition of *energy* to the system, be converted into a real particle. The virtual state is made possible by the concept of indeterminism expressed in the *uncertainty principle*.

VIRTUAL WORK. If a body, acted upon by a system of *forces*, is imagined to undergo a small displacement, then in general the forces will do *work*, termed the virtual work of the forces. If the body is in *equilibrium*, the total virtual work done is zero. This principle of virtual work is used to determine the positions of equilibrium of a body or a system of bodies under the action of given forces, and to determine relations between the forces acting on such a system in a given equilibrium position.

VIRUS. A disease-producing particle, too small to be seen by an optical *microscope* but visible with an *electron microscope*. Viruses are only capable of multiplication within a living *cell*, each type of virus requiring a specific host cell. The simplest viruses consist of a single helical strand of *ribonucleic acid* coated with *protein molecules* (see *tobacco mosaic virus*). The active principle of these viruses resides in the RNA as it is only this part of the particle which enters the cell. Other viruses are considerably more complex and may be up to 0·2 *microns* in diameter.

Viruses are considered to be on the borderline between the animate and the inanimate. See also *bacteriophage*.

VISCOMETER. Instrument for the measurement of *viscosity*.

VISCOSE. Thick, treacly, brownish *liquid*, consisting mainly of a *solution* of cellulose *xanthate* in dilute *sodium hydroxide*. Made from *cellulose* by the action of sodium hydroxide and *carbon disulphide*. Used for the production of viscose *rayon* and of cellulose film, of the type used for transparent wrappings.

VISCOSE RAYON. See *rayon*.

VISCOSITY. The property of a *fluid* whereby it tends to resist relative motion within itself. If different layers of a fluid are moving with different *velocities*, *viscous forces* come into play, tending to slow down the faster-moving layers and to increase the velocity of the slower-moving layers. For two parallel layers in the direction of flow, a short distance apart, this viscous force is proportional to the velocity gradient between the layers. The constant of proportionality is called the coefficient of viscosity of the fluid. The *C.G.S. unit* of measurement of viscosity is the *poise*.

VISCOSITY, KINEMATIC. The ratio of the coefficient of *viscosity* to the *density* of a *fluid*.

VISCOUS. Having high *viscosity*; a *liquid* which drags in a treacle-like manner.

VISUAL PURPLE. See *rhodopsin*.

VITALISTIC THEORY. The view that life, and all consequent biological phenomena, are due to a 'vital force'.

VITAMINS. Accessory food factors. A group of organic substances, occurring in various foods, which are necessary for a normal diet. Absence or shortage leads to various deficiency diseases. Before the chemical nature of any of the vitamins was known, they were named by the letters of the alphabet. Vitamin A, $C_{20}H_{29}OH$, occurs in milk, butter, green vegetables, and in liver, especially of fish. Deficiency causes 'night-blindness' (see *rhodopsin*) and ultimately more serious eye troubles; the resistance of the mucous membranes to infection also decreases. This vitamin can be made in the body from *carotene*. Vitamin B, originally regarded as a single substance, has been shown to be a whole group of *compounds* termed the vitamin B complex; these occur in wheat-germ, *yeast*, and other sources. B_1, *thiamin*, protects from neuritis, muscular weakness, and digestive disturbances; serious deficiency causes beri-beri. B_2, *riboflavin*, (also known as vitamin G) promotes growth in the young and probably plays an important part in the health of the skin. B_6, *pyridoxine*, is believed to be important in the utilization of *unsaturated fatty acids*. B_{12}, *cobalamine*, is required for the formation of *red blood cells*. See also other members of the complex; *nicotinic acid, pantothenic acid, biotin*, and *choline*. Vitamin C, *ascorbic acid*, occurs in the juice of lemons and oranges and in fresh vegetables; deficiency causes scurvy. Vitamin D consists of several different compounds, all of which are *sterols*. The most important is *calciferol* which is formed by the action of *ultra-violet radiation* on *ergosterol*. It controls the deposition of calcium compounds in the body; deficiency causes rickets. Vitamin E, *tocopherol*, is used to prevent abortion but its precise function in man is not known. Vitamin F, see *linoleic acid*. Vitamin K consists of naphthoquinone compounds whose deficiency causes haemorrhage.

VITREOSIL (reg. trade mark). Translucent form of *silica*, SiO_2, prepared from sand. Used for making laboratory apparatus which is required to withstand large and sudden changes in *temperature*; does not crack at such changes owing to very low expansion.

VITREOUS. Pertaining to, composed of, or resembling *glass*.

VITRIOL. Concentrated *sulphuric acid*, H_2SO_4, oil of vitriol; *copper sulphate*, $CuSO_4.5H_2O$, blue vitriol; *ferrous sulphate*, $FeSO_4.7H_2O$, green vitriol; zinc sulphate, $ZnSO_4.7H_2O$, white vitriol.

VOLATILE. Passing readily into *vapour*; having a high *vapour pressure*.

VOLT. Unit of *electromotive force* and *potential difference*. The absolute volt is 10^8 *electromagnetic units* of potential, and is that potential difference which, applied across the ends of a *conductor* having resistance of 1 absolute *ohm*, causes a current of 1 absolute *ampere* to flow. The former international volt was similarly defined in terms of the international ohm and international ampere. 1 international volt $= 1 \cdot 0035$ absolute volts.

VOLTAGE. The *electromotive force* of a supply of electricity, measured in *volts*.

VOLTAIC CELL. See *cell* (phys.).

VOLTAIC PILE. Earliest electric *battery*, devised by Volta. A number of *cells* joined in series, each consisting of a sheet of zinc and copper separated by a piece of cloth moistened with dilute *sulphuric acid*.

VOLTAMETER. Electrolytic cell in which a *metal*, generally silver or copper, is deposited by *electrolysis* of a *salt* of the metal upon the *cathode*. From the increase in *weight* of the cathode and a knowledge of the *electrochemical equivalent* of the metal, the quantity of electricity which has passed through the circuit may be found.

VOLTMETER. Instrument for measuring the *potential difference* between two points. In principle consists of an arrangement similar to an *ammeter* with a high *resistance* in series incorporated in the instrument, the scale being calibrated in *volts*. When the instrument is connected in parallel between the points where the P.D. is being measured, very little current flows through it, and a correct reading of the *voltage* is obtained.

VOLUME. The measure of bulk or space occupied by a body.

VOLUME, BRITISH UNITS OF.

> *Solids:* 1728 cubic inches = 1 cubic foot.
> 27 cubic feet = 1 cubic yard.
> (1 cubic inch = 16·387 c.c.)

> *Liquids :* 4 gills = 1 pint, 0·5682 litre.
> 2 pints = 1 quart.
> 4 quarts = 1 gallon, 4·546 litres.

VOLUME, METRIC UNITS OF.
> 1000 cubic millimetres = 1 cubic centimetre.
> 1000 c.c. = 1 *litre* very nearly.
> 1,000,000 c.c. = 1 *stere.*

VOLUMETRIC ANALYSIS. A group of methods of *quantitative chemical analysis* involving the measurement of *volumes* of the reacting substances. The amount of a substance present is determined by finding the volume of a *solution* of another substance, of known *concentration,* which is required to react with it. The added volume is measured by adding the reacting solution from a *burette;* the completion of the reaction is often shown by a suitable *indicator.*

VULCANITE. Hard insulating material made by the action of *rubber* on sulphur.

VULCANIZED RUBBER. Product obtained by heating *rubber* with sulphur.

W

WASHING-SODA. Crystalline *sodium carbonate,* $Na_2CO_3.10H_2O$.

WATER. H_2O. The normal *oxide* of hydrogen. Natural water (river, spring, rain, etc.) is never quite pure but contains dissolved substances. Pure water is a colourless, odourless *liquid,* m.p. 0° C., b.p. 100° C., which has a maximum *density* at 4° C. of 1·000 grams per c.c. Liquid water consists of associated *molecules,* $(H_2O)_n$.

WATER EQUIVALENT (phys.). See *heat capacity.*

WATER, EXPANSION OF. *Water* on cooling, reaches its maximum *density* at very nearly 4° C. At this *temperature* its density is, by definition, 1·000 gm. per millilitre (1/1000 of a *litre*); it then expands as its temperature falls to 0° C., the density at 0° being 0·99987; on freezing, it expands still further, giving *ice* with a density of 0·9168 at 0° C. This accounts for the bursting of water-pipes in frosts.

WATER GAS. *Fuel gas* obtained by the action of *steam* on glowing hot *coke,* giving *carbon monoxide* and hydrogen. The formation of water gas is accompanied by absorption of *heat* (an *endothermic* reaction); thus the coke is rapidly cooled and has to be re-heated at intervals by a blast of hot air, which causes partial *combustion* and makes the coke incandescent again.

WATER GLASS. Sodium silicate, Na_2SiO_3.

WATER OF CONSTITUTION. The portion of *water of crystallization* which, in some *hydrated salts,* is retained more tenaciously than the rest. Thus, *copper sulphate,* $CuSO_4.5H_2O$, when heated to 100° C. loses 4 *molecules* of water of crystallization and becomes $CuSO_4.H_2O$, but the last molecule is retained till the temperature reaches 250° C.

WATER OF CRYSTALLIZATION. A definite molecular proportion of water chemically combined with certain substances in the crystalline state; e.g. the *crystals* of *copper sulphate* contain 5 *molecules* of *water* with every molecule of copper sulphate, $CuSO_4.5H_2O$.

WATER SOFTENING. Removal of the causes of hardness of water (see *hard water*). Generally depends on the *precipitation* or removal from *solution* of the *metals* the *salts* of which cause the hardness.

WATER VAPOUR. *Water* in the gaseous or *vapour* state, present in the *atmosphere* in varying amounts. See *humidity*.

WATT, THE. Unit of *power*; the rate of *work* done in *joules* per second; the *energy* expended per second by an unvarying *electric current* of 1 *ampere* flowing through a *conductor* the ends of which are maintained at a *potential difference* of 1 *volt*. Equivalent to 10^7 *ergs* per second. The power in watts is given by the product of the current in amperes and the potential difference in volts. 1000 watts = 1 *kilowatt*; 746 watts = 1 *horse-power*.

WATT-METER. Instrument for the direct measurement of the *power*, in *watts*, of an electrical *circuit*.

WAVE FRONT. The locus of adjacent points in the path of a *wave motion* which possess the same *phase*.

WAVE FUNCTION. In *wave mechanics orbital electrons* are not treated as particles moving in precisely defined *orbits*, but as 3-dimensional stationary wave systems represented by a wave function, ψ, the magnitude of which represents the varying *amplitudes* of the wave system at various points around the *nucleus*. The volume containing all the points where ψ has an appreciable magnitude is called the *orbital* of the electron. Thus, according to wave mechanics, the precise position and *velocity* of an electron (which cannot be defined without error, see *uncertainty principle*) is replaced by a *probability* that an electron, visualized as a particle, will be at a certain point in *space* at a particular instant of time. The *probability distribution* of electrons is given by the magnitude of ψ^2.

WAVE GUIDE. Hollow *metal conductor* through which *microwaves* may be propagated. Used extensively in *radar*.

WAVE-LENGTH. The distance between successive points of equal *phase* of a *wave motion*; thus, the wave-length of the waves on water could be measured as the distance from crest to crest. The wave-length is equal to the *velocity* of the wave motion divided by its *frequency*.

WAVE MECHANICS. A development of *quantum mechanics*. Every particle is considered to be associated with a kind of periodic wave, whose *frequency* and *amplitude* are determined by rules which are derived partly by analogy with the propagation of *light*-waves, partly by ad hoc hypothesis from known quantum conditions, and partly from necessary conditions of continuity. These waves, however, are not conceived as having any real physical existence, the term 'wave' being really used only by analogy as a description of the mathematical relations employed, since in all but the simplest cases the waves would have to be imagined in a 'hyperspace' of very many dimensions. See also *wave function*.

WAVE MOTION. The propagation of a periodic disturbance carrying *energy*. At any point along the path of a wave motion, a periodic displacement or vibration about a mean position takes place. This may take the form of a displacement of air *molecules* (e.g. *sound* waves in air), of water molecules (waves on water), a displacement of elements of a string or wire, displacement of electric and magnetic *vectors* (*electromagnetic waves*), etc. The locus of these displacements at any instant is called the wave. The wave motion moves forward a distance equal to its *wave-length* in the time taken for the displacement at any point to undergo a complete *cycle* about its mean position. See *longitudinal waves*; *transverse waves*.

WAVE NUMBER. Number of waves in unit length. Reciprocal of *wave-length*.

WAVE THEORY OF LIGHT. The theory that *light* is propagated as a wave motion (see *electromagnetic radiation*); formerly the existence of a medium, the *ether*, was postulated for the transmission of light waves. This hypothesis has been rejected as unnecessary, and the classical wave theory has been modified to include the dual particle (*photon*) wave concept which is required to explain all the observed phenomena.

WAX. True waxes (e.g. *beeswax*) are simple *lipids* consisting of *esters* of higher *fatty acids* than are found in *fats and oils*, with monohydric *alcohols*. The term is often loosely applied to *solid*, non greasy, *insoluble* substances which soften or melt at fairly low *temperatures*, e.g. *paraffin wax*.

WEAK NUCLEAR INTERACTIONS. Interactions which are responsible for the *decay* of all particles except *protons*, *electrons*, *neutrinos*, and *photons*. Weak nuclear interactions are some 10^{12} times weaker than *strong nuclear interactions*.

WEIGHT. The *force* of attraction of the *Earth* on a given *mass* is the weight of that mass.

WEIGHT, BRITISH UNITS OF. Avoirdupois weights.

$437\frac{1}{2}$ grains	= 1 ounce = 28·3 gm.
7000 grains = 16 ounces	= 1 *pound*.
14 pounds	= 1 stone.
2 stone	= 1 quarter.
4 quarters	= 1 hundredweight.
2240 pounds = 20 cwt	= 1 ton.
2000 lb.	= 1 short ton.

WEIGHT, METRIC UNITS OF.

1000 milligrams	= 1 gram	= 15·432 grains.
1000 grams	= 1 *kilogram*	= 2·2046 lb.
1000 kilograms	= 1 tonne	= 0·9842 ton.

WELDING. Joining of two *metal* surfaces by raising their *temperature* sufficiently to melt and fuse them together.

WESTON CELL, cadmium cell. *Primary cell* used as a standard of *E.M.F.*

Produces 1·0183 *volts* at 20° C. Consists of a mercury *cathode* covered with mercurous sulphate and a cadmium *amalgam anode* coated with cadmium sulphate *crystals*. The *electrolyte* is a *saturated solution* of cadmium sulphate.

WET AND DRY BULB HYGROMETER. Instrument for determining the *relative humidity* of the *atmosphere*. Consists of a pair of *thermometers* side by side, the bulb of one being surrounded by moistened muslin. This one will indicate a lower temperature than the other, on account of loss of *heat* by *evaporation*; the difference in the readings will depend upon the relative humidity, which can be found by reference to special tables calculated for the purpose.

WETTING AGENT. A substance which lowers the *surface tension* of a *liquid*.

WHALE OIL. Animal *fat* obtained from the fatty layer of blubber of true whales. After extraction it is divided into various fractions and used for *soap* manufacture and other purposes; on *hydrogenation* a hard, tasteless, edible fat is obtained.

WHEATSTONE BRIDGE. A divided electrical *circuit* used for the measurement of *resistances*. When no current flows from C to D, as indicated by the absence of deflection on the *galvanometer* G, $R_1/R_2 = R_3/R_4$, where R_1, etc., are resistances. See Fig. 21. This principle is applied in the metre bridge. A wire, AB, of uniform resistance and generally 1 metre in length, corresponds to R_3 and R_4 in the Wheatstone bridge diagram; for R_1 a standard resistance is used, while R_2 is the resistance to be measured. By a sliding contact a point of no deflection in the galvanometer is found along AB, the resistances R_3 and R_4 being proportional to the lengths cut off.

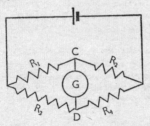

FIG. 21

WHISTLER. An *atmospheric* whistle of descending *pitch* which can be picked up under certain circumstances by a *radio* receiver. Caused by *electromagnetic radiations*, produced by *lightning* flashes, which follow the *lines of force* of the Earth's *magnetic field* and are reflected back to Earth by the *ionosphere*.

WHITE ARSENIC. Arsenious oxide, As_2O_3. Intensely poisonous white powder.

WHITE DWARF. A class of small, highly dense *stars* of low *luminosity*. They are the remnants of stars that have consumed nearly all their available hydrogen. Owing to their small size they have high surface *temperatures* and therefore appear white. See *supernovae*.

WHITE LEAD. Basic lead carbonate, $2PbCO_3.Pb(OH)_2$. Used in *paints*.

WHITE LIGHT. *Light* which can be resolved into a continuous *spectrum* of *wave-lengths* (i.e. *colours*); e.g. the light from an incandescent 'white-hot' *solid*.

WHITE SPIRIT. A *mixture* of *petroleum hydrocarbons* of boiling range 150°–200° C. Used as a *solvent* and in the *paint* and varnish industry.

WIDE-ANGLE LENS. A *camera lens* with a wide angle of view (up to 100°) and a short *focal length*.

WIEDEMANN-FRANZ LAW. The ratio of the thermal *conductivity* to the electrical conductivity is the same for all *metals* at a given *temperature*. This ratio is proportional to the *absolute temperature*. Most pure metals obey the law with reasonable accuracy at ordinary temperatures.

WIGNER EFFECT. The effect produced when the *atoms* in a *crystal* are displaced as a result of *irradiation*. If *graphite*, for example, is bombarded with *neutrons*, the shape of the crystal *lattice* is altered and the material suffers a change of physical dimensions. See also *Wigner energy*.

WIGNER ENERGY. *Energy* stored within a crystalline substance as a result of the *Wigner effect*. In a *nuclear reactor* in which *graphite* is used as the *moderator*, some of the energy lost by the *neutrons* is stored in the graphite, this is known as the Wigner energy.

WIGNER NUCLIDES. Pairs of *isobars* of odd *mass number* in which the *atomic number* and *neutron* number differ by one. E.g. ${}_1^3H$ and ${}_2^3He$.

WILSON CLOUD CHAMBER. See *cloud chamber*.

WIMSHURST MACHINE. Laboratory apparatus for generating static *electricity*.

WIND. A large-scale movement of air, generally caused by a *convection* effect in the *atmosphere*.

WIRELESS. See *radio*.

WOLFRAM. W. See *tungsten*.

WOLFRAMITE, 'wolfram'. Natural ferrous tungstate, $FeWO_4$.

WOLLASTON PRISM. *Prism* for obtaining plane-polarized light (see *polarization of light*). Constructed of *quartz*, this prism, like the *Rochon prism*, may be used for work in the ultra-violet. (See *ultra-violet radiation*.)

WOOD NAPHTHA. See *methyl alcohol*.

WOOD'S METAL. *Alloy* of 50% bismuth, 25% lead, 12·5% tin, 12·5% cadmium. M.p. 71° C.

WORK (phys.). The work done by a *force* f when it moves its point of application through a distance s is equal to $fs \cos \theta$, where θ is the *angle* between the line of action of the force and the displacement. For units, see *erg, joule, foot-pound, foot-poundal*.

WORK FUNCTION. At the *absolute zero* of temperature, the *free electrons* present in a *metal* are distributed amongst a large number of discrete *energy* states E_1, E_2, etc., up to a state of maximum energy E. At higher temperatures a small proportion of the electrons have energies greater than E. The work function of a metal is the energy which must be supplied to free electrons possessing energy E, to enable them to escape from the metal.

WORT. See *brewing*.

WROUGHT IRON. Purest commercial form of iron; iron nearly free from carbon. Very tough and fibrous; can be welded.

X

XANTHATES. *Salts* of the series of xanthic acids which have the general formula ROCSSH. Cellulose xanthate is the important intermediate product in the manufacture of *viscose*.

XENON. Element. A.W. 131·3. At. No. 54. *Inert gas* occurring in exceedingly minute amounts in the air.

XEROGRAPHY. A method of photographic copying in which an electrostatic image is formed on a surface coated with selenium when it is exposed to an optical image. A dark powder (consisting of *graphite* and and a *thermoplastic resin*), oppositely charged to the electrostatic image, is dusted on to the surface after exposure so that particles adhere to the charged regions; the image thus formed is then transferred to a sheet of charged paper and fixed by heating.

X-RAY CRYSTALLOGRAPHY. The study of crystalline substances by observation of the *diffraction* patterns which occur when a *beam* of *X-rays* is passed through a *crystal*. It is principally as a result of the use of X-ray crystallography that the structure of certain *proteins* (e.g. *haemoglobin*) and *nucleic acids* have been analysed.

X-RAY SPECTRUM. Each *element*, when bombarded by *cathode rays*, emits *X-rays* of a characteristic *frequency* which depends upon the *atomic number*; a *spectrum* photograph of lines corresponding to various elements may thus be obtained from the X-rays emitted.

X-RAYS, Röntgen rays. *Electromagnetic radiations* of the same type as *light*, but of much shorter *wave-length*, in the range of 5×10^{-7} cm. to 6×10^{-10} cm. approximately. Produced when *cathode rays* (a stream of *electrons*) strike a material object. X-rays affect a photographic plate in a way similar to light. The absorption of the rays by *matter* depends upon the *density* and the *atomic weights* of the material. The lower the A.W. and density, the more *transparent* is the material to X-rays. Thus, bones are more opaque than the surrounding flesh; this makes it possible to take an X-ray photograph (radiograph) of the bones of a living person.

X UNIT. X.U. Unit of length, 10^{-11} cm. Used mainly for expressing *X-ray wave-lengths*. It is now more usual to use *Ångström units* to express X-ray wave-lengths.

XYLAN. A complex *polysaccharide* which occurs closely associated with *cellulose* in plants.

XYLENE, xylol, dimethylbenzene, $C_6H_4(CH_3)_2$. *Liquid* resembling *toluene*; occurs in *coal-tar*. Exists in three *isomeric* forms. *Mixture* of these boils at 137°–140° C.

XYLOL. See *Xylene*.

XYLONITE*. Trade name for a *plastic* material of the *cellulose nitrate* type. See also *celluloid*.

Y

YARD. British unit of length. The Imperial standard yard is the distance, at 62° F., between the central traverse lines on two gold plugs in a certain *bronze* bar. 91·44 centimetres. The yard was redefined by the 1963 Weights and Measures Act as 0·9144 metres.

YEAR. Measure of time; commonly understood to be the time taken by the *Earth* to complete its *orbit* round the *Sun*. The civil year has an average value of 365·2425 mean *solar days*; 3 successive years consisting of 365 days, the fourth or leap year of 366. Century years do not count as leap years unless divisible by 400. The tropical or solar year, the average interval between two successive returns of the Sun to the first point of Aries, is 365·2422 mean solar days; the *sidereal year* is 365·2564 mean solar days.

YEASTS. *Unicellular micro-organisms* producing *zymase*, which converts *sugars* into *alcohol* and *carbon dioxide*. Used in *brewing* for the production of alcohol and in baking because the carbon dioxide produced causes the dough to 'rise'.

YIELD POINT. If a wire or rod of a material such as *steel* is subjected to a slowly increasing tension, the elongation produced is at first proportional to the tension (*Hooke's law*). If the tension is increased beyond the *elastic limit*, a point is reached at which a sudden increase in elongation occurs with only a small increase in tension; this is the yield point.

YOUNG'S MODULUS. *Elastic modulus* applied to a stretched wire or to a rod under tension or compression; the ratio of the *stress* on a cross-section of the wire or rod to the longitudinal *strain*.

YPERITE. See *mustard gas*.

YTTERBIUM. Yb. Element. A.W. 173·04. At. No. 70. See *lanthanides*.

YTTRIUM. Y. Element. A.W. 88·905. At. No. 39.

Z

ZEEMAN EFFECT. When a substance which emits a *line spectrum* is placed in a strong *magnetic field*, the single lines are split up into groups of closely spaced lines. From the separation of the lines in these groups information on atomic structure can be deduced.

ZENER CURRENT. The current in a *semiconductor*, consisting of *electrons* which have escaped from the *valence band* into the *conduction band* under the influence of a strong *electric field*.

ZENITH (astr.). Highest point; point on *celestial sphere* directly overhead.

ZEOLITE. Natural *hydrated* silicate of calcium and aluminium, term also now applied to artificial substances used in softening *hard water* by the 'base-exchange' method (see *ion exchange*). The calcium in the water replaces sodium in the zeolite; the process may be reversed and the zeolite restored by washing it with a *solution* of common *salt*.

ZERO. Nought; the starting-point of any scale of measurement.

ZERO POINT ENERGY. The *energy* possessed by the *atoms* or *molecules* of a substance at the *absolute zero* of temperature.

ZETA. Zero Energy Thermonuclear Apparatus. A *torus*-shaped apparatus used for studying controlled *thermonuclear reactions* at Harwell.

ZIEGLER CATALYSTS. *Catalysts* capable of initiating the *polymerization* of *ethylene* and *propylene* at normal *temperatures* and *pressures*, e.g. titanium trichloride and aluminium alkyl.

ZINC. Zn. Element. A.W. 65·37. At. No. 30. Hard, bluish-white *metal*; m.p. 419° C.; b.p. 907° C.; S.G. 7·14. Occurs as *calamine*, $ZnCO_3$, and *zinc blende*, ZnS. Extracted by roasting the ore to form the *oxide*, which is then reduced with carbon and the resulting zinc distilled. Used in *alloys*, especially *brass*, and in *galvanized iron*.

ZINC BLENDE. Natural zinc sulphide, ZnS. Important ore of zinc.

ZINC-COPPER COUPLE. Metallic zinc coated with a thin film of copper by immersing zinc in *copper sulphate solution*. Evolves hydrogen with hot *water*.

ZINC OXIDE. ZnO. White *amorphous* powder, widely used as a *pigment*.

ZIRCON. Zirconium silicate. $ZrSiO_4$. Colourless or yellowish gemstone.

ZIRCONIA. Zirconium oxide. ZrO_2. Used as a *pigment* and a *refractory* material.

ZIRCONIUM. Zr. Element. A.W. 91·22. At. No. 40. Rare *metal*, S.G. 6·4, m.p. 1900° C. Used in *alloys*.

ZODIAC. Zone of *celestial sphere* containing paths of *Sun, Moon,* and *planets*. Bounded by two circles, equidistant from the *ecliptic* and about 18° apart; divided into 12 signs of the zodiac, named after 12 constellations.

ZONE OF SPHERE. Portion of the surface of a *sphere* cut off by two parallel *planes*. Area is given by $2\pi rd$, where r is the radius of the sphere and d the distance between the two planes.

ZONES OF AUDIBILITY. An intense *sound*, e.g. due to an *explosion*, can usually be heard or detected at all points in a large area around the source of the sound, and also in distant zones of audibility separated from that area by regions in which the sound cannot be detected. Sound waves can reach these zones by reflection down from the *upper atmosphere*.

ZONES, FRESNEL. See *half-period zones*.

ZOOLOGY. The scientific study of animals.

ZWITTERION. *Ion* carrying both a positive and negative *electric charge*.

ZYGOTE. A fertilized *ovum*; the product of the union of two *gametes*.

ZYMASE. *Enzyme* present in *yeast*; acts on *sugar* with the formation of *alcohol* and *carbon dioxide*. See *fermentation*.

TABLE I. TABLE OF ELEMENTS, SYMBOLS, ATOMIC NUMBERS, AND ATOMIC WEIGHTS

(International Atomic Weights, 1961, based on Carbon-12.)

[A.W. values in brackets denote mass number of the most stable known isotope.]

Element	Symbol	At. No.	A.W.
Actinium	Ac	89	[227]
Aluminium	Al	13	26·9815
Americium	Am	95	[243]
Antimony	Sb	51	121·75
Argon	A	18	39·948
Arsenic	As	33	74·9216
Astatine	At	85	[210]
Barium	Ba	56	137·34
Berkelium	Bk	97	[247]
Beryllium	Be	4	9·0122
Bismuth	Bi	83	208·98
Boron	B	5	10·81
Bromine	Br	35	79·909
Cadmium	Cd	48	112·40
Caesium	Cs	55	132·905
Calcium	Ca	20	40·08
Californium	Cf	98	[249]
Carbon	C	6	12·011
Cerium	Ce	58	140·12
Chlorine	Cl	17	35·453
Chromium	Cr	24	51·996
Cobalt	Co	27	58·9332
Copper	Cu	29	63·54
Curium	Cm	96	[248]
Dysprosium	Dy	66	162·50
Einsteinium	Es	99	[254]
Erbium	Er	68	167·26
Europium	Eu	63	151·96
Fermium	Fm	100	[252]
Fluorine	F	9	18·9984
Francium	Fr	87	[223]
Gadolinium	Gd	64	157·25
Gallium	Ga	31	69·72
Germanium	Ge	32	72·59
Gold	Au	79	196·967
Hafnium	Hf	72	178·49
Helium	He	2	4·0026
Holmium	Ho	67	164·930

Element	Symbol	At. No.	A.W.
Hydrogen	H	1	1·00797
Indium	In	49	114·82
Iodine	I	53	126·9044
Iridium	Ir	77	192·2
Iron	Fe	26	55·847
Krypton	Kr	36	83·80
Lanthanum	La	57	138·91
Lawrencium	Lw	103	[257]
Lead	Pb	82	207·19
Lithium	Li	3	6·939
Lutetium	Lu	71	174·97
Magnesium	Mg	12	24·312
Manganese	Mn	25	54·938
Mendelevium	Md	101	[256]
Mercury	Hg	80	200·59
Molybdenum	Mo	42	95·94
Neodymium	Nd	60	144·24
Neon	Ne	10	20·183
Neptunium	Np	93	[237]
Nickel	Ni	28	58·71
Niobium	Nb	41	92·906
Nitrogen	N	7	14·0067
Nobelium	No	102	[253]
Osmium	Os	76	190·2
Oxygen	O	8	15·9994
Palladium	Pd	46	106·4
Phosphorus	P	15	30·9738
Platinum	Pt	78	195·09
Plutonium	Pu	94	[242]
Polonium	Po	84	[209]
Potassium	K	19	39·102
Praseodymium	Pr	59	140·907
Promethium	Pm	61	[145]
Protactinium	Pa	91	[231]
Radium	Ra	88	[226]
Radon	Rn	86	[222]
Rhenium	Re	75	186·20
Rhodium	Rh	45	102·905
Rubidium	Rb	37	85·47
Ruthenium	Ru	44	101·07
Samarium	Sm	62	150·35
Scandium	Sc	21	44·956
Selenium	Se	34	78·96
Silicon	Si	14	28·086
Silver	Ag	47	107·870

Element	Symbol	At. No.	A.W.
Sodium	Na	11	22·9898
Strontium	Sr	38	87·62
Sulphur	S	16	32·064
Tantalum	Ta	73	180·948
Technetium	Tc	43	[99]
Tellurium	Te	52	127·60
Terbium	Tb	65	158·924
Thallium	Tl	81	204·37
Thorium	Th	90	232·038
Thulium	Tm	69	168·934
Tin	Sn	50	118·69
Titanium	Ti	22	47·90
Tungsten	W	74	183·85
Uranium	U	92	238·03
Vanadium	V	23	50·942
Wolfram (Tungsten)	W	74	183·85
Xenon	Xe	54	131·30
Ytterbium	Yb	70	173·04
Yttrium	Y	39	88·905
Zinc	Zn	30	65·37
Zirconium	Zr	40	91·22

TABLE 2. THE SOLAR SYSTEM

Planet	Equatorial Diameter (miles)	Mass (Earth masses)*	Distance from Sun millions of miles	Sidereal period
Mercury	3,010	0·054	36·0	87·969 days
Venus	7,640	0·8150	67·24	224·701 days
Earth	7,926	1·000	92·96	365·256 days
Mars	4,220	0·107	141·63	686·980 days
Jupiter	88,730	317·89	483·64	11·86 years
Saturn	74,130	95·14	886·70	29·46 years
Uranus	29,270	14·52	1783·1	84·0 years
Neptune	27,840	17·46	2794·1	164·8 years
Pluto	3,600	0·1 (approx.)	3666·1	248·4 years
Sun	864,100	332,958	—	—
Moon	2,159·9	0·0123	0·2388 (to Earth)	27·32

* The Mass of the Earth is $5 \cdot 976 \times 10^{24}$ Kilograms.

TABLE 3. TABLE OF AMINO ACIDS

Name	Formula	Molecular weight
Glycine	$CH_2(NH_2).COOH$	75.1
Alanine	$CH_3CH.(NH_2).COOH$	89.1
Phenylalanine	$C_6H_5CH_2CH.(NH_2).COOH$	165.2
Tryosine	$C_6H_4OH.CH_2CH.(NH_2).COOH$	181.2
Valine	$(CH_3)_2CH.CH.(NH_2).COOH$	117.1
Leucine	$(CH_3)_2CH.CH_2CH.(NH_2).COOH$	131.2
Iso-leucine	$(CH_3).CH_2CH(CH_3)CH.(NH_2).COOH$	131.2
Serine	$CH_2OH.CH.(NH_2).COOH$	105.1
Threonine	$CH_3CHOH.CH.(NH_2).COOH$	119.1
Cysteine	$SH.CH_2CH.(NH_2).COOH$	121.1
Methionine	$CH_3.S.(CH_2)_2CH.(NH_2).COOH$	149.2
Asparagine	$NH_2CO.CH_2CH.(NH_2).COOH$	132.1
Glutamine	$NH_2CH.(CH_2)_2(CO.NH_2).COOH$	146.1
Lysine	$NH_2(CH_2)_4CH.(NH_2).COOH$	146.2
Arginine	$NH_2C(:NH).NH(CH_2)_3CH.(NH_2).COOH$	174.2
Aspartic	$COOH.CH_2CH.(NH_2).COOH$	133.1
Glutamic	$COOH.(CH_2)_2CH.(NH_2).COOH$	147.1
Histidine	$C_3H_3N_2.CH_2CH.(NH_2).COOH$	155.2
Tryptophane	$C_6H_4.NH.C_2H.CH_2CH.(NH_2).COOH$	204.2
Proline	$NH.(CH_2)_3CH.COOH$	115.1

TABLE 4. DIFFERENTIAL COEFFICIENTS AND INTEGRALS

y	$\dfrac{dy}{dx}$	$\int y.dx$
x^n	nx^{n-1}	$\dfrac{1}{n+1}.x^{n+1}$
$\dfrac{1}{x}$	$\dfrac{-1}{x^2}$	$\log_e x$
e^{ax}	ae^{ax}	$\dfrac{1}{a}.e^{ax}$
$\log_e x$	$\dfrac{1}{x}$	$x(\log_e x - 1)$
$\log_a x$	$\dfrac{1}{x}.\log_a e$	$x.\log_a \dfrac{x}{e}$
$\cos ax$	$-a.\sin ax$	$\dfrac{1}{a}.\sin ax$
$\sin ax$	$a.\cos ax$	$-\dfrac{1}{a}.\cos ax$
$\tan ax$	$a.\sec^2 ax$	$-\dfrac{1}{a}.\log_e \cos ax$
$\cos x$	$-\operatorname{cosec}^2 x$	$\log_e \sin x$
$\sec x$	$\tan x.\sec x$	$\log_e(\sec x + \tan x)$
$\operatorname{cosec} x$	$-\cot x.\operatorname{cosec} x$	$\log_e(\operatorname{cosec} x - \cot x)$
$\sin^{-1}\dfrac{x}{a}$	$\dfrac{1}{(a^2-x^2)^{\frac{1}{2}}}$	$x.\sin^{-1}\dfrac{x}{a} + (a^2-x^2)^{\frac{1}{2}}$
$\cos^{-1}\dfrac{x}{a}$	$\dfrac{-1}{(a^2-x^2)^{\frac{1}{2}}}$	$x.\cos^{-1}\dfrac{x}{a} - (a^2-x^2)^{\frac{1}{2}}$
$\tan^{-1}\dfrac{x}{a}$	$\dfrac{a}{a^2+x^2}$	$x.\tan^{-1}\dfrac{x}{a} - a\log_e(a^2+x^2)^{\frac{1}{2}}$

TABLE 5. THE PERIODIC TABLE OF THE ELEMENTS

I		II		III		IV		V		VI		VII		VIII	O
A	B	A	B	A	B	A	B	A	B	A	B	A	B		
												1 H			2 He
3 Li			4 Be		5 B		6 C		7 N		8 O		9 F		10 Ne
11 Na		12 Mg		13 Al			14 Si		15 P		16 S		17 Cl		18 A
19 K		20 Ca		21 Sc		22 Ti		23 V		24 Cr		25 Mn		23 27 28 Fe Co Ni	
	29 Cu		30 Zn		31 Ga		32 Ge		33 As		34 Se		35 Br		36 Kr
37 Rb		38 Sr		39 Y		4a Zr		41 Nb		42 Mo		43 Tc		44 45 46 Ru Rh Pd	
	47 Ag		48 Cd		49 In		50 Sn		51 Te		52 Sb		53 I		54 Xe
55 Cs		56 Ba		57* La		72 Hf		73 Ta		74 W		75 Re		76 77 78 Os Ir Pt	
	79 Au		80 Hg		81 Tl		82 Pb		83 Bi		84 Po		85 At		86 Rn
87 Fr		88 Ra		89† Ac											

*Lanthanides	57 La	58 Ce	59 Pr	60 Nd	61 Pm	62 Sm	63 Eu	64 Gd	65 Tb	66 Dy	67 Ho	68 Er	69 Tm	70 Yb	71 Lu
†Actinides	89 Ac	90 Th	91 Pa	92 U	93 Np	94 Pu	95 Am	96 Cm	97 Bk	98 Cf	99 Es	100 Fm	101 Mv	102 No	103 Lw

TABLE 6. SPECTRUM OF ELECTROMAGNETIC RADIATIONS

WAVE LENGTH IN METRES		FREQUENCY IN KILOCYCLES PER SECOND
10^{-17}	Cosmic rays	10^{22}
10^{-16}		10^{21}
10^{-15}		10^{20}
10^{-14}		10^{19}
10^{-13}	Gamma rays	10^{18}
10^{-12}		10^{17}
10^{-11}		10^{16}
10^{-10}	X-rays	10^{15}
10^{-9}		10^{14}
10^{-8}	Ultra-violet radiation	10^{13}
10^{-7}		
10^{-6}	Visible light	10^{12}
10^{-5}	Infra-red (heat) radiation	10^{11}
10^{-4}		10^{10}
10^{-3}		10^{9}
10^{-2}	EHF	10^{8}
10^{-1}	SHF	10^{7}
1	UHF	10^{6}
10	VHF	10^{5}
10^{2}	HF	10^{4}
10^{3}	MF	10^{3}
10^{4}	LF	10^{2}
10^{5}	VLF	10
		1

Radio frequencies